HIGHER ALGEBRA

Volumes I and II

HIGHER ALGEBRA

BY

HELMUT HASSE, Ph.D.
Professor of Mathematics, University of Hamburg

VOLUME I
Linear Equations

Translated from the third revised German edition
by

THEODORE J. BENAC, Ph.D.
Associate Professor of Mathematics, U.S. Naval Academy

FREDERICK UNGAR PUBLISHING CO.
NEW YORK

Printed in the United States of America

Library of Congress Catalog Card No. 54–7418

CONTENTS

Volume I

Linear Equations

CONTENTS

PAGE

Volume II

Equations of Higher Degree

Introduction

The Basic Problem of Algebra

The word *algebra* was handed down to us by the Arabs and literally means to carry a term from one side of an equation to the other side. Later on algebra came to be understood generally as the theory of solving equations (in this interpretation, only those equations are included which are formed by means of the four so-called elementary operations alone) with a number of unknown quantities. These two volumes are dedicated to this problem.

Here we will not be concerned with the objects, that is, the quantities, which are to be computed from the equations to be solved. Instead our attention will be directed to the solving process itself. This viewpoint is already implicitly contained in the explanation of the term algebra and characterizes the modern interpretation of the problems of this branch of knowledge. The objects themselves (for instance, the three sides of a triangle whose altitudes are given) are of interest to those who apply algebra (in our example, the geometer); while the algebraist is concerned only with the general formal rules (symbolisms, algorithms) by which the required quantities can be determined from the given equations (therefore, in the example, the rules for solving a system of three equations in three unknowns). If, according to this, algebra appears merely as an auxiliary science for other branches of mathematics, it can, nevertheless, justly claim to be recognized as an independent mathematical discipline. This is based, first, on its indispensability and multiform significance for nearly all parts of mathematics; secondly, because the methods and results of an algebra pursued for its own sake satisfy the criterion of closed logical structure, simplicity throughout, and consummate beauty, whose fulfillment must be required of a viable mathematical branch of knowledge.

In the sense of the previous remarks, it seems proper, in fact we seem to be directed, to base the presentation of algebra on a foundation of the greatest possible generality relative to the objects to be considered. Hence we will not only, as is self-evident, strip the quantities in question of every designation (metric, geometric, etc.) but also of their significance as numbers in the usual sense of the word number (natural, integral, rational, real, complex numbers). The *intuitive significance* as numbers of the symbols appearing in the equations is just as irrelevant as a possible nomenclature for the formalism which leads to the solution of the equations. The only thing which is important are the *formal rules* by which these symbols are to be manipulated, namely, the fact that the symbols to be used designate elements of a domain in which they can be manipulated according to the known rules characterizing addition, multiplication, subtraction and division. In Chapter I we will first be concerned with those domains called *fields*, among others; then we will give an exact formulation of the ***basic problem of algebra*** which we provisionally state here as follows:

To develop general formal methods for solving equations between known and unknown elements of a field in terms of the unknowns, where the equations are formed by means of the four elementary operations.

Before we can take up the solution of this problem we must clearly explain the concept of field and also what is to be understood by an *equation* in the sense of the problem. This is the objective of Chapter I. At the end of this chapter we will give an exact formulation of the basic problem of algebra and will call attention to its two most important subproblems. After this in Chapter II the elements of *group theory* will be explained.

Though this theory is used only superficially in the solution of the first subproblem, it will be a decisive tool for the solution of the second subproblem. In Chapters III and IV we will completely solve the first subproblem. At the end of Vol. 2 we will be concerned with investigations related to the second subproblem.

It is characteristic of the *modern* development of algebra that the tools specified above have given rise to far-reaching autonomous theories which are more and more replacing the basic problem of *classical* algebra, cited above, as the center of interest. Thus, in the modern interpretation algebra is no longer merely the theory of solving equations but the *theory of the formal calculating domains,* as fields, groups, etc., and its *basic problem* has now become that of obtaining an insight into the *structure of such domains* (for this purpose, cf. p. [31]). However, in the restricted space of these volumes it is not possible to put the more general modern viewpoint in the foreground. Therefore, we take the basic problem of classical algebra, expressed above, as a directing guide and defining frame for our presentation, though we will also be led, particularly in Vol. 2, to structural statements in the sense of modern algebra.

Though this theory is used only expeditiously in the solution of the first subproblem, it will be a decisive tool for the solution of the second subproblem. In Chapters III and IV we will completely solve the first subproblem. At the end of Vol. 2 we will be concerned with investigations related to the second subproblem.

It is characteristic of the modern development of algebra that the tools specified above have given rise to far-reaching autonomous theories which are more and more replacing the basic problem of classical algebra, cited above, as the center of interest. Thus, in the modern interpretation algebra is no longer merely the theory of solving equations but the theory of the formal calculating domains, as fields, groups, etc., and its basic problem has now become that of obtaining an insight into the structure of such domains (for this purpose, cf. p. 151). However, in the restricted space of these volumes it is not possible to put the more general modern viewpoint in the foreground. Therefore, we take the basic problem of classical algebra, expressed above, as a directing guide and delimiting frame for our presentation, though we will also be led, particularly in Vol. 3, to structural statements in the sense of modern algebra.

I. Rings. Fields. Integral Domains

1. Definition of Rings, Fields, Integral Domains

The formal characterization of the three elementary arithmetical operations, i. e., addition, subtraction, multiplication — the fourth, division, will be included only later — will set them free from the intuitive meaning of the symbols as numbers. This objective can be realized by the following postulates:

(a) *There is a* ***set*** B ***of distinct elements.*** *The number of elements in this set is finite (at least two, otherwise arbitrary) or infinite.*

We use letters $a, b, \ldots$ and combining symbols (for instance, the symbols $a+b, ab, \ldots$ which are to be explained later on) in order to communicate the results of logical postulations of elements of B, and simply call $a, b, \ldots$ the *elements* of B. The *distinctness* postulated in (a) requires that we are able to tell for any two such logical postulations a, b whether they are the same or different elements of B; we indicate this relationship by the notation $a = b$, or $a \neq b$, respectively.

(b) *For any two (not necessarily different) elements a, b of* B, *given in a definite order, there are defined* ***two rules of combination (operations),*** *that is, to every ordered pair of elements a, b of* B *there is in some way associated an element c (first rule of combination) and an element d (second rule of combination) of* B.

(a) and (b) are realized, for example, if B is the set of all even numbers, or all integers, or all rational numbers, or all real numbers, or all complex numbers, or all positive numbers of one of these systems (except for the complex numbers), and the rules of combination are chosen as addition ($c = a + b$) and multiplication ($d = ab$). As these special cases can be regarded as the starting point of our abstraction we will in general also call the two rules of combination in (b) *addition* and *multiplication*, and the elements c and d associated to the pair a, b their *sum* and *product*, respectively, and write $c = a + b$, $d = ab$. However, in adopting this terminology it should be kept in mind that the purely formal postulate (b) (as well as postulate (c), given below, on our rules of combination) gives us no reason for intuitively assuming that these operations must coincide with ordinary addition and multiplication if B is a set of numbers.

(c) *For arbitrary elements of* B *the two rules of combination specified in (b) satisfy the laws:*

(1) $a + b = b + a$, **(2)** $ab = ba$
(commutative law);

(3) $(a + b) + c = a + (b + c)$, **(4)** $(ab)c = a(bc)$
(associative law);

(5) $(a + b)c = ac + bc$
(distributive law);

(6) *To every ordered pair of elements a, c of* B *there exists a uniquely determined element b of* B, *such that $a + b = c$,*
(Law of unrestricted and unique subtraction).

According to (6) the operation of determining b from $a + b = c$ can be performed without restriction and uniquely in B. As already expressed in the parenthesis after law (6), this operation is called *subtraction*. In harmony with the terminology used under (b), we therefore introduce the notation $b = c - a$ (*difference*).

Definition 1. *If a set* B *satisfies the conditions specified in* (a), (b), (c), *then* B *is called a* ***ring*** *with respect to the rules of combination* (b).

The last additional statement must be made since a set B can be a priori a ring relative to two operations defined differently from those in (b). This means that a set may be a ring in several ways (cf. Vol. 3, Section 1, Exer. 4, 5). By a ring B plain and simple we always understand the set B together with its defining rules of combination. — We will always designate rings by upper case Greek letters, elements of a ring by lower case Latin or Greek letters.[1]

We will now first prove some properties of rings.

Theorem 1. *In any ring* B *there exists a uniquely determined element* 0, *called the* ***null element*** *or* ***zero*** *of* B, *with the property*

$$a + 0 = a \textit{ for all } a \textit{ in } B.$$

Proof: Let $a, b, \ldots$ be elements of B. Then by (6) the differences $a - a, b - b, b - a, \ldots$ exist in B. By definition these differences have the property

$$a + (a - a) = a,\ b + (b - b) = b,\ a + (b - a) = b, \ldots$$

On applying (1) and (3) to the first and third of these relations we now have

$$b + (a - a) = [a + (b - a)] + (a - a) =$$
$$= [a + (a - a)] + (b - a) = a + (b - a) = b.$$

On comparing this with the second relation and using the uniqueness in (6) we obtain

$$a - a = b - b.$$

Therefore all differences $a - a, b - b, \ldots$ are the same element 0 of B. This element has the property specified in the theorem, and by (6) is uniquely determined by a single one of the conditions $a + 0 = a$.

[1] The letters $i, k, l, m, n, p, q, r, s; \iota, \varkappa, \lambda, \mu, \nu, \varrho, \sigma$, however, are reserved for ordinary integers, for instance, indices and exponents.

Theorem 2. $0c = 0$ *is valid for any* c *in* B.

Proof: By (5) and Theorem 1 we have for any c in B

$$0c = (0 + 0)c = 0c + 0c,$$

therefore, by (6) and Theorem 1, $0c = 0$.

Up to now we have paid no attention to division. We will now take it into consideration by adjoining the following postulate to the postulates (1) to (6) specified under (c).

(7) *To every ordered pair of elements* a, c *of* B, *where* $a \neq 0$, *there exists a uniquely determined element* b *of* B, *such that* $ab = c$, **(Law of unrestricted and unique division).**

If (7) is valid in B, the operation of determining b from $ab = c$ can be performed in B without restriction and uniquely provided that $a \neq 0$. Analogous to the case of subtraction we denote this operation as *division* and introduce the notation $b = \frac{c}{a}$ *(quotient).*

The restriction $a \neq 0$ imposed in (7) is not an arbitrary convention, for it is necessary if (a), (b), (c) and (7) are to be consistent with one another. This can be shown as follows: Let us assume that this restriction is not specified and that c is an arbitrary element of B. Then, from the existence of an element b satisfying $0b = c$, by Theorem 2 we would have $c = 0$. Hence B would contain only the one element 0 in contradiction to (a). These remarks suggest the question: Are the postulates (a), (b), (c), (7), given above, consistent? In answer we merely note that a contradiction in (a), (b), (c), (7) would imply a contradiction in the system of rational numbers, since this system satisfies all of these postulates.

The table of postulates (1) and (2), (3) and (4), and (6) and (7) is symmetric relative to addition and multiplication except for the restriction $a \neq 0$ in (7). It should be further noted that this nonsymmetry must naturally go back to the nonsymmetry of law (5) which connects the two individual operations, as the above deduction of that restriction also shows (proof of Theorem 2).

Definition 2. *If* (7) *as well as* (a), (b), (c) *is valid in a ring* B, *then* B *is called a* ***field*** *with respect to the rules of combination* (b).

Analogous to Theorem 1, fields moreover satisfy

Theorem 3. *In any field* K *there exists a uniquely determined element* $e \neq 0$, *called the* ***unity element*** *or* ***identity*** *of* K, *with the property*

$$ae = a \text{ for all } a \text{ in } K.$$

Proof: By (a) there exists in K an element $a \neq 0$. The proof of the theorem for such an element follows, as in the case of Theorem 1, by using (7) instead of (6). Furthermore, by Theorem 2 it is clear that $ae = a$ is also valid for $a = 0$. Finally, the assumption $e = 0$ would imply $a = ae = a0 = 0$ for every a in K, which contradicts (a).

Besides rings and fields there is another kind of concept which is used in algebra and stands logically between these two, namely, that of *integral domain.* It arises from the concept of ring by assuming in addition only a part of postulate (7) which led to the concept of field. On the one hand, we omit from (7) the unrestricted existence of quotients and only require the uniqueness of division in those cases in which it can be performed:

(7 a) *If* $ab = ab'$ *and* $a \neq 0$, *then* $b = b'$ ***(Uniqueness of division).***

On the other hand, however, the existence of the special quotients $\frac{a}{a}, \frac{b}{b}, \ldots$, where $a, b, \ldots \neq 0$, is required. According to the preceding this amounts to postulating the validity of the analogue to Theorem 3:

(7 b) *There exists an element* e *in* B *such that* $ae = a$ *for all* a *in* B ***(Existence of the unity element).***

Definition 3. *If* (7 a) *and* (7 b) *as well as* (a), (b), (c) *are valid in a ring* B, *then* B *is called* an ***integral domain*** *with respect to the rules of combination* (b).

Every field is an integral domain since (7 a) and (7 b) are consequences of (7), and every integral domain is a ring by Def. 3.

We use the term *domain*[2] as a common designation for rings, fields, integral domains. We call the rules of combination defined in a domain. i. e., *addition, subtraction, multiplication,* possibly *division,* the *first three,* or *four,* respectively, *elementary operations.*

In the following we will be mainly concerned with integral domains. For such systems (therefore, in particular, for fields) the converse of Theorem 2 is also valid:

Theorem 4. *If the product of two elements of an integral domain is zero, then at least one of the factors is zero, that is,* $ab = 0$, $a \neq 0$, *implies* $b = 0$.

Proof: Let $ab = 0$, $a \neq 0$. Since $a0 = 0$ by Theorem 2, $ab = a0$, and (7 a) implies that $b = 0$.

Not only is it true, as shown above, that Theorem 4 is a consequence of (7 a), but the converse is also valid. The proof rests on the fact that if the equation $ab = ab'$ exists for an element $a \neq 0$, then $a(b - b') = 0$. For, if the analogue to Theorem 4 is valid in a ring, the latter relation yields $b - b' = 0$, that is, $b = b'$.

Addendum to Definition 3. *The postulates* (7 a), (7 b) *of Def.* 3 *can also be replaced by the postulate that the analogues to Theorem* 3 *and Theorem* 4 *shall be valid in* B.

[2] Accordingly, *domain* actually means the same as *ring;* however, the neutral term *domain* is more familiar in the sense given above, while the term *ring* is ordinarily used only if the system is actually not an integral domain.

Here it is enough merely to mention that all general operating rules of elementary algebra with respect to addition, subtraction and multiplication, especially the rules for removing parentheses, can be derived by simple inferences from postulates (a), (b), (c) for rings. Furthermore, if (7) is assumed in addition, the general formulae for operating with fractions are also valid. It is left to the reader to carry out the details.

When operating in a domain B it is convenient to use the following abbreviating notations:

$$-a \text{ for } 0-a,$$

$$\ldots, (-2)\, a, (-1)\, a, 0\, a, 1\, a, 2\, a, \ldots \text{ for } \ldots -(a+a), -a, 0, a, a+a, \ldots \quad \textit{(integral multiples of } a),$$

$$\ldots, a^{-2}, a^{-1}, a^0, a^1, a^2, \ldots \text{ for } \ldots, \frac{e}{aa}, \frac{e}{a}, e, a, aa, \ldots \quad \textit{(integral powers of } a).$$

(Naturally the powers $a^{-1}, a^{-2}, \ldots$ are used only in so far as they are uniquely defined, for instance, if B is a field and $a \neq 0$.) By (1) to (7) and Theorems 1 to 4 it easily follows from the definition of the arithmetical operations in the domain of integers that

$$(m+n)a = m\, a + n\, a, \quad a^{m+n} = a^m a^n, \quad (a^m)^n = a^{mn},$$
$$(m\, n)e = (me)(n\, e), \quad e^m = e, \quad m0 = 0, \quad 0m = 0,$$

where m, n are integers, provided that the elements occurring in these expressions have a unique sense on the basis of the preceding.

Examples

1. On the basis of the preceding expositions we may state as known from the elements of arithmetic:

Theorem 5. *The* $\left\{\begin{array}{l}\textit{integers}\\ \textit{rational numbers}\end{array}\right\}$ form $\left\{\begin{array}{l}\textit{an integral domain } \Gamma\\ \textit{a field } \mathsf{P}\end{array}\right\}$ *if the rules of combination are taken as ordinary addition and multiplication. The numbers* 0 *and* 1 *are the null and unity elements of* Γ *and* P.

2. Furthermore, all real numbers, as well as all complex numbers, form a field with respect to ordinary addition and multiplication.

3. The even numbers form a ring but not an integral domain, since they do not satisfy (7b). Rings which satisfy (7b) but not (7a) will be met in Vol. 2, Section 2. An example of an integral domain which is not a field has already been given, namely Γ.

4. The following field may be cited as an example of a field whose elements are not numbers and which contains only finitely many elements.

For the two elements 0 and e let us define the two rules of combination by the conventions

$$\begin{array}{ll} 0+0=0 & 00=0 \\ 0+e=e+0=e & 0e=e0=0 \\ e+e=0 & ee=e \end{array}$$

It is easy to establish that (1) to (7) are valid. Hence this is a field which consists only of its null- and unity elements. The results of Vol. 2, Section 20 show that this field is not an uninteresting exceptional case. It will there be shown that finite fields exist such that the number of their elements is an arbitrary power of a prime number.

2. Subdomains. Congruence Relations. Isomorphism

In Section 1 we started off with postulate (a) which asserts the existence of a *set of distinct elements*, the *basic data of set theory*. Through the addition of postulates (b), (c), etc., they are transformed into the *basic data of algebra*, that is, into the *domain*. Therefore, in the study of our domains we should expect to meet, among other things, concepts and facts which follow from (a) alone, namely, which belong to the theory of sets. The question then arises as to what use can be made of them in studying the domains obtained through the addition of (b), (c), etc. Here we must restrict ourselves to making a brief list of the set-theoretic foundations, to which we will have recourse from the so-called *naive standpoint*, without entering into the details of conceptual difficulties arising in recent times through the paradoxes of the theory of sets. These can be removed by a correct *axiomatic approach*, as has been done in Section 1 for domains, based on the concept of set. In particular, we will abstain from any precise definition of the concept of set that does not satisfy the naive standpoint.

1. *Subsets*

Let M be a **set,** whereby we always *understand,* as in Section 1, (a), a *set of distinct elements.* A set M_1 is called a **subset** of M or **contained** in M, if every element of M_1 also occurs in M. We also think of the set M itself as well as of the *empty set* containing no elements *(null set)* as subsets of M. All other subsets of M are called *true* or *proper* subsets.

Let $M_1, M_2, \ldots$ be any finite or infinite number of subsets of a set M. Then there are two definite subsets of M associated to these subsets, namely, their **intersection** Δ and their **union** E. The intersection Δ consists of all and only those elements of M which are contained in M_1 *as well as* in $M_2, \ldots$. It can also be the null set. The union E consists of all and only those elements of M which are contained *either* in M_1 *or* in $M_2, \ldots$ E can also be defined as the intersection of all subsets of M containing $M_1, M_2, \ldots$ and in this sense it is the *smallest* subset of M containing $M_1, M_2, \ldots$ Similarly, Δ can be defined as the union of all subsets of M contained in $M_1, M_2, \ldots$ and in this sense it is the *largest* subset of M contained in $M_1, M_2, \ldots$

2. *Equivalence Relations and Partitions*

By a decomposition of a set M into *mutually exclusive* subsets we mean a representation of M as the union of subsets such that the intersection of any pair of these subsets is the null set. These decompositions are especially important in algebra. We call *such a decomposition a* **partition** *of* M, *and the subsets thereby determined its* **classes.** If such a partition is submitted and if the symbol $\sim$ or the symbol $\dashv\vdash$ is placed between any two elements a, b of M, given in a definite order, according as a occurs in the same subset as b or not, then the following facts are obvious:

(α) $a \sim a$ (*law of* **reflexivity).**

(β) $a \sim b$, implies $b \sim a$ (*law of* **symmetry).**

(γ) $a \sim b$, $b \sim c$ implies $a \sim c$ (*law of* **transitivity).**

For the existence of these facts, no matter what the meaning attributed to the symbols $\sim$, -|- may be, we introduce a special terminology:

(I) *If one and only one of the two symbols* $\sim$, -|- *can be placed between any two elements of* M, *given in a definite order, such that the conditions* (α), (β), (γ) *are valid, then we say that an* ***equivalence relation*** $\sim$ *is defined in* M.

We then have:

(A) *Every partition of* M *leads to an equivalence relation in* M *by placing* $\sim$ *between the elements of a class and* -|- *between the elements of different classes.*

The converse of this statement is used very widely not only in algebra but also in nearly every branch of mathematics. Hence we will establish it in detail.

(B) *Every equivalence relation in* M *arises according to* (A) *from one and only partition in* M.

Proof: a) Let an equivalence relation be given in M. Then a subset M_1 of M can have the property E which states that there is an element c of M such that M_1 consists of all and only those elements d of M for which $c \sim d$. For the present, we call M_1 an E-subset of M which is generated by c. Every element c of M generates an E-subset but naturally the same E-subset can in general be generated by different elements. We now consider the totality of E-subsets of M and show that these are the classes of a partition of M from which the equivalence relation under consideration arises in the sense of (A).

First, different E-subsets M_1, M_2 of M are mutually exclusive. For, if the element a were contained in M_1 and M_2, where M_1 is generated by c_1, M_2 by c_2, then $c_1 \sim a$, $c_2 \sim a$, therefore, by (β), (γ) it would follow that $c_1 \sim c_2$. Consequently, if d_1 is an element of M_1, d_2 an element of M_2, which means that $c_1 \sim d_1$, $c_2 \sim d_2$, then by (β), (γ) it would also be valid that $c_1 \sim d_2$, $c_2 \sim d_1$; therefore, d_2 would be contained in M_1, d_1 in M_2. This would imply that M_1 and M_2 were identical contrary to the assumption.

Secondly, the union of all E-subsets is the set M, that is, every element a of M actually belongs to an E-subset. For, by (α) a belongs to the E-subset generated by a.

This means that the E-subsets of M are the classes of a partition of M. We will now show that the equivalence relation under consideration follows from this partition in the sense of (A).

First, two elements a, b belonging to the same E-subset M_1 are related by the symbol $\sim$. For, if M_1 is generated by c, then $c \sim a$, $c \sim b$; therefore by (β), (γ) we also have $a \sim b$.

Secondly, two elements a, b belonging to different E-subsets M_1, M_2 of M are related by the symbol $\nsim$. For, if it were true that $a \sim b$, where M_1 is generated by c_1, M_2 by c_2, then from $c_1 \sim a$, $c_2 \sim b$ and (β), (γ) it would also follow that $c_1 \sim c_2$. This would contradict the assumption that M_1 and M_2 were different.

b) An equivalence relation cannot arise from two different partitions of M, for the class containing an element a must include all and only those elements b for which $a \sim b$; therefore, it is uniquely determined by the equivalence relation (as the E-subset of M generated by a).

If a partition of M is given, then every subset of M which contains one and only one element from each class is called a **complete system of representatives** for this partition.

The simplest equivalence relation is the *logical identity*, that is, the relation defined in Section 1 under (a) by the symbols $=$, $\neq$. The partition thereby determined is the separation of M into its distinct elements.

3. *Equipotency. Cardinal numbers*

From a set M a new set M' can be derived by replacing the elements of M, in any way whatever, by new elements, provided that the distinctness of the elements of M is preserved (say by replacing the element a by 'concept of the element a'). If the symbol $\longleftrightarrow$, or $\not\longleftrightarrow$, is placed between the two elements a of M and a' of M' according as a' is obtained from a by this substitution or not, then the following facts are obvious:

(δ.) *to every a of M there is an a' of M' such that $a \longleftrightarrow a'$,* (δ′) *to every* a' *of* M′ *there is an* a *of* M *such that* $a \longleftrightarrow a'$,

(ε) *if* $a \longleftrightarrow a'$, $b \longleftrightarrow b'$ *and* $a = b$, *then* $a' = b'$,

(ε′) *if* $a \longleftrightarrow a'$, $b \longleftrightarrow b'$ *and* $a' = b'$, *then* $a = b$.

For the existence of these facts in the case of two given sets M and M′, no matter what the *meaning* attached to the symbols $\longleftrightarrow$, $\leftarrow\!\!|\!\!\rightarrow$ may be, we introduce a special terminology:

(II) *If one and only one of the two symbols* $\longleftrightarrow$, $\leftarrow\!\!|\!\!\rightarrow$ *can be placed between any element* a *of a set* M *and* a' *of a set* M′ *so that the conditions* (δ), (δ′), (ε), (ε′) *are satisfied, then we say that a* ***one-to-one (or biunique) correspondence*** $\longleftrightarrow$ ***exists between*** M ***and*** M′. If such a correspondence is possible between M and M′, *we say that* M *and* M′ *are* ***equipotent.***

It is evident that equipotency is an equivalence relation in the sense of (I). In the case of two finite sets M and M′ the statement of equipotency is obviously equivalent to saying that the *number* of elements in M and M′ is the same. Hence the class of equipotent sets generated according to (B) by a finite M is the totality of all sets with the same number of elements as M. This class can directly be used for the unique characterization of this number.[3] Consequently, following *Cantor*, the classes which belong, according to (B), to the equivalence relation (II) in the set of all sets (that is, the totalities of all sets equipotent to any set, respectively) are called in general **cardinal numbers** (or **powers**). They generalize the number concept to include infinite sets. By thinking of all equipotent sets as a logical unit (the class) we just disregard any special meaning of the elements of the individual sets and look upon the *totality* [(δ), (δ′)] of the elements together with their *distinctness* [(ε), (ε′)] alone as characterizing the number concept.

The set of natural numbers 1, 2, . . . , n may be used to represent the finite cardinal number n. The set of natural numbers 1, 2, . . . represents another cardinal number important for us. Such sets are called **countable.** Consequently, a countable set is equipotent to the

[3] *R. Dedekind* (*Was sind und was sollen die Zahlen?* What are numbers, and what purpose do they serve? Braunschweig 1887) actually used this concept for the definition of natural numbers as the numbers of finite sets.

set of all natural numbers, that is, it is a set whose elements can be biuniquely associated to the natural numbers by *indexing*: $a_1, a_2, \ldots$.

The set of all real numbers is an example of the fact that not every infinite set is countable.[4]

We will now apply the concepts of set theory explained above to some important appropriate concepts in the case of domains.

1. *Subdomains*

An immediate consequence of the concept of subset is

Definition 4. *If the elements of a subset* B_1 *of a domain* B *form a* 1) *ring,* 2) *field,* 3) *integral domain with respect to the same rules of combination defined in* B, *then* B_1 *is called a* 1) ***subring*** 2) ***subfield*** 3) ***integral subdomain*** *of* B, *and* B *an* ***extension domain (ring, field, integral domain)*** *of* B_1.

In order to decide whether a subset B_1 of an integral domain B is a subring, subfield, integral subdomain of B, it is not necessary to prove all conditions specified in Section 1, but only those cited in the following theorem:

Theorem 6. *A necessary and sufficient condition for a subset* B_1 *consisting of at least two elements of an integral domain* B *to be a* 1) *subring of* B *is that if the first three elementary operations defined in* B *are applied to the elements of* B_1, *they always again yield elements of* B_1; 2) *subfield of* B *if in addition the fourth operation (division) can always be carried out for the elements of* B_1 *(provided that the denominator is different from*

[4] If an enumeration $\alpha_1, \alpha_2, \ldots$ is given of the real numbers written as decimal fractions (avoiding the repeating $00\ldots$), then a decimal fraction α can easily be formed (of the same kind) which is different from $\alpha_1, \alpha_2, \ldots$ and so would not yet have been counted. Thus, it could be chosen so that for every $n = 1, 2, \ldots$ the n-th numeral of α after the decimal point is different from the n-th numeral of α_n after the decimal point (*Cantor's diagonal method*).

zero) and always yields elements of B_1; 3) *integral subdomain of* B *if* B_1 *is a subring of* B *and contains the unity element of* B.

Proof: a) By Def. 1 to 4 it is clear that these conditions are necessary. b) If these conditions are satisfied, then they imply that the following conditions of Section 1 are valid for B_1: (a), (b), the existence requirement in (6), eventually the existence in (7) or (7b). On the other hand, the remaining conditions required in Section 1, namely (1) to (5), the uniqueness in (6), eventually the uniqueness in (7) or (7a), are satisfied a fortiori in B_1, since they are valid in B.

The criterion of Theorem 6, of course, can accordingly be extended to rings B. However, we will need it only for the cases cited in Theorem 6. For a simpler way of speaking we will also formulate the following Theorem 7 as well as Def. 5 only for *fields*, since they will be applied later on only to this case.

Regarding *intersections* in the case of fields we have

Theorem 7. *If* $K_1, K_2, \ldots$ *are any (finite or infinite*[5] *number of) subfields whatsoever of a field* K, *then the intersection of the sets* $K_1, K_2, \ldots$ *is also a subfield of* K. *This is called the* ***intersection field*** *or briefly* ***intersection*** *of the fields* $K_1, K_2, \ldots$

Proof: The intersection contains at least two elements; for, all $K_1, K_2, \ldots$ have the two distinct elements 0 and e of K in common, since they are subfields of K. Thereupon the statement immediately follows from Theorem 6.

In the *case of the union,* however, a corresponding theorem is not valid. For, if a_1 is in K_1, a_2 in K_2, then $a_1 + a_2$, for instance, does not have to be contained in any of the fields $K_1, K_2, \ldots$. Instead, an analogue to the concept of union is introduced based

[5] The enumeration used here and in the following Def. 5 should not be interpreted as meaning that there are at most a countable number of terms.

on the generalization of the fact given on p. 21 that the union can be expressed as an intersection.

Definition 5. *If* $K_1, K_2, \ldots$ *are any (finite or infinite number of) subfields of a field* K, *then the intersection of all subfields of* K *containing* $K_1, K_2, \ldots$ *as subfields is called the* ***composite*** *of* $K_1, K_2, \ldots$ *or the* ***field composed from*** $K_1, K_2, \ldots$

That the intersection can be formed at all, follows from the fact that there exists at least one field on which its formation can be based, namely, K.

The composite of $K_1, K_2, \ldots$ contains the union of the sets $K_1, K_2, \ldots$; in general, however, it contains more than this. It is the *smallest* subfield of K containing $K_1, K_2, \ldots$ as subfields just as the intersection of $K_1, K_2, \ldots$ is the *largest* subfield of K contained in $K_1, K_2, \ldots$ as subfield.

2. *Congruence Relations and Residue Class Rings*

A *domain* B being given, we add to the conditions (α), (β), (γ) for an equivalence relation in the *set* B two more postulates, formed in a natural manner, on the behavior of the equivalence relation toward the two rules of combination of B, and define:

Definition 6. *If an equivalence relation* $\equiv$ *in a domain* B *not only satisfies* (α), (β), (γ) *but also the conditions:*

(1) $a_1 \equiv b_1,\ a_2 \equiv b_2$ *implies* $a_1 + a_2 \equiv b_1 + b_2$,

(2) $a_1 \equiv b_1,\ a_2 \equiv b_2$ *implies* $a_1 a_2 \equiv b_1 b_2$,

then we call it a ***congruence relation*** *in* B *and the classes thereby determined the* ***residue classes*** *in* B *relative to it.*[6]

[6] The set M of all $a \equiv 0$ relative to a congruence relation in B is exactly what is meant by an *ideal in* B. This concept is basic for the divisibility theory (cf. Vol. 2, Section 2) in general domains (cf. *E. Noether, Idealtheorie in Ringbereichen.* Theory of Ideals in Rings, Math. Ann. 83, 1921).

We next take as a basis in Section 1, (a) the set $\overline{B}$ of residue classes relative to a congruence relation $\equiv$ in B. This requires that at least two such residue classes exist, so that all elements of B are not congruent to one another. Let r and s be two residue classes. Now, form all sums $a+b$ and products ab for any element a of r, and b of s. Then by (1) and (2) it follows that all these sums belong to a definite residue class t, of B, and all these products to a definite residue class u. Through the conventions $r+s=t$ and $rs=u$, Section 1, (b) is realized. We will refer to these rules of combination as the *elementwise* addition and multiplication, respectively, of the residue classes. We now prove that Section 1, (c) is also realized, i. e.,

Theorem 8. *Let a congruence relation* $\equiv$ *be given in a domain* B, *by which not all elements of* B *are congruent to one another, and let two rules of combination be defined in the set* $\overline{B}$ *of residue classes relative to the congruence relation through elementwise addition, and multiplication, then* $\overline{B}$ *is a ring with respect to these rules of combination;* $\overline{B}$ *is called the* ***residue class ring*** *of* B *relative to the congruence relation* $\equiv$.

Proof: The validity of Section 1, (1) to (5) is an immediate consequence of the validity of these laws in the domain B. Furthermore, if a and c are elements of the residue classes r and t, respectively, then the existence of an element b satisfying $a+b=c$ follows from Section 1, (6). Now, if s is the residue class which contains b, then by (1) and our definition of addition it follows that $r+s=t$. Finally, this residue class s is also the unique solution of $r+s=t$. For, if $r+s'=t$ is also true and b' is an element of s', then $a+b\equiv a+b'$, because both sides belong to the same residue class t. Now the relation $(-a)\equiv(-a)$ is surely valid by (α.) Hence by (1) these two relations yield

$b \equiv b'$, that is, $s = s'$. Consequently, subtraction can be carried out without restriction and uniquely in $\overline{\mathsf{B}}$, that is, Section 1, (6) is satisfied.

Furthermore, it should be noted, that, if B is an integral domain, $\overline{\mathsf{B}}$ does not also have to be an integral domain, since even though Section 1, (7 b) is satisfied in $\overline{\mathsf{B}}$, Section 1, (7 a) need not be. (Cf. Vol. 2, Theorem 28.) The case in which B is actually a field is uninteresting, since there are then only trivial residue class partitions in B (cf. Vol. 3, Section 2, Exer. 10).

3. *Isomorphisms and Types of Domains*

Two domains B and B' being given, we add to the conditions (δ), (δ'), (ε), (ε') for the equipotency of the two sets B and B' two postulates, formed in a natural manner, on the behavior of the one-to-one correspondence toward the two rules of combination of B and B'. We first prove

Theorem 9. *The following convention yields an equivalence relation in the set of all domains: Let* $\mathsf{B} \cong \mathsf{B}'$ *if and only if* 1) B *and* B' *are equipotent;* 2) *if the one-to-one correspondence between the elements* $a, b, \ldots$ *of* B *and* $a', b', \ldots$ *of* B' *can be chosen so that the conditions:*

(3) *If* $a \longleftrightarrow a'$, $b \longleftrightarrow b'$, *then* $a + b \longleftrightarrow a' + b'$,

(4) *If* $a \longleftrightarrow a'$, $b \longleftrightarrow b'$, *then* $ab \longleftrightarrow a'b'$.

exist.

Proof: It is immediately obvious that the conditions (α), (β), (γ) valid for equipotency are preserved even if the postulates (3) and (4) are added.

Similarly, it is immediately obvious:

Corollary to Theorem 9. *Extension domains of a fixed domain* B_0 *satisfy an analogue to Theorem* 9 *even if the further condition is added to conditions* (3) *and* (4) *that the elements*

a_0 *of* B_0 *shall correspond to themselves under the one-to-one correspondence between* B *and* B':

(5) $a_0 \longleftrightarrow a_0$ *for all* a_0 *in* B_0.

As a consequence of Theorem 9 we now define:

Definition 7. *A one-to-one correspondence between two domains* B *and* B' *with the properties* (3), (4) *is called an* ***isomorphism*** *between* B *and* B', *and* B *and* B' *themselves are then said to be* ***isomorphic.*** *The equivalence relation* $\mathsf{B} \cong \mathsf{B}'$ *specified in Theorem 9 for domains is called an* ***isomorphism;*** *the classes thereby determined, the* ***types*** *of the domain.*

As a consequence of the Corollary to Theorem 9 we analogously define:

Addendum to Definition 7. *An isomorphism between two extension domains* B *and* B' *of a domain* B_0 *with the property* (5) *is called an* ***isomorphism relative to*** B_0, *and* B *and* B' *are said to be* ***isomorphic relative to*** B_0. *The equivalence relation for extension domains of* B_0 *specified in the Corollary to Theorem 9 is called an* ***isomorphism relative to*** B_0, *the classes thereby determined the* ***extension types relative to*** B_0.

The conditions which must be satisfied by the relation $\mathsf{B} \cong \mathsf{B}'$ are given in Theorem 9. They tell us what happens in passing from B to B' or from B' to B by the correspondence under consideration. First, (δ), (δ') specifies that to every element of B there corresponds an element of B' and conversely, or, briefly stated, the *totality* of the elements is preserved. Secondly, (ε), (ε') specifies that distinct elements of B correspond to distinct elements of B' and conversely, or, briefly stated, the *distinctness* of the elements is preserved. Thirdly, (3) and (4) specify that every combination by addition and multiplication, respectively, in B goes over to like combinations of the corresponding elements of B' and conversely, or, briefly stated, the combinations of addition and of multiplication are preserved. Now, if the meaning of the elements is not taken into account, the *domain* B is characterized according to Section 1 merely by the given *totality* B

of elements together with their *distinctness* [Section 1, (a)] and the manner in which addition and multiplication are defined in it [Section 1, (b)]. This means that any statement about domains independent of the meaning of the elements of B (only such statements are of interest to us from the abstract point of view formulated in the introduction) is formed merely from the relations $=$, $\neq$ and the combinations of addition and of multiplication, to which subtraction and division are also reducible according to Section 1. Therefore, such statements are preserved, in the above sense, by the correspondence under consideration in passing from B to B′ as well as conversely in passing from B′ to B. In other words, within the limits prescribed, the domains B and B′ are *not to be distinguished at all.* Consequently, from our standpoint it is a matter of complete indifference whether such statements are made about B or B′.

Furthermore, let B and B′ be two extension domains of B_0 which are isomorphic relative to B_0. Then any statement which expresses a relationship between the elements of B and those of the subdomain B_0, based only on equality, distinctness and the four elementary operations, goes over into a valid statement on replacing the elements of the first domain by the elements in B′ corresponding to them. The converse is also true for the corresponding passage from B′ to B. To be brief, the extension domains B and B′ of B_0 are *not to be distinguished within* the limits prescribed. Consequently, it is again a matter of complete indifference whether such statements are made about B or B′.

Accordingly, when studying domains in algebra we are interested only in those statements which are common to all domains of a type; and when studying extension domains of a fixed domain B_0, only in such statements that are common to all domains of an extension type of B_0. This shows that the terms *type* and *extension type* introduced in Def. 7 and the Addendum to Def. 7 are in harmony with the usual meaning attached to the word "type." Statements of the specified kind are also said to deal with the *structure of domains.* It was stated at the end of the introduction that the deduction of such statements was the principal problem of modern algebra.

This exposition may seem to imply that in algebra no distinction whatever is drawn between isomorphic domains. This implication has to be qualified. True, the basic problem of algebra, as formulated in the introduction, is indifferent to whether it deals with a domain B or a B′ isomorphic to B. However, if the isomorphic domains B and B′ are both subdomains of another domain B*, then a distinction between them arises in a natural way, namely, their elements are distinct (with respect to considerations inside B*) in virtue of the individuality of the elements of B* (cf. the examples on p. 45 and p. 66).

In addition, it should be noted that the above exposition implies that the special property of being a field or an integral domain belongs at the same time to *all* domains of a type. Hence besides the general *ring types* we can speak in particular of *field types* and *types of integral domains.*

Examples

1. Every domain B is a subdomain and extension domain of itself. Any other subdomain and extension domain of B is called *true* or *proper.*

2. Without further exposition examples 1 to 3 of Section 1 yield clear examples of subdomains and extension domains.

3. If K_1, K_2 are subfields of K, their intersection is identical with K_1 and their composite with K_2 if and only if K_1 is a subfield of K_2. This is easy to demonstrate by Theorem 7 and Def. 5.

4. Further examples of subdomains and extension domains as well as of isomorphisms of domains will be given in Sections 3, 4.

5. The partition of the integers into *even* and *odd* yields according to (A) an equivalence relation. It is easy to show that this is a congruence relation in the integral domain Γ (Theorem 5 [19]). The residue class ring thereby determined is isomorphic to the field specified in Section 1, Example 4; therefore, it is a residue class *field.*

6. Further examples of congruence relations and residue class rings will be given in Vol. 2, Section 2.

3. The Quotient Field of an Integral Domain

It is important for us to prove that every integral domain can be extended to a field by adjoining all "quotients" which can be formed from its elements. We show, namely:

Theorem 10. *To every integral domain* I *there exists an extension field* K *all of whose elements can be represented as quotients of elements in* I. *The extension type of* K *relative to* I *is uniquely determined by this condition.*

Proof: [7]

a) *Proof of uniqueness*

Let K be a field with the properties specified in the theorem. Being a field it also contains conversely all quotients $\frac{a}{b}$ of elements a, b ($b \neq 0$) in I, that is, it consists of the totality of all these quotients (naturally, they need not all be different). By postulates Section 1, (1) to (7) for fields the following facts are then valid in K:

(1) $\frac{a}{b} = \frac{a'}{b'}$ if and only if $ab' = a'b$,

(2) $\frac{a_1}{b_1} + \frac{a_2}{b_2} = \frac{a_1b_2 + a_2b_1}{b_1b_2}$,

(3) $\frac{a_1}{b_1}\frac{a_2}{b_2} = \frac{a_1a_2}{b_1b_2}$,

(4) $\frac{a_1}{b_1} - \frac{a_2}{b_2} = \frac{a_1b_2 - a_2b_1}{b_1b_2}$,

(5) $\frac{a_1}{b_1}\Big/\frac{a_2}{b_2} = \frac{a_1\,b_2}{a_2\,b_1}$, if $\frac{a_2}{b_2} \neq 0$, that is $a_2 \neq 0$ (besides b_1, $b_2 \neq 0$).

[7] We stress here, as also in the case of the corresponding proof to Theorem 11 in Section 4, the logical framework of the proof. The facts cited at the individual steps are always easy to prove by means of Sections 1, 2. As a rule we will merely point out the parts of Sections 1, 2 which are involved in the proof and leave the more detailed exposition to the reader.

Now, let $\overline{\mathsf{K}}$ be another field as specified in the theorem, α an element of K and $\frac{a}{b}$ an arbitrary representation of α as a quotient of elements in I. Set up a correspondence whereby α is mapped on that element $\overline{\alpha}$ of $\overline{\mathsf{K}}$ which is represented by the same quotient. By the above remarks and (1) this is a one-to-one correspondence [Section 2, (δ), (δ'), (ε), (ε')] between the totality of elements of K and $\overline{\mathsf{K}}$. By (2) and (3) it satisfies the conditions Section 2, (3) and (4). Obviously, it also satisfies condition Section 2, (5) with respect to I as the ground domain. Therefore $\overline{\mathsf{K}} \cong \mathsf{K}$ relative to I. This proves the unique determination of the extension type of K relative to I.

b) *Introductory Remarks to the Existence Proof*

On principle the proof of the existence of a field K as specified in the theorem can be carried through only by the construction of K, that is, by producing its elements and their combinations. While doing so, of course, we are not allowed to operate with the quotients $\frac{a}{b}$, since these have a sense only on the basis of the existence of K. Consequently, for the construction we take away from the fraction line in $\frac{a}{b}$ its significance as a division symbol, think of $\frac{a}{b}$ merely as an ordered pair of elements from I and write it as (a, b) in order to avoid confusion with the quotients $\frac{a}{b}$ which may partly have been already defined in I. We will then draw from (1) to (3) the necessary general principles for specifying the elements of K and their combinations.

c) *Construction of a Field K' Isomorphic to K*

In the set M of all ordered pairs of elements (a, b), where a, b belong to I and $b \neq 0$, we define an equivalence relation by the convention:

(1′) $(a, b) \sim (a', b')$ if and only if $ab' = a'b$.

It is easy to confirm that this relation satisfies Section 2, (α), (β), (γ), so that this is actually an equivalence relation in the sense of Section 2, (I).

On the basis of (1′) M splits into classes. We think of these classes as forming a set K′ of distinct elements. The class generated by (a, b) is designated by $\{a, b\}$.

By (1′) and the analogue to Theorem 3 [17] $\{0, e\} \neq \{e, e\}$. Therefore Section 1, (a) is valid in K′.

Define in K′ two rules of combination, addition and multiplication, by the conventions:

(2′) $\{a_1, b_1\} + \{a_2, b_2\} = \{a_1 b_2 + a_2 b_1, b_1 b_2\}$,
(3′) $\{a_1, b_1\}\{a_2, b_2\} = \{a_1 a_2, b_1 b_2\}$.

By Theorem 4 [18] $b_1 b_2 \neq 0$ if both b_1 and b_2 are different from zero. Therefore the right sides in (2′) and (3′) are actually definite classes in K′.

Now, it is true that these conventions were first given in terms of the particular representatives (a_1, b_1) and (a_2, b_2) of the classes on the left. However, they are independent of the choice of these representatives inside their classes. It is easy to verify that it is only the representatives and not the classes on the right which are changed if (a_1, b_1) and (a_2, b_2) on the left are replaced by equivalent (a_1', b_1') and (a_2', b_2'). Consequently, in virtue of (2′) and (3′), Section 1, (b) is also realized in K′.

Finally, the operations defined in (2′) and (3′) satisfy postulates Section 1, (1) to (7). Thus, Section 1, (1) to (5) follow easily from the validity of each postulate in I, and Section 1, (6) and (7) follow from the validity of Section 1, (6) and (7a) in I. Hence differences and quotients are uniquely determined in K′ and are always given by

(4′) $\{a_1, b_1\} - \{a_2, b_2\} = \{a_1 b_2 - a_2 b_1, b_1 b_2\}$,

(5′) $\dfrac{\{a_1, b_1\}}{\{a_2, b_2\}} = \{a_1 b_2, a_2 b_1\}$, if $\{a_2, b_2\} \neq 0$.

The condition $\{a_2, b_2\} \neq 0$ laid down in (5′) implies $a_2 \neq 0$; for by (2′) or (4′) the class $\{0, e\}$ is the null element of K' and by (1′) $\{a, b\} = \{0, e\}$ implies $a = 0$.

Consequently, K' is a field with respect to the rules of combination (2′) and (3′).

d) *Construction of* K

The field K' contains the subset I' of the special classes $\{a, e\}$. By (2′) to (4′) and Theorem 6 [25] this subset is an integral subdomain of K'; furthermore by (1′) to (3′) and Def. 7 [30] it is isomorphic to I on the basis of the correspondence $\{a, e\} \longleftrightarrow a$. We now form a set K out of K'. It consists of the elements a in I corresponding to the elements $\{a, e\}$ in K' belonging to I' and the elements in K' not belonging to I'. Then K is a set of distinct elements which corresponds biuniquely to K'. Next, in K we define two rules of combination, addition and multiplication, by going back to the rules of combination defined for the corresponding elements of K', in other words, based on conditions (3) and (4) of Theorem 9 [29]. These, too, are unique, satisfy postulates Section 1, (1) to (7), and are identical for the subset I with the rules of combination already existing in I. The domain K thereby determined is an extension field of I isomorphic to K'.

This field K has the property specified in the theorem. Thus, by (3′) or (5′) every element $\{a, b\}$ of K' has a representation

$\{a, b\} = \dfrac{\{a, e\}}{\{b, e\}}$ as the quotient of two elements of I' —

($\{b, e\} \neq 0$ since $b \neq 0$). Hence the corresponding element of K has the representation $\frac{a}{b}$ as a quotient of two elements of I.

This completes the proof of Theorem 10.

The following corollary sharpens somewhat the uniqueness statement of Theorem 10. The existence statement of the corollary follows from Theorem 6 [25] and (2) to (5).

Corollary. *Within an arbitrary extension field* K^* *of* I *there is one and only one representative of the extension type specified in Theorem* 10, *namely, the field* K *which is formed by quotients constructed in* K^* *from elements of* I.

Proof: If in the previous proof under a) the assumption is added that K and $\overline{\mathsf{K}}$ are both subfields of one and the same extension field K^* of I, then it even follows that $\overline{\mathsf{K}} = \mathsf{K}$, since in this case the quotients $\frac{a}{b}$ in K and $\overline{\mathsf{K}}$ have one and the same meaning established through K^*.

In view of the remarks after Def. 7 [30] it is therefore proper to think of isomorphic extension fields of I of the type specified in Theorem 10 as not distinct and to define with the *definite article:*

Definition 8. *The field* K *specified in Theorem* 10 *is called the* ***quotient field*** *of the integral domain* I.

Examples

1. If I itself is already a field, then its quotient field is identical with I, and conversely.

2. The quotient field of the integral domain Γ cited in Theorem 5 is the field P given there, too. In fact, the construction process used under c) goes over in the case of I = Γ into the well-known construction of rational numbers from the integers.

3. Cf. Section 4, Def. 10.

4. The Integral Domain of Integral Rational Functions of *n* Indeterminates over I and the Field of Rational Functions of *n* Indeterminates over K.

The concept of integral rational function and of rational function used in algebra is basically different from the usual one in analysis.

In analysis the functions are defined as correspondences of function values to the elements of a set of arguments. Accordingly, in the sense of analysis we would speak of a function f of n variables over an integral domain I if to every ordered system of elements $x_1, \ldots, x_n$ in I there corresponds an element $f(x_1, \ldots, x_n)$ in I. In particular, an integral rational function is a correspondence for all $x_1, \ldots, x_n$ in I which applies one and the same calculating process to $x_1, \ldots, x_n$ and fixed elements of I, where this process is composed of finitely many additions, subtractions and multiplications, as defined in I. Similarly, a rational function of n variables over a field K is defined in the sense of analysis if division is also included as an operation. In this case, however, since division by 0 is not defined for a given calculating process, it may happen that not every system $x_1, \ldots,\ x_n$ in K is allowable as a system of arguments; later this will be formulated more precisely. It is obvious that the set of integral rational functions of n variables over I, as well as the set of rational functions over K, in the sense of analysis, form a *ring*, if the rules of combination are defined by addition and multiplication applied to all (defined) function values.

In algebra this function concept is insufficient, for reasons to be developed later in detail (after Theorem 12 [49]). In analysis a function is characterized primarily by the *correspondence* and secondarily by the kind of correspondence — in the case of the rational functions, the *calculating process*. On the contrary, in algebra, where we are concerned only with rational functions, the calculating expression is regarded as primary and the correspondence that it yields as secondary.[8] In accord with the latter standpoint in the following we develop a theory of integral rational, or rational, calculating expressions in $x_1, \ldots, x_n$ over I, or K, respectively. On account of the formal analogy these, too, will be called, as usual, integral rational, or rational, functions of $x_1, \ldots, x_n$ over I, or K, respectively. However, in order to avoid falling back into the correspondence standpoint, the $x_1, \ldots, x_n$ are deprived of their previous meaning as variables in I, or K, by introducing them as fixed elements outside of I, or K, respectively, namely, as so-called *indeterminates.*[9]

The domain of integral rational functions in the sense of algebra of $x_1, \ldots, x_n$ over an integral domain I is obtained through an abstract construction, entirely analogous to that in Section 3, by proving:

Theorem 11. *To any integral domain* I *there exists an extension integral domain* I_n *with the property:*

There exist n elements $x_1, \ldots, x_n$ *in* I_n, *such that every element of* I_n *can be uniquely represented in the form*

$$\sum_{k_1, \ldots, k_n = 0}^{\infty} a_{k_1, \ldots, k_n} x_1^{k_1} \ldots x_n^{k_n},$$ [10]

---

[8] This is, then, the function concept, more primitive from the standpoint of analysis, which historically precedes the modern function concept in the sense of analysis mentioned above. The following developments show that, on the contrary, the function concept regarded as the more primitive in analysis is the deeper-reaching in algebra.

[9] For this terminology, see the explanation after Def. 9 [46].

[10] The meaning of the summation symbol Σ with the attached indices for the summation domain is assumed as known. — It should be noted that here we are actually representing a finite sum formally as an infinite sum with only a finite number of summands $\neq 0$. In doing so we tacitly assume that a sum of infinitely many zeros is again zero. This is done only for reasons of notation. Otherwise, the formulation of the uniqueness of our representation would become quite complicated; so also would the formulae, to be met later, for operating with the elements thus represented.

where the $a_{k_1, \ldots, k_n}$ are elements of I, *among which there are only a finite number different from zero.*

The extension type of I_n *relative to* I *is uniquely determined by this condition.*

Proof: [11] First, we prove the theorem for $n = 1$. This case is handled in a way completely analogous to the proof of Theorem 10 in Section 3.

a) *Uniqueness Proof*

For $n = 1$, let I_1 be an integral domain of the kind specified in the theorem, and x the element in I_1 previously designated by x_1. Being an integral domain, I_1 also contains conversely all expressions $\sum_{k=0}^{\infty} a_k x^k$, where the a_k are elements in I, with only finitely many $\neq 0$. This means that I_1 consists of the totality of all these expressions. On account of the uniqueness condition of the theorem and by postulates Section 1, (1) to (6) for rings, the following facts are valid in I_1:

(1) $\sum_{k=0}^{\infty} a_k x^k = \sum_{k=0}^{\infty} a'_k x^k$ if and only if $a_k = a'_k$ for all k,

(2) $\sum_{k=0}^{\infty} a_k x^k + \sum_{k=0}^{\infty} b_k x^k = \sum_{k=0}^{\infty} (a_k + b_k) x^k$,

(3) $\sum_{k=0}^{\infty} a_k x^k \sum_{k=0}^{\infty} b_k x^k = \sum_{k=0}^{\infty} \Big(\sum_{\substack{\lambda, \mu = 0 \\ \lambda + \mu = k}}^{k} a_\lambda b_\mu \Big) x^k$,

(4) $\sum_{k=0}^{\infty} a_k x^k - \sum_{k=0}^{\infty} b_k x^k = \sum_{k=0}^{\infty} (a_k - b_k) x^k$.

Now, let $\overline{\mathsf{I}}_1$ be another integral domain of this kind, $\bar{x}$ the element of $\overline{\mathsf{I}}_1$ designated in the theorem by x_1. Furthermore, let the element $\sum_{k=0}^{\infty} a_k x^k$ of I_1 always be mapped on an element $\sum_{k=0}^{\infty} a_k \bar{x}^k$

[11] Cf. footnote 7 [33] to the proof of Theorem 10.

of $\overline{\mathsf{I}}_1$. Then, just as in Section 3, a), (1) to (3) imply that $\overline{\mathsf{I}}_1 \cong \mathsf{I}_1$ relative to I on the basis of this correspondence. This shows that the extension type of I_1 relative to I is uniquely determined.

b) *Introductory Remarks to the Existence Proof*

On principle the proof of the existence of an integral domain I_1, as specified in the theorem, can be carried through only by the construction of I_1, that is, by producing its elements and their combinations. While doing so, of course, we are not permitted to operate with the element x and the sum representations $\sum_{k=0}^{\infty} a_k x^k$, since these have a sense only on the basis of the existence of I_1. Hence for the construction we deprive x of its significance as an element, i.e., as something which can be subjected along with the elements of I to the first three elementary operations; also, we take away from $\sum_{k=0}^{\infty} a_k x^k$ the significance of calculating expressions. Instead, we look upon such expressions merely as ordered systems $(a_0, a_1, \ldots)$ of elements in I. We then draw from (1) to (3) the general principles required for specifying the elements of I_1 and their combinations.

c) *Construction of an Integral Domain* I_1' *Isomorphic to* I_1.

Let I_1' be the set of all ordered systems of elements $(a_0, a_1, \ldots)$, where each system contains a countable infinity of elements in I such that only finitely many $a_k \neq 0$. We think of it as a set of distinct elements where

(1′) $(a_0, a_1, \ldots) = (a_0', a_1', \ldots)$ if and only if $a_k = a_k'$ for all k.

Since $(0, 0, \ldots) \neq (e, 0, \ldots)$, then Section 1, (a) is valid in I_1'.

Next, in I_1' we define two rules of combination, addition and multiplication, by the conventions:

(2′) $(a_0, a_1, \ldots) + (b_0, b_1, \ldots) = (a_0 + b_0, a_1 + b_1, \ldots)$,

(3′) $(a_0, a_1, \ldots)(b_0, b_1, \ldots)$
$$= (a_0 b_0, a_0 b_1 + a_1 b_0, a_0 b_2 + a_1 b_1 + a_2 b_0, \ldots).$$

It is easy to show that the right-hand sides of (2′) and (3′) have again only finitely many terms $\neq 0$ and therefore belong to I_1', so that Section 1, (b) is valid in virtue of (2′) and (3′).

Furthermore, the operations defined in (2′) and (3′) satisfy postulates Section 1, (1) to (6). Thus, Section 1, (1) to (5) easily follows from the validity of each law in I; likewise, Section 1, (6) follows on the basis of the validity of Section 1, (6) in I. Consequently, differences are determined uniquely in I_1' and are always given by

(4′) $(a_0, a_1, \ldots) - (b_0, b_1, \ldots) = (a_0 - b_0, a_1 - b_1, \ldots)$

However, a more detailed exposition is needed to prove that postulate Section 1, (7 a) is valid in I_1'. Instead of this we will prove here the statement equivalent to it, by the Addendum to Def. 3 [18], that the analogue to Theorem 4 [18] is valid in I_1'. Since it follows from (2′) or (4′) that the element $(0, 0, \ldots)$ is the null element of I_1', the assumption

$$(a_0, a_1, \ldots)(b_0, b_1, \ldots) = 0$$

indicates that all terms of this product system formed according to (3′) are zero. Now, if $(a_0, a_1, \ldots) \neq 0$, $(b_0, b_1, \ldots) \neq 0$ were true, so that there would be a last $a_\nu \neq 0$ and a last $b_\mu \neq 0$, then the $(\nu + \mu)$-th term

$$a_0 b_{\mu+\nu} + \cdots + a_{\nu-1} b_{\mu+1} + a_\nu b_\mu + a_{\nu+1} b_{\mu-1} + \cdots + a_{\nu+\mu} b_0$$

of the product system, after the choice of a_ν and b_μ, would be equal to $a_\nu b_\mu$, and therefore would be different from zero on account of the validity of Theorem 4 in I, contradicting the assumption. Therefore, the analogue to Theorem 4 is valid in I_1'.

Finally, Section 1, (7b), that is, the analogue to Theorem 3 [17] in I'_1, is also valid, because by (3′) the element $(e, 0, 0, \ldots)$ is the unity element of I'_1.

Consequently, I'_1 is an integral domain with respect to the operations (2′) and (3′).

d) *Construction of* I_1

The integral domain I'_1 contains the subset I' of the special elements $(a, 0, 0, \ldots)$. By (2′) to (4′) and Theorem 6 [25] this subset is an integral subdomain of I'_1; furthermore, by (1′) to (3′) and Def. 7 [30] it is isomorphic to I through the correspondence $(a, 0, 0, \ldots) \longleftrightarrow a$. Just as in Section 3, d), we can then derive from I' an extension integral domain I_1 of I isomorphic to I'_1 by replacing each element of I' by the element of I corresponding to it.

This integral domain I_1 has the property specified in the theorem. Thus, if x denotes the special element $(0, e, 0, 0, \ldots)$ of I'_1, so that by (3′)

$$x^0 = e = (e, 0, 0, \ldots),\ x^1 = x = (0, e, 0, 0, \ldots),$$
$$x^2 = (0, 0, e, 0, 0, \ldots), \ldots,$$

is valid and $(a_0, a_1, \ldots)$ is any element of I'_1, then by (2′) and (3′)

$$(a_0, a_1, \ldots) = (a_0, 0, 0, \ldots)\, x^0 + (a_1, 0, 0, \ldots)\, x^1 + \cdots.$$

Since x does not belong to the subdomain I' of I'_1, it remains unchanged in passing over to I_1. Hence the corresponding element of I_1 has the representation $\sum_{k=0}^{\infty} a_k x^k$.

Finally, this representation is unique. For, $\sum_{k=0}^{\infty} a_k x^k = \sum_{k=0}^{\infty} a'_k x^k$, on passing over to the isomorphic I'_1, implies $(a_0, a_1, \ldots) = (a'_0, a'_1, \ldots)$; by (1′) this yields $a_k = a'_k$ for all k.

This completes the proof of Theorem 11 for $n=1$. For the proof in the case of arbitrary n the following two methods are at our disposal:

Either the integral domain I_n can be successively constructed. For this purpose, let us designate by $I[x]$ the integral domain I_1 generated from an arbitrary integral domain I by the part of the theorem already proved. Then we form successively

$$I_1 = I[x_1],\ I_2 = I_1[x_2], \ldots, I_n = I_{n-1}[x_n].$$

The statements of the theorem for I_n can then be proved altogether by mathematical induction relative to n.

Or, the development of the above proof for $n=1$ is applied to any n. This procedure leads to no difficulties. Instead of (1) to (3) we then have:

(1a) $\sum\limits_{k_1,\ldots,k_n=0}^{\infty} a_{k_1,\ldots,k_n} x_1^{k_1}\ldots x_n^{k_n} = \sum\limits_{k_1,\ldots,k_n=0}^{\infty} a'_{k_1,\ldots,k_n} x_1^{k_1}\ldots x_n^{k_n}$ if and only if $a_{k_1,\ldots,k_n} = a'_{k_1,\ldots,k_n}$ for all systems $(k_1,\ldots,k_n)$,

(2a) $$\sum_{k_1,\ldots,k_n=0}^{\infty} a_{k_1,\ldots,k_n} x_1^{k_1}\ldots x_n^{k_n} + \sum_{k_1,\ldots,k_n=0}^{\infty} b_{k_1,\ldots,k_n} x_1^{k_1}\ldots x_n^{k_n}$$
$$= \sum_{k_1,\ldots,k_n=0}^{\infty} (a_{k_1,\ldots,k_n} + b_{k_1,\ldots,k_n})\, x_1^{k_1}\ldots x_n^{k_n},$$

(3a) $$\sum_{k_1,\ldots,k_n=0}^{\infty} a_{k_1,\ldots,k_n} x_1^{k_1}\ldots x_n^{k_n} \sum_{k_1,\ldots,k_n=0}^{\infty} b_{k_1,\ldots,k_n} x_1^{k_1}\ldots x_n^{k_n}$$
$$= \sum_{k_1,\ldots,k_n=0}^{\infty} \Big(\sum_{\substack{\lambda_1,\mu_1=0,\ldots,\lambda_n,\mu_n=0\\ \lambda_1+\mu_1=k_1,\ldots,\lambda_n+\mu_n=k_n}}^{\infty}\cdots\sum^{\infty} a_{\lambda_1,\ldots,\lambda_n} b_{\mu_1,\ldots,\mu_n}\Big)\, x_1^{k_1}\ldots x_n^{k_n}.$$

From this it is immediately evident how to choose the elements of I_n [namely, all systems $a_{k_1,\ldots,k_n}$ $(k_1,\ldots,k_n = 0, 1, \ldots)$ in an n-dimensional scheme of elements in I with only finitely many $\neq 0$] and their combinations.

It is left to the reader to carry out the details of the two methods in accordance with these hints.

The first method is significant theoretically, besides having the advantage of getting along on the computationally simple development of the proof carried out for $n = 1$. For, many theorems about I_n can be proved only by mathematical induction with respect to n, i. e., by reduction to the indicated recursive construction of I_n (cf., for instance, Vol. 2, Theorem 49 [208]). The second method, however, is more satisfactory because it immediately renders the special consideration of the case $n = 1$ superfluous. Moreover, in contrast to the first method, it takes into account an important property of I_n, namely, the *symmetry* in $x_1, \ldots, x_n$. This means, as is obvious from Theorem 11, that I_n goes into itself if the roles of the elements $x_1, \ldots, x_n$ are interchanged in any way whatever.

Here, in contrast to Section 3, Theorem 10, Corollary [37], there can actually exist within an arbitrary extension integral domain I^* several different representatives of the extension type specified in Theorem 11 (for instance, if $I^* = I[x_1, \ldots, x_n, x_{n+1}, \ldots, x_{n+m}]$, all $I[x_{i_1}, \ldots, x_{i_n}]$, where $i_1, \ldots, i_n$ are any n different numerals from the sequence $1, \ldots, n+m$). However, it is obvious that any such representative within I^* is determined uniquely by giving those elements of I^* which play the role of $x_1, \ldots, x_n$; this means that each representative is the totality of expressions in these elements, where each expression has the form specified in Theorem 11.

In view of the remarks after Def. 7 we are therefore again justified in defining with the *definite* article:

Definition 9. *The integral domain I_n specified in Theorem 11 is called the* ***integral domain of the integral rational functions of the n indeterminates*** *$x_1, \ldots, x_n$ over I. It will be designated by $I[x_1, \ldots, x_n]$, its elements by $f(x_1, \ldots, x_n), \ldots$ or, more briefly, by $f, \ldots$.*

The unique representations of these elements in the form of Theorem 11 are called their ***normal representations*** *and the elements $a_{k_1, \ldots, k_n}$ of I appearing therein, the* ***coefficients*** *of this representation.*

In designating the x_i as *indeterminates* we mean that each individual x_i, with respect to I, admits of no *determination* other than the negative one, that no equation $\sum_{k=0}^{\infty} a_k x_i^k = 0$ (with only finitely many coefficients $a_k \neq 0$) exists except the trivial one, where all $a_k = 0$. The x_i are therefore neither elements of I, nor do they satisfy algebraic equations in I (see Section 5, [56] and Vol. 2, Def. 21, [223]). Hence *Steinitz* called them *transcendental* elements relative to I. Nor, on account of (1 a), are the x_i mutually connected through positive determinations (algebraic equations). Therefore, to be more precise, *Steinitz* called them a system of *algebraically independent* elements relative to I.

$I[x_1, \ldots, x_n]$ is always a *proper* extension domain of I, since the uniqueness of the normal representation implies that the elements $x_1, \ldots, x_n$, for instance, do not belong to I.

$I[x_1, \ldots, x_n]$ is never a field (even if I is a field). On the basis of the successive construction given above it is sufficient to prove this for $I[x]$. It is easy to see that $I[x]$ does not contain the quotient $\frac{e}{x}$, because for any

$$f(x) = \sum_{k=0}^{\infty} a_k x^k \text{ from } I[x] \text{ we have } x f(x) = \sum_{k=0}^{\infty} a_k x^{k+1}$$
$$= 0 + a_0 x + a_1 x^2 + \cdots \neq e + 0x + 0x^2 + \cdots = e.$$

We will now include the *rational* calculating expressions in $x_1, \ldots, x_n$, which were specified at the beginning of this section. For this purpose we extend $I[x_1, \ldots, x_n]$ to the quotient field. In doing this the subdomain I will be, in particular, extended to the quotient field. Consequently, it is sufficient to start with a field K and the corresponding integral domain $K[x_1, \ldots, x_n]$.

Definition 10. *If* K *is a field, then the quotient field of the integral domain* $K[x_1, \ldots, x_n]$ *is called the* ***field of the rational functions of the n indeterminates*** $x_1, \ldots, x_n$ *over* K. *It will be designated by* $K(x_1, \ldots, x_n)$, *its elements by* $\varphi(x_1, \ldots, x_n), \ldots$ *or more briefly by* $\varphi, \ldots$

The integral rational functions over I, and the rational functions over K, in the sense of analysis will now be derived from the integral rational functions over I, and the rational functions over K, defined above from an algebraic standpoint, by attaching to the foregoing *indeterminates* $x_1, \ldots, x_n$ the significance of elements of I or K, respectively. First, for I $[x_1, \ldots, x_n]$ we form:

Definition 11. *By the* ***integral rational function in the sense of analysis associated*** *to an element f of* I $[x_1, \ldots, x_n]$ *we understand that function over* I *in the sense of analysis which is generated by associating to every system of elements* $x_1, \ldots, x_n$ *in* I *the function value consisting of the elements of* I *yielded by the normal representation of f.*

For the present, let the ring of integral rational functions of $x_1, \ldots, x_n$ over I in the sense of analysis, mentioned at the beginning of this section, be designated by $\overline{\mathsf{I}[x_1, \ldots, x_n]}$. For this ring we prove the following fact which is of basic importance in passing from I $[x_1, \ldots, x_n]$ to $\overline{\mathsf{I}[x_1, \ldots, x_n]}$ and which we call the **principle of substitution:**

Theorem 12. *In passing from* $\mathsf{B} = \mathsf{I}[x_1, \ldots, x_n]$ *to* $\mathsf{B}' = \overline{\mathsf{I}[x_1, \ldots, x_n]}$ *by the correspondence defined in Def.* 11 *the conditions, Section* 2, (δ), (δ′), (ε), (3), (4), (5) *remain valid though* (ε) *need not. This transition maps the totality of elements of* I $[x_1, \ldots, x_n]$ *upon the totality of the elements of* $\overline{\mathsf{I}[x_1, \ldots, x_n]}$; *it preserves equality and all relations arising from the rules of combination, though not necessarily the distinctness of the elements of* I $[x, \ldots, x_n]$. *If and only if Section* 2, (ε′) *also is satisfied do we have* $\mathsf{I}[x_1, \ldots, x_n] \cong \overline{\mathsf{I}[x_1, \ldots, x_n]}$ *on the basis of the above correspondence.*

Proof: a) The validity of Section 2, (δ), (ε.) naturally follows from the fact that the correspondence rule of Def. 11 is unique and applicable to any element in $\mathsf{I}[x_1, \ldots, x_n]$.

b) The validity of Section 2, (3), (4), (5) is easy to see from the above formulas (2a), (3a). For this purpose we merely note that in the latter the normal representation of the sum and product of two elements of $\mathsf{I}[x_1, \ldots, x_n]$ is calculated from that of the summands or factors, respectively, by applying only postulates Section 1, (1) to (5) valid in $\mathsf{I}[x_1, \ldots, x_n]$. For, since these postulates are valid in I, these transformations are also permissible if $x_1, \ldots, x_n$ are elements in I.

c) In order to comprehend the validity of Section 2, (δ′) we have to show that conversely any integral rational function of $x_1, \ldots, x_n$ over I in the sense of analysis also corresponds according to Def. 11 to an element f of $\mathsf{I}[x_1, \ldots, x_n]$. Let us now consider calculating processes which consist of finitely many additions, subtractions and multiplications applied to $x_1, \ldots, x_n$ and fixed elements of I. If, for the present, $x_1, \ldots, x_n$ are regarded as indeterminates, namely, as elements of $\mathsf{I}[x_1, \ldots, x_n]$, then such a calculating process yields an element f of $\mathsf{I}[x_1, \ldots, x_n]$, simply because these operations can be carried out without restriction in the integral domain $\mathsf{I}[x_1, \ldots, x_n]$. Furthermore, according to the proofs already given in b) all relations arising from the rules of combination are preserved in passing from $\mathsf{I}[x_1, \ldots, x_n]$ to $\overline{\mathsf{I}[x_1, \ldots, x_n]}$ by our correspondence. If this is applied to that relation which expresses the element f in terms of the elements $x_1, \ldots, x_n$ and fixed elements of I, then it follows that the function values produced by the calculating process mentioned above are the same as those produced by the normal representation of f. Consequently, the submitted integral rational function in the sense of analysis is identical with the one corresponding to f.

d) Section 2, (ε') is not satisfied, for instance, if we choose for I the field K (Section 1, Example 4) consisting only of 0 and e. For, in this case to the two distinct elements $x+x^2$ and 0 of $\mathsf{K}[x]$ there corresponds the same function 0 in the sense of analysis, because $x+x^2$ is also zero for all x in K (that is, for $x=0$ and $x=e$).

Moreover, in Vol. 2, Theorem 49, [208] and Vol. 3. Section 4, Exer. 7, 8 as well as Section 1, Exer. 9 we will see that Section 2, (ε') is satisfied if and only if I has infinitely many elements. In other words, if I is infinite, then $\overline{\mathsf{I}[x_1, \ldots, x_n]} \cong \mathsf{I}[x_1, \ldots, x_n]$ relative to I; if I is finite, this is never valid.

It is because of the possibility existing under d) that the aims of algebra are not served by the function concept which is dependent on the concept of correspondence and accordingly characterizes the functions by their *function values*; instead, in algebra we need the formal function concept set forth above, which yields a more refined characterization of functions by means of their *calculating expressions*. True, as implied in the remarks under *d*) this distinction is actually necessary only for finite integral domains. However, methodical viewpoints based on the foundations given in Section 1 naturally keep deciding in favor of the *calculating expression* as superior to the *function values* yielded by it.

In the preceding we have deliberately refrained from introducing a notation for distinguishing whether $x_1, \ldots, x_n$ are to be regarded as indeterminates or as elements of I. Instead, we have left it to the context to make this distinction so that the passage from the first to the second meaning of $x_1, \ldots, x_n$, to be carried out so often in the following, would not always lead to a change of notation. On the basis of Theorem 12, it is also permissible, with regard to the *rules of combination*, to let

$f(x_1, \ldots, x_n)$ designate the associated function values as well as the elements of $I[x_1, \ldots, x_n]$. Consequently, we will keep using $f(x_1, \ldots, x_n)$ to designate the function value associated to f for the system of elements $x_1, \ldots, x_n$ in I; for the sake of brevity, such a *function value* will also be called simply an integral rational *function* of $x_1, \ldots, x_n$ over I. However, the notation f (without arguments) shall only be used for the element of $I[x_1, \ldots, x_n]$. [Accordingly, $f(x_1, \ldots, x_n)$ is not at the same time a symbol for the function in the sense of analysis associated to f but only for a particular value of this function, which itself is formed only through the totality of all function values $f(x_1, \ldots, x_n)$.] Hence we only have to introduce in some way a notation which will distinguish between the two entirely different statements of *equality*:

$f(x_1, \ldots, x_n) = g(x_1, \ldots, x_n)$ as elements of $I[x_1, \ldots, x_n]$,

$f(x_1, \ldots, x_n) = g(x_1, \ldots, x_n)$ as function value for the system of elements $x_1, \ldots, x_n$ over I.

Therefore, we make the further convention that the symbol $\equiv$ (contrariwise, $\not\equiv$) shall be used to designate the first of the two statements.[12] On the basis of what has already been agreed upon, however, we can and will use the expression $f = g$ as equivalent to $f(x_1, \ldots, x_n) \equiv g(x_1, \ldots, x_n)$. By these conventions it unequivocally follows from the chosen designation which of the two possible interpretations of $x_1, \ldots, x_n$ is valid in a relation of equality or inequality.

[12] The relation $f(x_1, \ldots, x_n) \equiv g(x_1, \ldots, x_n)$ implies that the relation: $f(x_1, \ldots, x_n) = g(x_1, \ldots, x_n)$ for *all* $x_1, \ldots, x_n$ in I is valid; by the above, however, the converse need not be valid. Consequently, the symbol $\equiv$ has in general a more far-reaching meaning than is often understood by it, namely *equality* for all $x_1, \ldots, x_n$. — Any confusion between the relation $\equiv$ herein described and the congruence relation in the sense of Def. 6 [27] is excluded through the context.

Finally, the following definition enables us to make the transition from the elements of $K(x_1, \ldots, x_n)$ to the rational functions in the sense of analysis:

Definition 12. *By the* ***rational function in the sense of analysis associated*** *to an element* φ *of* $K(x_1, \ldots, x_n)$ *we understand that function in the sense of analysis over* K *which is formed when to any system of elements* $x_1, \ldots, x_n$ *in* K, *for which there exists at least one representation* $\frac{f}{g}$ *of* φ *as quotient of two elements of* $K[x_1, \ldots, x_n]$ *with* $g(x_1, \ldots, x_n) \neq 0$, *there corresponds as function value the quotient* $\frac{f(x_1, \ldots, x_n)}{g(x_1, \ldots, x_n)}$ *of the function values of f and g.*

Analogous to Theorem 12 the **principle of substitution** is valid here:

Theorem 13. *For the field* $K(x_1, \ldots, x_n)$ *and the ring* $\overline{K(x_1, \ldots, x_n)}$ *of the rational functions of* $x_1, \ldots, x_n$ *over* K *in the sense of analysis we have in virtue of the correspondence defined in Def.* 12 *that the analogue to Theorem* 12 *is valid except that here any possible nonvalidity of Section* 2, (ε') *always implies the nonvalidity of Section* 2, (δ).

Proof: a) In order to prove that Section 2, (ε) is satisfied, it must be shown that the function in the sense of analysis corresponding by Def. 12 to an element φ of $K(x_1, \ldots, x_n)$ is determined by φ alone independently of the particular choice (satisfying the condition of Def. 12) of its representation as a quotient $\frac{f}{g}$. Now, if $\frac{f}{g}$ and $\frac{f'}{g'}$ are two representations (satisfying these conditions) of φ as quotients, then from the relation $fg' = f'g$, existing by Section 3, (1), it follows by Theorem 12 that

$$f(x_1, \ldots, x_n)\, g'(x_1, \ldots, x_n) = f'(x_1, \ldots, x_n)\, g(x_1, \ldots, x_n)$$

is also valid. Hence by the assumption of Def. 12 regarding g and g it follows further that $\frac{f(x_1, \ldots, x_n)}{g(x_1, \ldots, x_n)} = \frac{f'(x_1, \ldots, x_n)}{g'(x_1, \ldots, x_n)}$.

b) By going back to the formulae, Section 3, (2) and (3) and applying Theorem 12, it likewise follows that Section 2, (3), (4), (5) are satisfied.

c) The validity of Section 2, (δ') follows just as in the proof of Theorem 12 under c); for the precise statement and derivation, see Vol. 3, Section 5, Exer. 1.

d) That Section 2, (ε') need not be valid is shown by the same example as above. It is obvious that this situation arises if and only if there exists at least one element g in $\mathsf{K}[x_1, \ldots, x_n]$ such that $g \neq 0$ but $g(x_1, \ldots, x_n) = 0$ for *all* $x_1, \ldots, x_n$ in K. On the one hand, if this is the case, the element $\frac{e}{g}$ in $\mathsf{K}(x_1, \ldots, x_n)$ has the property that there is *no* system of elements $x_1, \ldots, x_n$ in K for which it can be represented as a quotient whose denominator has a function value different from zero; for, by Section 3, (1) $\frac{f}{gf}$ is its most general quotient representation, where f is an arbitrary element of $\mathsf{K}[x_1, \ldots, x_n]$. In such a case there would be no function in the sense of analysis corresponding to $\frac{e}{g}$, since by Def. 12 the function values are undefined for *every* $x_1, \ldots, x_n$ in K. On the other hand, if there exists no such g in $\mathsf{K}[x_1, \ldots, x_n]$, then a function value can be associated according to Def. 12 to the quotient $\frac{f}{g}$ for at least one system of elements $x_1, \ldots, x_n$ in K.

On the basis of Theorem 13 the remarks about $\mathsf{I}[x_1, \ldots, x_n]$ made in connection with Theorem 12 may accordingly be applied to $K(x_1, \ldots, x_n)$, too. Hence our notational convention shall also be valid for the elements of $K(x_1, \ldots, x_n)$.

5. Detailed Formulation of the Basic Problem of Algebra

By means of the concepts explained in the preceding, we will now give an exact formulation of the basic problem of algebra specified in the introduction.

According to the formulation of the introduction, we obtain an **"equation"** formed by means of the four elementary operations between known and unknown elements of a field K, if we submit two calculating processes applied to the unknowns $x_1, \ldots, x_n$ and given (known) elements of K and ask for which systems of elements $x_1, \ldots, x_n$ in K do both processes yield the same result. This implies that the unknowns $x_1, \ldots, x_n$ have at first the character of indeterminates, and that the submitted calculating processes are two elements φ and φ' in $K(x_1, \ldots, x_n)$. The question implied in the "equation" refers then, in a certain analogy to the last developments of Section 4, to the replacement of the indeterminates $x_1, \ldots, x_n$ by systems of elements $x_1, \ldots, x_n$ in K and amounts to asking for which of these systems of elements is the equation $\varphi(x_1, \ldots, x_n) = \varphi'(x_1, \ldots, x_n)$ valid.

Since such an "equation" written as a *condition* or *question* has logically a meaning altogether different from the usual, similarly designated, *fact* of the existence of the equation, we will introduce a special symbol $\doteq$ (contrariwise, $\not\doteq$) to designate conditional equality. Hence the question specified above is designated by $\varphi(x_1, \ldots, x_n) \doteq \varphi'(x_1, \ldots, x_n)$.

First by applying the principle of substitution to the relation $\varphi - \varphi' = \psi$ the equation $\varphi(x_1, \ldots, x_n) \doteq \varphi'(x_1, \ldots, x_n)$ becomes equivalent to an equation of the form $\psi(x_1, \ldots, x_n) \doteq 0$, where ψ is again an element of $\mathsf{K}(x_1, \ldots, x_n)$.

Before reducing this equation further we must deal with the following situation. On the one hand, the calculating process leading to ψ in the sense of the stated problem (which process, according to $\psi = \varphi - \varphi'$, is composed of the two processes given originally and leading to φ and φ') consists, on closer inspection, of a chain of individual operations. Each operation is an addition, subtraction, multiplication or division of two elements, each of which is either an element of K or one of the $x_1, \ldots, x_n$ or is obtained from one of the preceding operations. On the other hand, as ψ is an element of $\mathsf{K}(x_1, \ldots, x_n)$, its normal representation can be written in the simple form of a quotient $\frac{f}{g}$ of two elements of $\mathsf{K}[x_1, \ldots, x_n]$. By the principle of substitution the result of substituting a system of elements $x_1, \ldots, x_n$ of K is indifferent to whether this substitution is made *before* the process is carried out (in other words, as implied in the sense of the problem, whether we calculate freely from the beginning with the $x_1, \ldots, x_n$ as elements of K), or whether the substitution in a quotient representation $\frac{f}{g}$ is made only *after* the process has been carried out. It should be understood, of course, that this statement is valid *only if we restrict ourselves to those substitutions for which neither the denominator g nor any one of the denominators appearing in the successive application of the calculating processes is zero.* Now, at the outset we are not at all sure that the denominator g is actually different from zero for those systems of elements of K for which the successive denominators of the process were not zero and *which would therefore be allowable in the sense of the stated problem.* However, it can be shown that among all quotient representations of ψ there is one (at least) with this property (see Vol. 3, Section 5, Exer. 1). Such a quotient representation $\psi = \frac{f}{g}$, adapted in a natural way to the problem, is taken as a basis in the following.

In virtue of a quotient representation $\psi = \frac{f}{g}$ (of the kind just characterized in detail) the solution of the equation $\psi(x_1, \ldots, x_n) \doteq 0$ can now be reduced further, by Section 3 and the principle of substitution, to the determination of all those solutions of $f(x_1, \ldots, x_n) = 0$ which are also solutions of $g(x_1, \ldots, x_n) \doteq\!\!\!/\, 0$. Now, since the solutions of the latter inequality are known if those of the equation $g(x_1, \ldots, x_n) \doteq 0$ are known, the problem reduces itself to considering equations of the form

$$f(x_1, \ldots, x_n) \doteq 0,$$

where f is an element of $\mathsf{K}[x_1, \ldots x_n]$.

Although, in principle, the common solutions of a number of equations are under control if the solutions of each individual equation are known, it is still useful from a theoretical as well as a practical viewpoint to consider such *systems of equations* as a whole. Consequently, we formulate the **problem of algebra** to be used as our guide in the following way:

Let K *be a field and* $f_1, \ldots, f_m$ *elements of* $\mathsf{K}[x_1, \ldots, x_n]$. *There shall be developed*[13] *methods for obtaining all solutions of the system of equations*

$$f_i(x_1, \ldots, x_n) = 0 \quad (i = 1, \ldots, m).$$

A systematic complete theory for the solution of this problem in its full generality would require more space than is available in this presentation. Therefore, we shall consider here only the following two specializations of the general case:

---

[13] This problem suggests the following two generalizations:

1. The number of equations and unknowns may also be allowed to be countably infinite;
2. Instead of the field K an integral domain (or even only a ring) may be used as a basis.

In recent times both cases have been studied.

1) The elements $f_1, \ldots, f_m$ are *linear*, that is, all coefficients in the normal representation (Def. 9 [45]) of these elements are zero except at most the $n+1$ coefficients

$$a_{0,\ldots,0}\,,\quad a_{1,0,\ldots,0}\,,\ldots,\quad a_{0,\ldots,0,1}.$$

In this case we are concerned with a system of equations which can be written in the form

$$(1) \qquad \sum_{k=1}^{n} a_{ik} x_k \doteq a_i \quad (i=1,\ldots,m),$$

where a_{ik} and a_i are elements of K. A system of equations of the form (1) is called a **system of linear equations** in K.

2) Let $m=n=1$. We are then concerned with a single equation of the form

$$\sum_{k=0}^{\infty} a_k x^k \doteq 0,$$

where the a_k are elements of K with only finitely many $\neq 0$. We can disregard the trivial case where all $a_k = 0$, since in this case any x in K is a solution of the equation. Consequently, there exists a last $a_r \neq 0$. The index r so determined is called the *degree* of the leftmost element of $K[x]$. The case $r=0$ is also trivial, since the assumption $a_0 \neq 0$ implies that there is no x in K which satisfies the equation. Consequently, an equation of the form

$$(2) \qquad \sum_{k=0}^{r} a_k x^k \doteq 0 \quad (a_r \neq 0, \quad r \geqq 1)$$

is to be considered. An equation of the form (2) is called an **algebraic equation of r-th degree** in K.

In Vol. 1, Chapters III and IV we will consider the subproblem 1); in Vol. 2, the subproblem 2).

II. Groups

6. Definition of Groups

One speaks of a group if the following postulates are realized:

(a) *A* ***set*** 𝔊 ***of distinct elements*** *is submitted which contains either an arbitrary finite or an infinite number of elements.*

See the remarks to Section 1, (a). Here, however, we will not require that 𝔊 have at least two different elements. We designate groups by capital German letters, elements of groups by capital Latin letters.

(b) *For any two elements A, B of 𝔊, given in a definite order,* ***one rule of combination*** *is defined, that is, to every ordered pair of elements A, B of 𝔊 there corresponds somehow an element C of 𝔊.*

See the remarks to Section 1, (b). We call the rule of combination *multiplication,* though on occasion addition in a domain will also be regarded as a group operation. We write $C = AB$ and call C the *product* of A and B.

(c) *For arbitrary elements of 𝔊 the rule of combination specified in (b) satisfies the laws:*

(1) $(AB)C = A(BC)$ ***(associative law);***

(2) *To every ordered pair of elements A, C of 𝔊, there exist uniquely determined elements B_1 and B_2 of 𝔊 such that $AB_1 = C$ and $B_2A = C$* ***(Law of the unrestricted and unique right and left division).***

We note the omission of the commutative law in contrast to its inclusion in both the addition and multiplication postulates of Section 1 for fields. Hence in (2) we must distinguish between right[1] division

[1] These designations refer to the position of the quotients B_1, B_2.

(determination of B_1 from $AB_1 = C$) and left[1] division (determination of B_2 from $B_2A = C$). As a consequence the notation $\frac{C}{A}$ cannot be used. On occasion authors write $B_1 = A \diagdown C$, $B_2 = C/A$; however, the notation of Theorem 15 is more widely adopted. Naturally, the restriction $a \neq 0$ in postulate Section 1, (7) corresponding to (2) is not imposed here; for, since a second rule of combination is not submitted, there is no distributive law [cf. the remark after Section 1, (7)].

Definition 13. *If the postulates specified under* (a), (b), (c) *are realized in a set* $\mathfrak{G}$, *then* $\mathfrak{G}$ *is called a* ***group*** *with respect to the rule of combination* (b). *The number of elements of* $\mathfrak{G}$ *(whether it be finite or infinite) is called the* ***order*** *of* $\mathfrak{G}$. *In particular, if the commutative law*

(3) $$AB = BA$$

is also satisfied, $\mathfrak{G}$ *is called an* ***Abelian group.***

The analogue to Theorem 3 [17] is also valid for groups:

Theorem 14. *In every group* $\mathfrak{G}$ *there exists a uniquely determined element E, called the* ***unity element*** *or* ***identity*** *of* $\mathfrak{G}$, *with the property:*

$$AE = EA = A \text{ for all } A \text{ in } \mathfrak{G}.$$

Proof: For all $A, B, \ldots$ in $\mathfrak{G}$, by (2) there exist in $\mathfrak{G}$ elements $E_A, E_B, \ldots$ and $F_A, F_B, \ldots$, such that

$$AE_A = A, \quad BE_B = B, \ldots$$
$$F_A A = A, \quad F_B B = B, \ldots$$

Furthermore, to every pair of elements A, B of $\mathfrak{G}$, by (2) elements C and D can be chosen such that

$$AC = B, \quad DA = B.$$

By (1) this implies that

[1] These designations refer to the position of the quotients B_1, B_2.

$$BE_A = (DA)E_A = D(AE_A) = DA = B = BE_B,$$
$$F_A B = F_A(AC) = (F_A A)C = AC = B = F_B B,$$

therefore $E_A = E_B$, $F_A = F_B$ on account of the uniqueness in (2). Hence E_A, E_B, ... are all the same element E; F_A, F_B, ... are all the same element F; and $AE = A$, $FA = A$ is valid for every A in $\mathfrak{G}$. In particular, this implies that for $A = F$, and E, $FE = F$, and $FE = E$, respectively; therefore, $E = F$. That E is determined uniquely by the stipulation of the theorem naturally follows from the uniqueness in (2).

In regard to division in a group we further prove:

Theorem 15. *To every element A of a group $\mathfrak{G}$ there exists a uniquely determined element A^{-1} of $\mathfrak{G}$, called the* ***inverse*** *of A, with the property*

$$AA^{-1} = A^{-1}A = E.$$

It is valid that

$$(AB)^{-1} = B^{-1}A^{-1}.$$

The elements B_1 and B_2 (right and left quotient of C and A) specified in (2) *are given by*

$$B_1 = A^{-1}C, \quad B_2 = CA^{-1}.$$

Proof: a) By (2) there exist uniquely determined elements A_1 and A_2 in $\mathfrak{G}$ such that

$$AA_1 = A_2 A = E.$$

By (1) and Theorem 14 it then follows that

$$A_1 = EA_1 = (A_2 A)\, A_1 = A_2 (AA_1) = A_2 E = A_2.$$

Therefore the element $A^{-1} =: A_1 = A_2$ has the property specified in the theorem and is uniquely determined by A.

b) From
$$(AB)(B^{-1}A^{-1}) = A(BB^{-1})\,A^{-1} = AEA^{-1}$$
$$= AA^{-1} = E$$

and the uniqueness of $(AB)^{-1}$ it follows that $(AB)^{-1} = B^{-1}A^{-1}$.

c) By (1), Theorem 14, and the proofs under a) the elements $B_1 = A^{-1}C$, $B_2 = CA^{-1}$ satisfy the equations $AB_1 = C$,

$B_2A = C$; therefore, by (2) they are the uniquely determined solutions of those equations.

Analogously to the conventions agreed upon at the end of Section 1, we write

$\ldots, A^{-2}, A^{-1}, A^0, A^1, A^2, \ldots$ for $\ldots, A^{-1}A^{-1}, A^{-1}, E, A, AA, \ldots$
(*integral powers of A*).

By taking into account the formula

$$(A^{-1})^{-1} = A,$$

which is valid by Theorem 15, it then follows by the definition of the arithmetical operations in the domain of the integers that

$$A^m A^n = A^{m+n}, \ (A^m)^n = A^{mn}$$

for arbitrary integers m, n. In particular, $E^m = E$ is valid for every integer m.

We formulate the following two theorems especially on account of later application. The first is merely a rephrasing of postulate (2).

Theorem 16. *If A is a fixed element of a group $\mathfrak{G}$, then each of the products AB and BA runs through all elements of $\mathfrak{G}$, each once, if B does.*

Theorem 17. *The inverse B^{-1} runs through all elements of $\mathfrak{G}$, each once, if B does.*

Proof: a) If A is any element of $\mathfrak{G}$, then by Theorem 15 $A = (A^{-1})^{-1}$; therefore A is the inverse B^{-1} of $B = A^{-1}$.

b) From $B_1^{-1} = B_2^{-1}$ it follows that $(B_1^{-1})^{-1} = (B_2^{-1})^{-1}$; therefore $B_1 = B_2$, again by Theorem 15.

In order to prove that a set is a group, condition (2), namely, that all left and right quotients exist and are uniquely determined, can be replaced by two simpler conditions as a consequence of

Theorem 18. *Under the assumption that* (a), (b) *and* (1) *are satisfied, postulate* (2) *is equivalent to the two postulates*:

(2 a) *There exists an element E in $\mathfrak{G}$ such that $AE = A$ for all A in $\mathfrak{G}$* ***(existence of the right-hand unity element).***

(2 b) *To every A in $\mathfrak{G}$ there exists an element A^{-1} of $\mathfrak{G}$, such that $AA^{-1} = E$* ***(existence of the right-hand inverse).***

Proof: a) If (a), (b), (1), (2) are satisfied, then by the preceding (2 a) and (2 b) are also satisfied.

b) Let (a), (b), (1), (2 a), (2 b) be satisfied. Then by (2 b) the right-hand inverse of A^{-1} also exists. If it is $(A^{-1})^{-1}$, then on multiplying the relation $A^{-1}(A^{-1})^{-1} = E$ on the left by A it follows from (1), (2 a), (2 b) that $E(A^{-1})^{-1} = A$. On the one hand, this means that $EA = E(A^{-1})^{-1} = A$, that is, E is also a left-hand unity element; on the other hand, $(A^{-1})^{-1} = A$, therefore $A^{-1}A = E$. Consequently A^{-1} is also the left-hand inverse of A. By (2 b) as well as (1) this implies that the equations $AB_1 = C$ and $B_2A = C$ are equivalent to the relations $B_1 = A^{-1}C$ and $B_2 = CA^{-1}$, respectively; namely, the latter are obtained from the former by left and right multiplication, respectively, by A^{-1} and conversely by A. These equations will therefore be uniquely solved by these expressions B_1, B_2. Hence (2) is satisfied.

Examples

1. Obviously every ring is an Abelian group with respect to the ring addition as the group operation. The unity element of this group is the null element of the ring. Furthermore, the elements of a field different from zero also form an Abelian group with respect to the field multiplication as the group operation.

2. If the set $\mathfrak{E}$ consists only of a single element E and if we set $EE = E$, then $\mathfrak{E}$ is an Abelian group of order 1 with respect to this operation, the so-called *identity group* or *unity group*. E is its unity element.

3. If $\mathfrak{G}$ contains only two elements E, A and we set

$$EE = E, \; EA = AE = A, \; AA = E,$$

then it is easy to see that $\mathfrak{G}$ is an Abelian group of order 2 with respect to this rule of combination. This group arises from the field specified in Section 1, Example 4, if the operation of addition in this field is taken as the group operation and we identify 0 with E and e with A.

4. Let an equilateral triangle be given in space whose three vertices and two surfaces are taken to be distinct. We consider all rotations which take this triangle as a whole into itself (without its being necessary for each individual vertex or surface to be turned into itself) and characterize these rotations only by the end position of the vertices and surfaces of the triangle relative to its initial position (therefore, neither by the intermediary positions nor by the absolute initial or end position). The set $\mathfrak{G}$ of distinct elements hereby defined obviously consists of the following rotations:

a) The identity rotation E (no change in position);

b) Two rotations A_1, A_2, one through the angle $\frac{2\pi}{3}$, the other $\frac{4\pi}{3}$ about the axis which is perpendicular to the plane of the triangle and passes through the center of the triangle;

c) Three rotations B_0, B_1, B_2, each through the angle π, about one of the three medians of the triangle.

In setting up this set the rotation sense submitted in b) as well as the rotation axes specified in c) may be regarded as fixed in space, that is, not subjected to the rotations of the triangle.

Proceeding from a fixed initial position these rotations can be illustrated by their end positions as follows:

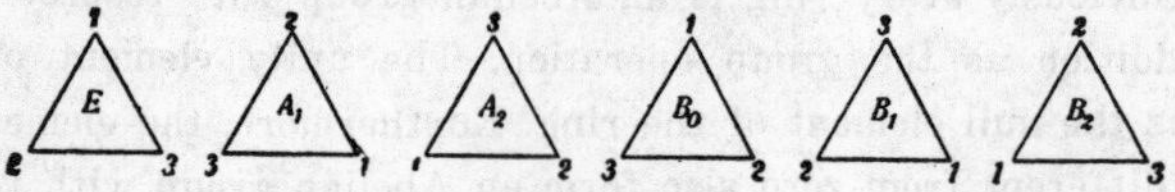

Now, if multiplication in $\mathfrak{G}$ is defined as the successive application of the rotations in question, then $\mathfrak{G}$ is a finite group of order 6 with respect to this multiplication. For, after what has been said, (a), (b) are realized in $\mathfrak{G}$; furthermore, (1) is obviously satisfied; finally, (2 a) and (2 b) are valid, since $\mathfrak{G}$ contains the identity rotation E as unity element and to any rotation C the rotation D generated by reversing the sense of the motion, for which $CD = E$ is obviously valid. As immediately implied by the above illustration, the elements of $\mathfrak{G}$ different from E can be expressed in terms of $A = A_1$ and $B = B_0$ as follows:

$$A_1 = A,\ A_2 = A^2,\ B_0 = B,\ B_1 = BA,\ B_2 = BA^2.$$

Furthermore, the following relations arise from the rule of combination:

$$A^3 = E,\ B^2 = E,\ AB = BA^2;$$

all remaining relations can be deduced from these. The last of these relations shows that $\mathfrak{G}$ is not an Abelian group. The inverses are

$$E^{-1} = E,\ A^{-1} = A^2, \qquad (A^2)^{-1} = A^{-2} = A,$$
$$B^{-1} = B,\ (BA)^{-1} = BA,\ (BA^2)^{-1} = BA^2.$$

In Vol. 2, Section 4 the application of the group concept pointed out in Example 1 will yield an important insight into the structure of integral domains and fields. In addition, at two crucial places (the definition of determinant in Vol. 1, Section 17, and the definition of the Galois group in Vol. 2, Section 15), we will be concerned with finite groups, not necessarily Abelian, whose elements are *not* at the same time elements of those domains on which we base the solution of the problems of algebra.

7. Subgroups. Congruence Relations. Isomorphism

In this section the developments of Section 2 will be applied to groups. As the analogue to Def. 4 [25] we have:

Definition 14. *If the elements of a subset $\mathfrak{H}$ of a group $\mathfrak{G}$ form a group with respect to the multiplication defined in $\mathfrak{G}$, then $\mathfrak{H}$ is called a* ***subgroup*** *of $\mathfrak{G}$.*

Just as in the case of Theorem 6 [25] in Section 2, we prove here

Theorem 19. *A subset $\mathfrak{H}$ of the group $\mathfrak{G}$ is a subgroup of $\mathfrak{G}$ if and only if the products as well as the left and right quotients*

of elements of $\mathfrak{H}$, *as they are defined within* $\mathfrak{G}$, *always again belong to* $\mathfrak{H}$.

In order to show that the quotients belong to $\mathfrak{H}$ it is obviously sufficient by Section 6 to require that $\mathfrak{H}$ contains the unity element E of $\mathfrak{G}$ as well as the inverse B^{-1} of every element B of $\mathfrak{H}$. For the case of a finite $\mathfrak{G}$ we even have

Theorem 20. *If* $\mathfrak{G}$ *is a finite group, then the statement of Theorem 19 is also valid if only the products of elements of* $\mathfrak{H}$ *(not also the quotients) are taken into account.*

Proof: Let A be a fixed element of $\mathfrak{H}$. Then by Section 6, (2) the elements AB, as well as BA, are all distinct if B runs through the elements of $\mathfrak{H}$, each once. Therefore, the two sets that are generated must each consist of exactly the same elements as are in $\mathfrak{H}$. This implies that all left and right quotients of elements of $\mathfrak{H}$ exist in $\mathfrak{H}$.

We will carry over Theorems 7 to 9 [26 to 29] and Definitions 5 to 7 [27 to 30] of Section 2 by merely formulating the corresponding theorems and definitions; for the rest, we refer to the corresponding proofs and expositions of Section 2.

Theorem 21. If $\mathfrak{H}_1, \mathfrak{H}_2, \ldots$ *are any [finite or infinite*[2] *number of] subgroups whatsoever of a group* $\mathfrak{G}$, *then the intersection of the sets* $\mathfrak{H}_1, \mathfrak{H}_2, \ldots$ *is also a subgroup of* $\mathfrak{G}$; *this is called the* ***intersection group*** *or briefly* ***intersection*** *of the groups* $\mathfrak{H}_1, \mathfrak{H}_2, \ldots$

Definition 15. *If* $\mathfrak{H}_1, \mathfrak{H}_2, \ldots$ *are any (finite or infinite number of) subgroups of a group* $\mathfrak{G}$, *then the intersection of all subgroups of* $\mathfrak{G}$ *containing* $\mathfrak{H}_1, \mathfrak{H}_2, \ldots$ *as subgroups is called the*

---

[2] Cf. the statement about numbering in footnote 5 to Theorem 7 [26] .

composite *of* $\mathfrak{H}_1, \mathfrak{H}_2, \ldots$ *or also the* ***group composed*** from $\mathfrak{H}_1, \mathfrak{H}_2, \ldots$

Definition 16. *If an equivalence relation* $\equiv$ *in a group* $\mathfrak{G}$ *satisfies not only the conditions Section 2,* (α), (β), (γ) *but also:*

(1) $A_1 \equiv A_2$, $B_1 \equiv B_2$ *implies* $A_1 B_1 \equiv A_2 B_2$,

then we call it a ***congruence relation*** *in* $\mathfrak{G}$ *and the classes thereby determined the* ***residue classes*** *of* $\mathfrak{G}$ *relative to it.*

Theorem 22. *Let a congruence relation* $\equiv$ *be given in a group* $\mathfrak{G}$. *In the set* $\overline{\mathfrak{G}}$ *of residue classes relative to this congruence relation let a rule of combination be defined by elementwise multiplication. Then* $\overline{\mathfrak{G}}$ *is a group with respect to this operation;* $\overline{\mathfrak{G}}$ *is called the* ***residue class group*** *of* $\mathfrak{G}$ *relative to the congruence relation* $\equiv$.

Theorem 23. *The following convention yields an equivalence relation in the set of all groups: Write* $\mathfrak{G} \cong \mathfrak{G}'$ *if and only if* 1) $\mathfrak{G}$ *and* $\mathfrak{G}'$ *are equipotent, and* 2) *the one-to-one correspondence between the elements* $A, B, \ldots$ *of* $\mathfrak{G}$ *and* $A', B', \ldots$ *of* $\mathfrak{G}'$ *can be chosen such that the condition:*

(2) *if* $A \longleftrightarrow A'$, $B \longleftrightarrow B'$, *then* $AB \longleftrightarrow A'B'$

is valid.

Definition 17. *A one-to-one correspondence between two groups* $\mathfrak{G}$ *and* $\mathfrak{G}'$ *with the property* (2) *is called an* ***isomorphism*** *between* $\mathfrak{G}$ *and* $\mathfrak{G}'$; $\mathfrak{G}$ *and* $\mathfrak{G}'$ *themselves are said to be* ***isomorphic.*** *The equivalence relation* $\mathfrak{G} \cong \mathfrak{G}'$ *specified in Theorem* 23 *for groups is called an* ***isomorphism,*** *the classes thereby determined the* ***types*** *of the groups.*

Examples

1. Every group contains the following subgroups: a) itself; b) the identity subgroup (Section 6, Example 2) consisting only of its unity element. All other subgroups of $\mathfrak{G}$ are called *true* or *proper*.

2. All groups of order 1 are isomorphic, that is, there is only one group type of order 1. Within a group $\mathfrak{G}$ there is only one subgroup of order 1; for by Section 6, (2) and Theorem 14 [58] $AA = A$ implies that $A = E$. Hence it is appropriate to speak of *the* identical group $\mathfrak{E}$ and *the* identity subgroup $\mathfrak{E}$ of $\mathfrak{G}$.

3. The group specified in Section 6, Example 3, has no proper subgroups.

4. It is easy to confirm that the group $\mathfrak{G}$ of Section 6, Example 4, has the following proper subgroups and no others:

a) E, A, A^2; b$_0$) E, B; b$_1$) E, BA; b$_2$) E, BA^2.

Let us designate them by $\mathfrak{N}, \mathfrak{H}_0, \mathfrak{H}_1, \mathfrak{H}_2$. Evidently, the intersection of any two is $\mathfrak{E}$; the composite of any two is $\mathfrak{G}$. Furthermore, $\mathfrak{H}_0, \mathfrak{H}_1, \mathfrak{H}_2$ are isomorphic to one another (cf. the remark after Def. 7 | [32] |).

8. Partition of a Group Relative to a Subgroup

Equivalence relations, and their partitions, which are more general than congruence relations (Def. 16 [65]) are introduced in group theory, due to the omission of the commutative law. In studying these we will obtain a deeper insight into the nature of congruence relations in groups. They arise as follows:

Theorem 24. *Let $\mathfrak{H}$ be a subgroup of the group $\mathfrak{G}$. Then each of the following two conventions yields an equivalence relation in the set $\mathfrak{G}$: If S and S' are elements of $\mathfrak{G}$, then*

(1 a) $S \overset{(r)}{\equiv} S' (\mathfrak{H})$ *if and only if* $S = S'A$ *with* A *in* $\mathfrak{H}$,

(1 b) $S \overset{(l)}{\equiv} S' (\mathfrak{H})$ *if and only if* $S = AS'$ *with* A *in* $\mathfrak{H}$,

that is, if the right and left, respectively, quotient of S and S' belongs to $\mathfrak{H}$.

Proof: Section 2, (α) is valid because E belongs to $\mathfrak{H}$; Section 2, (β), because A and A^{-1} belong to $\mathfrak{H}$ at the same time; Section 2, (γ) because A_1A_2 and A_2A_1 belong to $\mathfrak{H}$ with A_1, A_2, as immediately follows from Def. 14 [63] or Theorem 19 [63].

On the basis of Theorem 24 we now define:

Definition 18. *The equivalence relations specified in Theorem 24 are called* ***right*** *and* ***left,*** *respectively,* ***equivalences relative to*** $\mathfrak{H}$; *the classes of elements of* $\mathfrak{G}$ *thereby determined the* ***left*** *and* ***right,*** *respectively,* ***cosets*** *(or* ***residue classes)***[3] ***relative to*** $\mathfrak{H}$; *the partition of* $\mathfrak{G}$ *thereby obtained, the* ***right*** *and* ***left,*** *respectively,* ***partition of*** $\mathfrak{G}$ ***relative to*** $\mathfrak{H}$; *and a complete system of representatives for these, a* ***complete right*** *and* ***left,*** *respectively,* ***residue system of*** $\mathfrak{G}$ ***relative to*** $\mathfrak{H}$.

Each of the cosets relative to $\mathfrak{H}$ is generated by an arbitrary element S belonging to it by forming all products SA and AS, respectively, where A runs through the elements of $\mathfrak{H}$. To indicate their structure we usually denote them by $S\mathfrak{H}$ and $\mathfrak{H}S$, respectively (cf. Section 9, Def. 20 [70]). Furthermore, if $S_1, S_2 \ldots$ and $T_1, T_2, \ldots$[4] is a complete right and left, respectively, residue system of $\mathfrak{G}$ relative to $\mathfrak{H}$, then we write:

$$\mathfrak{G} = S_1\mathfrak{H} + S_2\mathfrak{H} + \cdots \text{ and } \mathfrak{G} = \mathfrak{H}T_1 + \mathfrak{H}T_2 + \cdots$$

for the right and left, respectively, partition of $\mathfrak{G}$ relative to $\mathfrak{H}$, where the symbol $+$ has the usual significance assigned to it in the theory of sets (i. e., formation of the union of mutually exclusive sets).

---

[3] Translator's note: In the case of groups the designation *coset* is used more frequently than *residue class*. The latter nomenclature is sometimes reserved for the special case considered in Vol. 2, Section 2.

[4] Cf. the statement about numbering in footnote 5 to Theorem 7 [26].

The left as well as the right coset generated by the unity element E, or by any other element of $\mathfrak{H}$, is obviously the group $\mathfrak{H}$ itself.

In the next section, after defining the concept of *normal divisor*, we will deal in greater detail with the way in which two equivalence relations (1 a) and (1 b) as well as the partitions determined by these equivalence relations are connected.

If $\mathfrak{G}$, and therefore $\mathfrak{H}$, is a finite group, an especially important conclusion can be drawn from the partition of $\mathfrak{G}$ relative to $\mathfrak{H}$. Thus, from Section 6, (2) we immediately have:

Theorem 25. *If $\mathfrak{G}$ is a finite group of order n and $\mathfrak{H}$ is a subgroup of $\mathfrak{G}$ of order m, then each of the left as well as the right cosets relative to $\mathfrak{H}$ has the same number of elements, namely, m. If j is the number of cosets, the so-called* ***index*** *of $\mathfrak{H}$ in $\mathfrak{G}$, then $n = mj$. This means that the order m as well as the index j of any subgroup of $\mathfrak{G}$ is a divisor of the order n of $\mathfrak{G}$.*

Examples

1. If $\mathfrak{H} = \mathfrak{G}$, then $\mathfrak{H}$ is itself the only coset relative to $\mathfrak{H}$; if $\mathfrak{G}$ is finite of order n, then $m = n$, $j = 1$. If $\mathfrak{H} = \mathfrak{E}$, then the elements of $\mathfrak{G}$ are the cosets relative to $\mathfrak{H}$; if $\mathfrak{G}$ is finite of order n, then $m = 1$, $j = n$.

2. In the case of Example 4 considered in Sections 6, 7 we have:

$\mathfrak{N}$ is a subgroup of order 3 and index 2,

$\mathfrak{H}_0, \mathfrak{H}_1, \mathfrak{H}_2$ are subgroups of order 2 and index 3.

The partitions

$$\mathfrak{G} = \mathfrak{N} + B\mathfrak{N} = \mathfrak{N} + \mathfrak{N}B,$$

$$\mathfrak{G} = \mathfrak{H}_0 + A\mathfrak{H}_0 + A^2\mathfrak{H}_0 = \mathfrak{H}_0 + \mathfrak{H}_0 A + \mathfrak{H}_0 A^2$$

are valid. The right and left equivalences and partitions relative to $\mathfrak{N}$ must actually coincide, since there are only two cosets, one of which is $\mathfrak{N}$; the other must therefore consist of the elements B, BA, BA^2 of $\mathfrak{G}$ not belonging to $\mathfrak{N}$. However, the right and left equivalences and partitions relative to $\mathfrak{H}_0$ are different, their distinctness being not only the sequence of the classes (which in itself is not to be counted as a distinguishing characteristic). For, $A\mathfrak{H}_0$ contains the elements A, BA^2; $A^2\mathfrak{H}_0$, the elements A^2, BA; $\mathfrak{H}_0 A$, the elements A, BA; $\mathfrak{H}_0 A^2$, the elements A^2, BA^2.

9. Normal Divisors. Conjugate Subsets of a Group. Factor Groups

As to be seen from the last example of the previous section, the two equivalence relations $\overset{(l)}{\equiv}$ and $\overset{(r)}{\equiv}$ need not coincide in a group $\mathfrak{G}$ relative to a subgroup $\mathfrak{H}$. We now define:

Definition 19. *A subgroup $\mathfrak{H}$ of the group $\mathfrak{G}$ is called a **normal divisor** or **invariant subgroup** of $\mathfrak{G}$ if and only if the right and left equivalences relative to $\mathfrak{H}$ are the same, that is, if and only if for every S in $\mathfrak{G}$ the left cosets $S\mathfrak{H}$ coincide with the right cosets $\mathfrak{H}S$.*

If $\mathfrak{H}$ is a normal divisor of $\mathfrak{G}$, then the left partition of $\mathfrak{G}$ relative to $\mathfrak{H}$ (except for the undetermined sequence of the classes) is identical with the right partition of $\mathfrak{G}$ relative to $\mathfrak{H}$; and, conversely, if the two partitions relative to a subgroup $\mathfrak{H}$ are identical it also follows, according to Section 2, (A), (B), that the left and right congruences relative to $\mathfrak{H}$ are the same. Therefore, $\mathfrak{H}$ is a normal divisor of $\mathfrak{G}$.

In the case of a normal divisor $\mathfrak{H}$ of $\mathfrak{G}$ we naturally no longer need to characterize the left and right equivalences relative to $\mathfrak{H}$, nor the left and right cosets relative to $\mathfrak{H}$, by the designation "left" and "right."

If $\mathfrak{G}$ is an Abelian group, then by Section 6, (3) and Theorem 24 [66] the left and right equivalences are surely the same. Consequently,

Theorem 26. *If $\mathfrak{G}$ is an Abelian group, then every subgroup $\mathfrak{H}$ of $\mathfrak{G}$ is a normal divisor of $\mathfrak{G}$.*

In order to obtain a more penetrating insight into the significance of the concept of *normal divisor*, we will introduce another equivalence relation of group theory which refers to the set of all subsets of a group. For the present, however, we will not connect this equivalence relation with Def. 19. We will first generalize to arbitrary subsets of $\mathfrak{G}$ the designations $S\mathfrak{H}$ and $\mathfrak{H}S$, given above for the left and right, respectively, congruence classes of S relative to $\mathfrak{H}$, that is, for the set of all elements SA and AS, respectively, where A runs through the elements of $\mathfrak{H}$. This will simplify the notation and the conclusions to be derived.

Definition 20. *Let $\mathfrak{M}$ and $\mathfrak{N}$ be subsets of the group $\mathfrak{G}$. Then by $\mathfrak{M}\mathfrak{N}$ we will understand that subset of $\mathfrak{G}$ which consists of all products AB, where A runs through the elements of $\mathfrak{M}$, B those of $\mathfrak{N}$.*

Since multiplication in $\mathfrak{G}$ satisfies the associative law Section 6, (1), we immediately have

Theorem 27. *The "elementwise multiplication" defined in Def. 20 in the set of all subsets of a group $\mathfrak{G}$ satisfies the associative law.*

This implies the validity of Section 6, (a), (b), (1) in the set of all subsets of $\mathfrak{G}$. Yet, in case $\mathfrak{G} \neq \mathfrak{E}$ this set of subsets is not a group with respect to the operation of Def. 20. For, if $\mathfrak{M} = E$ and $\mathfrak{N}$ consists of E and $A \neq E$, then no subset $\mathfrak{L}$ exists such that $\mathfrak{N}\mathfrak{L} = \mathfrak{M}$.

Let T, S be arbitrary elements of $\mathfrak{G}$. Then, by Theorem 27 $T\mathfrak{M}S$ has the uniquely determined sense $(T\mathfrak{M})S = T(\mathfrak{M}S)$. Furthermore, we have the relation $T'(T\mathfrak{M}S)S' = (T'T)\mathfrak{M}(SS')$, which will frequently be used in the following.

We now prove:

Theorem 28. *Let $\mathfrak{M}$ and $\mathfrak{M}'$ be two subsets of a group $\mathfrak{G}$ and let us put $\mathfrak{M} \sim \mathfrak{M}'$ if and only if $\mathfrak{M}' = S^{-1}\mathfrak{M}S$ for an S in $\mathfrak{G}$. Then, this is an equivalence relation in the set of all subsets of $\mathfrak{G}$.*

Proof: Section 2, (α) is satisfied, since $E^{-1}\mathfrak{M}E = \mathfrak{M}$; Section 2, ($\beta$), since $\mathfrak{M}' = S^{-1}\mathfrak{M}S$ implies

$$\mathfrak{M} = S\mathfrak{M}'S^{-1} = (S^{-1})^{-1}\mathfrak{M}'S^{-1};$$

Section 2, (γ), since

$$\mathfrak{M}' = S^{-1}\mathfrak{M}S,\ \mathfrak{M}'' = T^{-1}\mathfrak{M}'T \text{ implies}$$
$$\mathfrak{M}'' = T^{-1}(S^{-1}\mathfrak{M}S)T = (T^{-1}S^{-1})\mathfrak{M}(ST)$$
$$= (ST)^{-1}\mathfrak{M}(ST).$$

The formation of $\mathfrak{M}' = S^{-1}\mathfrak{M}S$ from $\mathfrak{M}$ is called the **transformation of $\mathfrak{M}$ by S.**

On the basis of Theorem 28 we define:

Definition 21. *If $\mathfrak{M} \sim \mathfrak{M}'$ in the sense of Theorem 28, then $\mathfrak{M}$ and $\mathfrak{M}'$ are called* ***conjugate subsets*** *of $\mathfrak{G}$. The classes determined by this equivalence relation in the set of all subsets of $\mathfrak{G}$ are called the* ***classes of conjugate subsets*** *of $\mathfrak{G}$.*

Regarding these classes the following special cases may be cited:

a) The **classes of conjugate elements** of $\mathfrak{G}$, that is, those classes which are generated by a subset containing only one element A of $\mathfrak{G}$. Such a class, therefore, consists of the totality of elements $S^{-1}AS$, where S runs through the elements of $\mathfrak{G}$.

One such class is generated by the unity element E and contains only the unity element itself. If $\mathfrak{G}$ is Abelian, then $S^{-1}AS = S^{-1}SA = EA = A$; therefore all classes of conjugate elements of $\mathfrak{G}$ contain only one element. If $\mathfrak{G}$ is not Abelian, there is at least one such class which contains more than one element, since $AS \neq SA$ implies $S^{-1}AS \neq A$.

b) The **classes of conjugate subgroups** of $\mathfrak{G}$, that is, those classes which are generated by a subgroup $\mathfrak{H}$ of $\mathfrak{G}$. Such a class, therefore, consists of the totality of subsets $S^{-1}\mathfrak{H}S$, where S runs through the elements of $\mathfrak{G}$.

The designation *conjugate subgroups* is justified by the following theorem:

Theorem 29. *The conjugate subsets* $S^{-1}\mathfrak{H}S$ *of a subgroup* $\mathfrak{H}$ *of a group* $\mathfrak{G}$ *are again subgroups of* $\mathfrak{G}$. *Moreover, they are isomorphic to* $\mathfrak{H}$ *and therefore also to one another.*

Proof: By Theorem 27 we have

$$(S^{-1}\mathfrak{H}S)\,(S^{-1}\mathfrak{H}S) = S^{-1}\,(\mathfrak{H}\mathfrak{H})\,S = S^{-1}\,\mathfrak{H}S,$$

since $\mathfrak{H}\mathfrak{H} = \mathfrak{H}$ is obvious from the group property, Section 6, (b) of $\mathfrak{H}$ and by Theorem 16 [60] . According to Def. 20 this relation says that all products of elements of $S^{-1}\mathfrak{H}S$ again belong to $S^{-1}\mathfrak{H}S$. Now, the element $E = S^{-1}\,ES$ belongs to $S^{-1}\mathfrak{H}S$, since E is contained in $\mathfrak{H}$; also, if $A' = S^{-1}\,AS$ belongs to $S^{-1}\mathfrak{H}S$ so does $A'^{-1} = S^{-1}\,A^{-1}\,S$, since if A is contained in $\mathfrak{H}$ so is A^{-1}. Consequently $S^{-1}\mathfrak{H}S$ is a subgroup of $\mathfrak{G}$ (Theorem 19 [63]).

Let a correspondence be set up between the elements of $\mathfrak{H}$ and $S^{-1}\mathfrak{H}S$ by the convention $A \longleftrightarrow S^{-1}\,AS$. Then Section 2, (δ) and Section 2, (ε) are satisfied, since to every A in $\mathfrak{H}$ there corresponds a unique element of $S^{-1}\mathfrak{H}S$; Section 2, (δ′), since every A' in $S^{-1}\mathfrak{H}S$ by definition of this subset can be represented as $S^{-1}\,AS$ with A in $\mathfrak{H}$; and Section 2, (ε′), since $S^{-1}\,A_1S = S^{-1}\,A_2S$ implies through left and right multiplication by S and S^{-1}, respectively, that $A_1 = A_2$. Finally,

$$(S^{-1}A_1S)\,(S^{-1}A_2S) = S^{-1}(A_1A_2)S;$$

therefore, condition (2) of Theorem 23 [65] is also satisfied. Consequently, we actually have that $\mathfrak{H} \cong S^{-1}\,\mathfrak{H}S$.

In regard to the distinctness of conjugate subgroups, we prove:

Theorem 30. *Two subgroups* $S^{-1}\mathfrak{H}S$ *and* $T^{-1}\mathfrak{H}T$ *which are conjugates of the subgroup* $\mathfrak{H}$ *of the group* $\mathfrak{G}$ *are surely identical if* $S \overset{(l)}{\equiv} T(\mathfrak{H})$. *Hence, if* $T_1, T_2, \ldots$ *is a complete left residue system of* $\mathfrak{G}$ *relative to* $\mathfrak{H}$, *then the conjugate subgroups*

$$T_1^{-1}\mathfrak{H}T_1,\quad T_2^{-1}\mathfrak{H}T_2,\ldots$$

at most are different from one another, that is, every subgroup of $\mathfrak{G}$ *conjugate to* $\mathfrak{H}$ *is identical with one of these.*

Proof: If $S \overset{(l)}{\equiv} T(\mathfrak{H})$, which means that $S = AT$ with A in $\mathfrak{H}$, then, $S^{-1}\mathfrak{H}S = (AT)^{-1}\mathfrak{H}(AT) = (T^{-1}A^{-1})\mathfrak{H}(AT) = T^{-1}(A^{-1}\mathfrak{H}A)T = T^{-1}\mathfrak{H}T$, because by Theorem 16 [60] we obviously have $A^{-1}\mathfrak{H}A = A^{-1}(\mathfrak{H}A) = A^{-1}\mathfrak{H} = \mathfrak{H}$.

We will now relate the concept of *normal divisor* to the special classes of conjugate subsets specified in a) and b). We do so by the following two theorems, either of which could also have been used to define this concept.

Theorem 31. *A subgroup* $\mathfrak{H}$ *of the group* $\mathfrak{G}$ *is a normal subgroup of* $\mathfrak{G}$ *if and only if it is identical with all its conjugate subgroups, that is, if the class of* $\mathfrak{H}$ *in the sense of Def.* 21 *consists only of* $\mathfrak{H}$ *itself.*

Proof: The relations $S\mathfrak{H} = \mathfrak{H}S$ occurring in Def. 19 for the elements S of $\mathfrak{G}$ are equivalent to the relations $\mathfrak{H} = S^{-1}\mathfrak{H}S$. This follows through left multiplication by S^{-1} and S, respectively.

Theorem 32. *A subgroup* $\mathfrak{H}$ *of* $\mathfrak{G}$ *is a normal divisor of* $\mathfrak{G}$ *if and only if it is a union of classes of conjugate elements of* $\mathfrak{G}$, *that is, if all elements of* $\mathfrak{G}$ *conjugate to* A *belong to* $\mathfrak{H}$ *whenever* A *itself does.*

Proof: a) Let $\mathfrak{H}$ be a normal divisor of $\mathfrak{G}$. Then by Theorem 31 $S^{-1}\mathfrak{H}S = \mathfrak{H}$ for all S in $\mathfrak{G}$. Hence $\mathfrak{H}$ contains all elements $S^{-1}AS$, where S belongs to $\mathfrak{G}$ and A to $\mathfrak{H}$; that is, all elements of $\mathfrak{G}$ conjugate to A belong to the subgroup if A does.

b) Conversely, if the latter is the case, then $S^{-1}\mathfrak{H}S$ and $S\mathfrak{H}S^{-1}$ are contained in $\mathfrak{H}$ for every S in $\mathfrak{G}$. Through left and right multiplication, respectively, by S we obtain that $\mathfrak{H}S$ is contained in $S\mathfrak{H}$ and $S\mathfrak{H}$ in $\mathfrak{H}S$; therefore, $S\mathfrak{H} = \mathfrak{H}S$. This means that $\mathfrak{H}$ is a normal divisor of $\mathfrak{G}$.

By Theorem 31 a subgroup $\mathfrak{H}$ is also characterized as a normal divisor of $\mathfrak{G}$ if $\mathfrak{H}$ is preserved with respect to transformation by all elements S of $\mathfrak{G}$ (cf. the remark to Theorem 28). This is why the designation *invariant subgroup* was used in Def. 19.

A subgroup of $\mathfrak{G}$ is not always a normal divisor of $\mathfrak{G}$. However, two normal divisors can be derived from any subgroup by the following theorem.

Theorem 33. *If $\mathfrak{H}$ is a subgroup of $\mathfrak{G}$, then the intersection and the composite of all subgroups conjugate to $\mathfrak{H}$ are normal divisors of $\mathfrak{G}$.*

Proof: a) If A occurs in the intersection $\mathfrak{D}$ of all subgroups of $\mathfrak{G}$ conjugate to $\mathfrak{H}$, that is, in all $S^{-1}\mathfrak{H}S$, where S runs through the group $\mathfrak{G}$, then for any fixed T in $\mathfrak{G}$ $T^{-1}AT$ occurs in all $T^{-1}(S^{-1}\mathfrak{H}S)T = (ST)^{-1}\mathfrak{H}(ST)$. By Theorem 16 [60] we again have, if T is any fixed element of $\mathfrak{G}$, that these are all subgroups of $\mathfrak{G}$ conjugate to $\mathfrak{H}$. Hence by Theorem 32 $\mathfrak{D}$ is a normal divisor of $\mathfrak{G}$.

b) If $\mathfrak{K}$ is the specified composite, then $\mathfrak{K}$ contains all $S^{-1}\mathfrak{H}S$. This means, as above, that $T^{-1}\mathfrak{K}T$ and $T\mathfrak{K}T^{-1}$ contain all $S^{-1}\mathfrak{H}S$, too. Hence these subgroups of $\mathfrak{G}$ are the kind which should be used according to Def. 15 [64] to determine $\mathfrak{K}$ by the formation of intersections. Therefore $\mathfrak{K}$ is contained in $T^{-1}\mathfrak{K}T$ and $T\mathfrak{K}T^{-1}$ for every T in $\mathfrak{G}$. This implies, as in the proof to Theorem 32 under b), that $\mathfrak{K}$ is a normal divisor of $\mathfrak{G}$.

The most important property of normal divisors, which will be of fundamental significance in our application of group theory in Vol. 2, Section 17, is to be found in the close connection between the normal divisors of a group $\mathfrak{G}$ and the congruence relations possible in $\mathfrak{G}$. In this regard the following two theorems are valid:

Theorem 34. *If $\mathfrak{H}$ is a normal divisor of $\mathfrak{G}$, then the (simultaneously right and left) equivalence relative to $\mathfrak{H}$ is a congruence relation in $\mathfrak{G}$.*

Proof: By Def. 19, $\mathfrak{H}S = S\mathfrak{H}$ for every S in $\mathfrak{G}$. This implies by Def. 20 and Theorem 27 that

(1) $(\mathfrak{H}S)(\mathfrak{H}T) = \mathfrak{H}(S\mathfrak{H})T = \mathfrak{H}(\mathfrak{H}S)T = (\mathfrak{H}\mathfrak{H})(ST) = \mathfrak{H}(ST)$.

Consequently, all products of elements from two cosets $\mathfrak{H}S$, $\mathfrak{H}T$ relative to $\mathfrak{H}$ belong to one and the same coset, i. e. $\mathfrak{H}(ST)$, relative to $\mathfrak{H}$. This means that Section 7, (1) is satisfied for the equivalence relative to $\mathfrak{H}$.

Theorem 35. *Every congruence relation in $\mathfrak{G}$ is identical with the (simultaneously right and left) equivalence relative to a definite normal divisor $\mathfrak{H}$ of $\mathfrak{G}$. $\mathfrak{H}$ is the totality of elements of $\mathfrak{G}$ which are congruent to the unity element E, that is, the coset determined by E under the congruence relation.*

Proof: a) The set $\mathfrak{H}$ of elements of $\mathfrak{G}$ congruent to E is, first of all, a subgroup of $\mathfrak{G}$. We will show that the conditions of Theorem 19 [63] (cf. the remark adjoined to it) are satisfied. First, by (1) in Def. 16 [65] $E \equiv A$, $E \equiv B$ implies $E \equiv AB$; secondly, $E \equiv E$; thirdly, by (1) in Def. 16 $E \equiv A$, $A^{-1} \equiv A^{-1}$ implies $A^{-1} \equiv E$.

b) If $A \equiv B$, then by (1) in Def. 16 $AB^{-1} \equiv E$ and $B^{-1}A \equiv E$. Hence by Theorem 24 [66] $A \overset{(r)}{\equiv} B(\mathfrak{H})$ and $A \overset{(l)}{\equiv} B(\mathfrak{H})$. Conversely, by (1) in Def. 16 it follows from each of these relations that $A \equiv B$. Consequently, the right and left equivalences relative to the subgroup $\mathfrak{H}$ both coincide with our congruence, therefore with one another. This implies the statement of the theorem.

By the last two theorems the only congruence relations that exist in a group $\mathfrak{G}$ are the equivalence relations in the sense of Def. 18 [67] relative to normal divisors $\mathfrak{H}$ of $\mathfrak{G}$. In particular, the equivalence relations last specified are *not* congruence relations if $\mathfrak{H}$ is *not* a normal divisor of $\mathfrak{G}$.

We can also express the conclusion of Theorem 22 [65] as follows:

Theorem 36. *If $\mathfrak{H}$ is a normal divisor of $\mathfrak{G}$, then the (simultaneously left and right) cosets of $\mathfrak{G}$ relative to $\mathfrak{H}$ form a group $\overline{\mathfrak{G}}$ through elementwise multiplication, the residue class group of $\mathfrak{G}$ relative to $\mathfrak{H}$. $\overline{\mathfrak{G}}$ is also called the* ***factor group*** *of $\mathfrak{G}$ relative to $\mathfrak{H}$ and we write $\overline{\mathfrak{G}} = \mathfrak{G}/\mathfrak{H}$.*

To operate with the elements $\mathfrak{H}S, \mathfrak{H}T, \ldots$ of the factor group $\mathfrak{G}/\mathfrak{H}$ proceed in accordance with rule (1). For finite $\mathfrak{G}$ Theorem 25 [68] says that the order of $\mathfrak{G}/\mathfrak{H}$ is equal to the index of $\mathfrak{H}$ in $\mathfrak{G}$. Finally, we obviously have

Theorem 37. *If $\mathfrak{G}$ is an Abelian group and $\mathfrak{H}$ a subgroup of $\mathfrak{G}$, then $\mathfrak{G}/\mathfrak{H}$ is also Abelian.*

Examples

1. The improper subgroups $\mathfrak{E}$ and $\mathfrak{G}$ of $\mathfrak{G}$ are always normal divisors of $\mathfrak{G}$. For their factor groups we have $\mathfrak{G}/\mathfrak{E} \cong \mathfrak{G}$ and $\mathfrak{G}/\mathfrak{G} \cong \mathfrak{E}$.

2. For the group $\mathfrak{G}$ considered in Sections 6, 7, Example 4, as already stressed in the statements about $\mathfrak{G}$ in Section 8, Example 2, the subgroups $\mathfrak{H}_0, \mathfrak{H}_1, \mathfrak{H}_2$ are conjugate to one another and are not normal divisors; however, the subgroup $\mathfrak{N}$ is a normal divisor. This can also be seen by forming the classes of conjugate elements of $\mathfrak{G}$. It follows from the formulae of Section 6, Example 4, that these classes have the following composition:

a) E; b) A, $A^2 = B^{-1}AB$;
c) B, $BA = A^{-2}BA^2$, $BA^2 = A^{-1}BA$.

Hence the classes of the conjugates of $\mathfrak{H}_0$ are:

$$\mathfrak{H}_0, \qquad \mathfrak{H}_1 = A^{-2}\mathfrak{H}_0 A^2, \qquad \mathfrak{H}_2 = A^{-1}\mathfrak{H}_0 A,$$

whereas $\mathfrak{N}$ is the union of the classes a) and b). The factor group $\mathfrak{G}/\mathfrak{N}$ is Abelian of order 2 (cf. Section 6, Example 3).

3. The Abelian group $\mathfrak{G}$ of rational numbers $\neq 0$ with respect to ordinary multiplication has, for instance, the following subgroups: the group $\mathfrak{P}$ of positive rational numbers and the group $\mathfrak{U}$ of all those rational numbers which can be represented as quotients of odd integers. The following partitions of $\mathfrak{G}$ relative to $\mathfrak{P}$ and $\mathfrak{U}$, respectively, are obviously valid:

$$\mathfrak{G} = \mathfrak{P} + (-1)\,\mathfrak{P}, \quad \mathfrak{G} = \mathfrak{U} + 2\mathfrak{U} + 2^2\mathfrak{U} + \cdots + 2^{-1}\mathfrak{U} + 2^{-2}\mathfrak{U} + \cdots,$$

therefore $\mathfrak{G}/\mathfrak{P}$ is finite of order 2, but $\mathfrak{G}/\mathfrak{U}$ is infinite.[5]

4. The Abelian group $\mathfrak{G}$ of integers with respect to ordinary addition has, for example, the subgroup $\mathfrak{H}$ consisting of all even numbers. The partition

$$\mathfrak{G} = \mathfrak{H} + 1\,\mathfrak{H}$$

is valid so that $\mathfrak{G}/\mathfrak{H}$ is again finite of order 2.[6] In Vol. 2, Section 2 we will discuss in detail these and analogously formed subgroups of $\mathfrak{G}$ as well as their factor groups.

---

[5] In the case of $\mathfrak{U}$ that part of the fundamental theorem of arithmetic dealing with the unique factorization of rational numbers into powers of prime numbers is assumed as known in the case of the prime number 2. In Vol. 2, Section 1 this will be dealt with systematically.

[6] Here, too, we assume that Theorem 13 of Vol. 2, Section 1 is valid relative to the prime number 2, namely, that every integer g can be uniquely expressed in the form $g = 2q + r$, where q and r are integers and $0 \leqq r < 2$. $\mathfrak{H}$ then consists of the g with $r = 0$; $1\mathfrak{H}$, of the g with $r = 1$. — Naturally $1\mathfrak{H}$ indicates here that 1 is to be *added* to the elements of $\mathfrak{H}$.

III. Linear Algebra without Determinants

10. Linear forms. Vectors. Matrices

Let K be an arbitrary field. We will use this field as the *ground field* of *linear algebra* in the sense of Section 5, (1) throughout the remainder of Vol. 1.

To simplify our terminology we make the convention that in Chapters III and IV all elements designated by a, b, c, α, β, γ with or without indices shall be elements of K, even though this may not always be expressly stated. Likewise, $x_1, \ldots, x_n$ shall be elements of K whenever we pass over to the concept of function in the sense of analysis.

Before taking up the main problem, as formulated in Section 5, (1), we will introduce in this section some concepts, which in themselves are not essential, whose application, however, will extraordinarily simplify the following developments both from a notational and descriptive point of view.

a) Linear Forms

First, we introduce a special nomenclature for the integral rational functions of $x_1, \ldots, x_n$ which appear on the left sides of the system of equations Section 5, (1) under consideration.

Definition 22. *An element of* $K[x_1, \ldots, x_n]$ *whose normal representation is* $\sum_{k=1}^{n} a_k x_k$ *is called a* ***linear form*** *of* $x_1, \ldots, x_n$ *or also* ***linear*** *and* ***homogeneous*** *in* $x_1, \ldots, x_n$.

The significance of *linear* has already been explained in Section 5 in the case of (1); *form* or *homogeneous* shall mean that in the normal representation the coefficient which is designated by $a_{0,\ldots,0}$ in Theorem 11 is zero. The expression *linear form* by itself will always stand for a linear form of the n indeterminates $x_1, \ldots, x_n$ unless qualified otherwise by the context.

The following two definitions are very important for all further considerations:

Definition 23. *A linear form f is called a* ***linear combination of*** *or* ***linearly dependent on*** *the linear forms $f_1, \ldots, f_m$ if there exist $c_1, \ldots, c_m$ such that $f = \sum_{i=1}^{m} c_i f_i$ Otherwise, f is said to be* ***linearly independent of*** *$f_1, \ldots, f_m$.*

Hence, the null form $0 \equiv \sum_{k=1}^{n} 0 x_k$ is certainly a linear combination of *every* system $f_1, \ldots, f_m$ of linear forms. To show this we merely have to choose $c_1, \ldots, c_m = 0$. On taking this into account we further define:

Definition 24. *The linear forms $f_1, \ldots, f_m$ are said to be* ***linearly dependent*** *if there exist $c_1, \ldots, c_m$, which are not all zero, such that $\sum_{i=1}^{m} c_i f_i = 0$. Otherwise, $f_1, \ldots, f_m$ are said to be* ***linearly independent.***

In particular $(m = 1)$ every linear form $f \neq 0$ is linearly independent, whereas the form 0 is linearly dependent.

The two entirely distinct concepts of *linearly dependent on* (*linearly independent of*) and *linearly dependent* (*linearly independent*) introduced in Def. 23 and 24 are connected by a relation whose proof is so simple that it is left to the reader:[1]

Theorem 38. a) *If f is linearly dependent on $f_1, \ldots, f_m$,* then *$f, f_1, \ldots, f_m$ are linearly dependent.*

b) *If f is linearly independent of $f_1, \ldots, f_m$ and $f_1, \ldots, f_m$ are linearly independent, then $f, f_1, \ldots, f_m$ are linearly independent.*

---

[1] Above all it should be made clear that the *field* property [Section 1, (7)] plays an essential role in this proof, so that even these facts, upon which the following exposition is based, are not generally valid in integral domains. (Cf. point 2 in footnote 13 [55] to Section 5.)

a′) *If $f, f_1, \ldots, f_m$ are linearly dependent and there is a relation $cf + c_1f_1 + \cdots + c_mf_m = 0$ such that f has a coefficient $c \neq 0$ (in particular, this is the case if $f_1, \ldots, f_m$ are linearly independent), then f is linearly dependent on $f_1, \ldots, f_m$.*

b′) *If $f, f_1, \ldots, f_m$ are linearly independent, then f is linearly independent of $f_1, \ldots, f_m$, and $f_1, \ldots, f_m$ are also linearly independent.*

The successive application of b′) yields the following two mutually implicative inferences:

Theorem 39. *If $f_1, \ldots, f_m, f_{m+1}, \ldots, f_{m+l}$ are linearly independent, then $f_1, \ldots, f_m$ are also. If $f_1, \ldots, f_m$ are linearly dependent, then $f_1, \ldots, f_m, f_{m+1}, \ldots, f_{m+l}$ are also.*

Analogous to this, the following two mutually implicative inferences are also valid:

Theorem 40. *Let* $f_i = \sum_{k=1}^{n} a_{ik} x_k$, $g_i = \sum_{k=1}^{n+l} a_{ik} x_k$ $(i = 1, \ldots, m)$.

Then, if $f_1, \ldots, f_m$ are linearly independent so also are $g_1, \ldots, g_m$ and if $g_1, \ldots, g_m$ are linearly dependent so also are $f_1, \ldots, f_m$.

Proof: Let $\mathsf{K}[x_1, \ldots, x_n] = \mathsf{K}_n$. Then the g_i can be described as those elements (linear but not forms) of $\mathsf{K}_n[x_{n+1}, \ldots, x_{n+l}]$ whose function values are the elements f_i of K_n if the indeterminates $x_{n+1}, \ldots, x_{n+l}$ are replaced by the system $(0, \ldots, 0)$. Consequently, by the principle of substitution it follows that the relation $\sum_{i=1}^{m} c_i g_i = 0$ for the function values also satisfy the relation $\sum_{i=1}^{m} c_i f_i = 0$.

Furthermore, we have:

Theorem 41. *If $f_1, \ldots, f_m$ are linearly independent, then each of their linear combinations can be linearly composed from these in only one way. If $f_1, \ldots, f_m$ are linearly dependent, then each* *of their linear combinations can be linearly composed in at least two different ways.*

Proof: a) If $f_1, \ldots, f_m$ are linearly independent, then $\sum_{i=1}^{m} c_i f_i = \sum_{i=1}^{m} c'_i f_i$ implies $\sum_{i=1}^{m} (c_i - c'_i) f_i = 0$. Hence, by Def. 24 $c_i - c'_i = 0$, that is, $c_i = c'_i$ for $i = 1, \ldots, m$.

b) If $f_1, \ldots, f_m$ are linearly dependent, that is, $\sum_{i=1}^{m} c_i f_i = 0$, wherein at least one $c_i \neq 0$, then $f = \sum_{i=1}^{m} d_i f_i$ also implies that $f = \sum_{i=1}^{m} (d_i + c_i) f_i$, wherein at least one $d_i \neq d_i + c_i$.

By Theorem 41, for example, the special system of n linear forms $x_1, \ldots, x_n$, from which every linear form $\sum_{k=1}^{n} a_k x_k$ can be linearly composed, is linearly independent. For, by Theorem 11 this representation is unique, since it is the normal representation.

Finally we have:

Theorem 42. *If $g_1, \ldots, g_l$ are linear combinations of $f_1, \ldots, f_m$, then every linear combination of $g_1, \ldots, g_l$ is also a linear combination of $f_1, \ldots, f_m$.*

Proof: $g_k = \sum_{i=1}^{m} c_{ki} f_i$ $(k = 1, \ldots, l)$ and $g = \sum_{k=1}^{l} c_k g_k$ imply

$$g = \sum_{k=1}^{l} \left[c_k \left(\sum_{i=1}^{m} c_{ki} f_i \right) \right] = \sum_{i=1}^{m} \left[\left(\sum_{k=1}^{l} c_k c_{ki} \right) f_i \right].$$

In the following we will frequently apply the *rule* used above *regarding the interchange of the order of summation,* which is based on the addition postulates, Section 1, (1), (3), (5). Due to its validity the parentheses and brackets may be omitted without misunderstanding in the case of such operations.

b) Vectors

According to the conception underlying the construction of $\mathsf{K}[x_1, \ldots, x_n]$ from K in Section 4, c) and d), the linear forms

$\sum_{k=1}^{n} a_k x_k$, in particular, are formally nothing else but systems $(a_1, \ldots, a_n)$ of elements which are subject to the distinctness criterion and rules of combination given in Section 4, (1 a) to (3 a), where the abbreviating designations $x_1, \ldots, x_n$ were introduced for the special systems $(e, 0, \ldots, 0), \ldots, (0, \ldots, 0, e)$. Without using these abbreviations the laws, Section 4, (1 a) to (3 a), insofar as they refer to linear forms (which are now to be our only objects of study) and to the elements of the ground field, amount to the following:

(1) $(a_1, \ldots, a_n) = (a'_1, \ldots, a'_n)$ if and only if, $a_k = a'_k$ for $k = 1, \ldots, n$,

(2) $(a_1, \ldots, a_n) + (b_1, \ldots, b_n) = (a_1 + b_1, \ldots, a_n + b_n)$,

(3) $a(a_1, \ldots, a_n) = (aa_1, \ldots, aa_n)$.

Now, in linear algebra we have to handle not only systems of *coefficients* of linear forms but also systems of n elements of the ground field which are to be substituted for the *indeterminates* $x_1, \ldots, x_n$ in the linear forms. In doing so we frequently have to characterize these substitution systems by (1) as well as admit them in the right-hand formations of (2) and (3). This end could actually be attained merely by formally thinking of the substitution systems as systems of coefficients of linear forms. With respect to such an interpretation the substitution systems would be distinct if their associated linear forms were distinct, and the right-hand formations in (2) and (3) would be effected by carrying out the rules of combination on the left with these linear forms. However, such a way of thinking would complicate the terminology unduly. Moreover it could be very confusing, since in the case of the expression linear form we usually think of the possibility of replacing the indeterminates by elements of the ground field, which is naturally not the case for the "auxiliary linear forms" last mentioned. It is therefore advisable to devise a brief terminology which will make it possible to apply the formal rules (1) to (3) in another way.

Definition 25. *Systems of n elements satisfying the distinctness criterion and the rules of combination* (1) *to* (3) *are called* ***n-termed vectors.*** *We designate them by the small German letters corresponding to their terms.*

For example, $(a_1,\ldots, a_n)$ is designated by $\mathfrak{a}$; $(a_{i1},\ldots, a_{in})$, by $\mathfrak{a}_i$, etc. Unless otherwise specified, a *vector* is always understood as being n-termed.

By (2) the subtraction of vectors must naturally also be defined without restriction and uniquely. This can actually be done by the formula analogous to (2):

$$(a_1,\ldots, a_n) - (b_1,\ldots, b_n) = (a_1 - b_1,\ldots, a_n - b_n),$$

either by assuming that the rule of combination (2) satisfies postulates Section 1, (1), (3), (6), or simply in virtue of the formal identity with linear forms. The vector $(0,\ldots, 0)$ corresponding to the null form and playing the role of the *null vector* may again be designated by 0.

Since vectors and linear forms are formally the same, we can also think of the concepts introduced in Def. 23, 24 as explained for vectors; consequently, the analogues to Theorems 38 to 42 must also be valid when formulated in terms of vectors.

Written out in detail the statements "$\mathfrak{a}$ is linearly dependent on $\mathfrak{a}_1,\ldots,\mathfrak{a}_m$" and "$\mathfrak{a}_1,\ldots,\mathfrak{a}_m$ are linearly dependent" mean according to Def. 23, 24 that the relations

(4) $\sum_{i=1}^{m} c_i a_{ik} = a_k$ and (5) $\sum_{i=1}^{m} c_i a_{ik} = 0$, respectively, for $k = 1,\ldots, n$

are valid, where the latter contains at least one $c_i \neq 0$.

The special n linearly independent vectors $(e, 0,\ldots, 0), \ldots, (0,\ldots, 0, e)$, which correspond to the linear forms $x_1,\ldots, x_n$, are also called the n *unit vectors* and designated by $\mathfrak{e}_1,\ldots,\mathfrak{e}_n$. There exists then for any vector $\mathfrak{a}$ the representation $\sum_{k=1}^{n} a_k \mathfrak{e}_k$ in terms of these unit vectors. Through these representations we are naturally brought back (except for the difference of notation between $\mathfrak{e}_k$ and x_k) to the standpoint of linear forms.

Hitherto the conventions set up for vectors have been formally the same as those in the case of linear forms. Now, however, a convention is made which has no counterpart from the standpoint of linear forms.

Definition 26. *The **inner product** $\mathfrak{a}\mathfrak{b}$ of two vectors $\mathfrak{a}$ and $\mathfrak{b}$ is defined as the element* $\sum_{k=1}^{n} a_k b_k$.

In contrast to (3) in the *inner* product *both* factors are vectors, while the result of forming the inner product is not a vector but an element of the ground field. — In particular, we have

$$\mathfrak{a}\mathfrak{e}_k = a_k,\quad \mathfrak{e}_k\mathfrak{e}_{k'} = \begin{Bmatrix} e \text{ for } k = k' \\ 0 \text{ for } k \neq k' \end{Bmatrix},\quad \mathfrak{a}0 = 0.$$

Theorem 43. *The inner product of vectors is an operation satisfying the rules*

$$\mathfrak{a}\mathfrak{b} = \mathfrak{b}\mathfrak{a},\ c(\mathfrak{a}\mathfrak{b}) = (c\mathfrak{a})\mathfrak{b} = \mathfrak{a}(c\mathfrak{b}),\ (\mathfrak{a}+\mathfrak{b})\mathfrak{c} = \mathfrak{a}\mathfrak{c} + \mathfrak{b}\mathfrak{c}.$$

Proof: By Def. 25, 26 this immediately follows from postulates Section 1, (1) to (5).

The successive application of the last of these rules naturally gives rise to the still more general formula

$$\left(\sum_{i=1}^{m} \mathfrak{a}_i\right)\mathfrak{c} = \sum_{i=1}^{m} \mathfrak{a}_i \mathfrak{c}.$$

On writing this out in detail we obtain $\sum_{k=1}^{n}\sum_{i=1}^{m} a_{ik}c_k = \sum_{i=1}^{m}\sum_{k=1}^{n} a_{ik}c_k$. This is the rule mentioned in connection with Theorem 42 regarding the interchange of the order of summation. We will make essential use (Theorem 44) of it.

The inner product makes no use of the field property [Section 1, (7)] of the ground domain K. Hence the last developments are also valid for vectors over the integral domain $\mathsf{K}[x_1, \ldots, x_n]$.[2]

[2] To such vectors there would then correspond linear forms $f(\xi_1, \ldots, \xi_n)$ of the integral domain $\mathsf{K}_n[\xi_1, \ldots, \xi_n]$ over $\mathsf{K}_n = \mathsf{K}[x_1, \ldots, x_n]$; however, for our purposes we have no need of this interpretation (cf. the exposition before Def. 25).

The vector $\mathfrak{x}$ of the indeterminates is the only vector of this kind we need.

By using this vector we can also designate a linear form $f(x_1, \ldots, x_n)$ by $f(\mathfrak{x})$. In doing so we agree to interpret $\mathfrak{x}$ as a vector of the ground domain, and to use the symbols $\equiv$ and $=$ in accord with the conventions given in the footnote to Theorem 12 [50].

By Def. 26 any linear form $f(x_1, \ldots, x_n) \equiv \sum_{k=1}^{n} a_k x_k$ also has the representation $f(\mathfrak{x}) \equiv \mathfrak{a}\mathfrak{x}$ as an inner product. On the basis of the formulae of Theorem 43 this representation leads to an extraordinarily simple rule for operations with the function values of a linear form. We especially stress the following fact in connection with the remark after Theorem 43:

Theorem 44. *If $f(\mathfrak{x})$ is a linear form, then for a linear combination $\mathfrak{x} = \sum_{i=1}^{m} c_i \mathfrak{x}_i$ of $\mathfrak{x}_1, \ldots, \mathfrak{x}_m$ the formula*

$$f(\mathfrak{x}) = \sum_{i=1}^{m} c_i f(\mathfrak{x}_i)$$

is valid, that is, the function value of f for a linear combination of m vectors is the corresponding linear combination of the m function values for these vectors.

Proof: If $f(\mathfrak{x}) \equiv \mathfrak{a}\mathfrak{x}$, then by Theorem 43

$$f\Big(\sum_{i=1}^{m} c_i \mathfrak{x}_i\Big) = \mathfrak{a}\Big(\sum_{i=1}^{m} c_i \mathfrak{x}_i\Big) = \sum_{i=1}^{m} \mathfrak{a}(c_i \mathfrak{x}_i) = \sum_{i=1}^{m} c_i(\mathfrak{a}\mathfrak{x}_i) = \sum_{i=1}^{m} c_i f(\mathfrak{x}_i).$$

In our remarks before Def. 25 we had in mind particularly the facts and calculations which occur in Theorem 44 and its proof. In view of Theorem 44 the appropriateness of the introduction of vectors becomes obvious.

Finally, in line with the remarks of Section 4, we point out that in the case of linear forms the formal function concept of algebra coincides with the function concept in the sense of analysis.

Namely, on passing over to the linear forms the condition in question, Section 2, (ε'), is satisfied in the sense of analysis by

Theorem 45. *For linear forms f and g over* K, *the relation*

$$f(\mathfrak{x}) \equiv g(\mathfrak{x})$$

is equivalent to the relation

$$f(\mathfrak{x}) = g(\mathfrak{x}) \text{ for all } \mathfrak{x} \text{ in K}.$$

Proof: a) It is clear that the former relation implies the latter.

b) If $f(\mathfrak{x}) = g(\mathfrak{x})$ for all $\mathfrak{x}$ in K, then in particular $f(\mathfrak{e}_k) = g(\mathfrak{e}_k)$ $(k = 1,\ldots,n)$. Now, $f(\mathfrak{x}) \equiv \mathfrak{a}\mathfrak{x}$ implies $f(\mathfrak{e}_k) = \mathfrak{a}\mathfrak{e}_k = a_k$. Hence the corresponding coefficients of f and g must be the same, that is $f(\mathfrak{x}) \equiv g(\mathfrak{x})$.

c) Matrices

In the systems of coefficients from the left sides of systems of linear equations we encounter systems of m n-termed vectors, which we can think of as combined into an $(m\,n)$-termed vector. These $(m\,n)$-termed vectors can also be thought of as formed by combining, in some other way, n m-termed vectors, where each vector consists of the coefficients of a fixed indeterminate. It is advisable to introduce a special terminology for these two combining processes as well as, conversely, for the decomposition of an $(m\,n)$-termed vector in one of these two ways. For this purpose we define:

Definition 27. *An $(m\,n)$-termed vector, insofar as it is thought of as being formed by combining m n-termed or n m-termed vectors into a rectangular array*

$$\begin{pmatrix} a_{11} & \cdots\cdots & a_{1n} \\ \cdots & \cdots\cdots & \cdots \\ a_{m1} & \cdots\cdots & a_{mn} \end{pmatrix}, \textit{briefly } (a_{ik}) \quad \begin{pmatrix} i = 1,\ldots, m \\ k = 1,\ldots, n \end{pmatrix},$$

is called an ***(m, n)-rowed matrix.*** *The horizontal and vertical component vectors are called the* ***rows*** *and* ***columns,*** *respectively, of the matrix. We also designate matrices by the capital letters corresponding to their terms.*

For example, (a_{ik}) is designated by A; (α_{ik}), by A,... The (m, n)-rowed *null matrix* corresponding to the (mn)-termed null vector can again be designated by 0. — We will also omit the addendum *(m, n)-rowed* when the numbers m and n follow from the context.

According to Def. 27 the concept *(m, n)-rowed matrix* is narrower than the concept *(mn)-termed vector*, just as the concept "the integer $l = mn$ decomposed into factors" is narrower than the concept "the integer l." In the case of matrices the distinctness criterion and the rules of combination, namely, the analogues to (1), (2), (3)

$$\left.\begin{array}{l}(1')\,(a_{ik}) = (a'_{ik}) \text{ if and only if } a_{ik} = a'_{ik}\\ (2')\,(a_{ik}) + (b_{ik}) = (a_{ik} + b_{ik})\\ (3')\,a(a_{ik}) = (aa_{ik})\end{array}\right\}\begin{pmatrix} i = 1,\ldots,m\\ k = 1,\ldots,n\end{pmatrix},$$

do not actually bring this out. The restriction lies rather in the rectangular array imposed on the (mn)-termed vector, whereby the terms standing in each row or column are conceptually combined.

As a rule the index i is used for numbering the rows; k, for the columns. Hence, if an (m, n)-rowed matrix (a_{ik}) is submitted, then (a_{ki}) stands for the (n, m)-rowed matrix

$$\begin{pmatrix} a_{11} \cdots a_{m1}\\ \cdots\cdots\cdots\\ a_{1n} \cdots a_{mn}\end{pmatrix}$$

obtained by interchanging the rows and columns; for, here it is the first index which enumerates the columns, the second index the rows.

Definition 28. *The (n, m)-rowed matrix (a_{ki}) obtained from an (m, n)-rowed matrix (a_{ik}) by interchanging its rows and columns is called the* ***transpose*** *of (a_{ik}). If (a_{ik}) is denoted by A, then (a_{ki}) is denoted by A'.*

Besides the rules of combination (2′) and (3′), in the so-called matrix calculus there is still another extremely important rule of combination which is used to obtain a new matrix from two given matrices. We are referring to the so-called *matrix product* which can be defined, however, only within the set of all matrices (not only those with fixed m and n). The formation of matrix product actually contains the formation of inner vector product as a special case;[3] however, it does not simply amount to the inner product of the vectors corresponding to the matrices. Even though the so-called matrix calculus in question plays a very important role in linear algebra and especially contributes far more than the vector notation towards the clear statement of the developments and results of linear algebra, we still must refrain from investigating it further in the limited space at our disposal. For such a treatment we refer to more extensive texts.[4]

11. Nonhomogeneous and Homogeneous Systems of Linear Equations

We next begin the systematic treatment of the problem formulated in Section 5, (1). Besides investigating the proper system of linear equations

$$\text{(J)} \qquad f_i(x_1, \ldots, x_n) \equiv \sum_{k=1}^{n} a_{ik} x_k \doteq a_i \quad (i = 1, \ldots, m)$$

we consider independently the system of linear equations

$$\text{(H)} \qquad f_i(x_1, \ldots, x_n) \equiv \sum_{k=1}^{n} a_{ik} x_k \doteq 0 \quad (i = 1, \ldots, m).$$

(H) is said to be the *system of homogeneous equations associated to* (J), whereas (J) is said to be *nonhomogeneous*.

The fact that (J) and (H) have been assigned opposite names implies that we do not wish to regard, as it seems natural

---

[3] From the standpoint of the product of matrices the two factors of the inner vector product are a $(1, n)$-rowed and an $(n, 1)$-rowed matrix and the result a $(1, 1)$-rowed matrix. The latter is formally, but not conceptually, an element of the ground field.

[4] See also Vol. 3, Section 10, Exer. 3, as well as many other exercises in the following sections of Vol. 1 and Vol. 2.

to do at first, the special case of (J), where all $a_i = 0$, as *formally* identical with (H). On the contrary, in order that the results to be deduced may be neatly formulated, we make the following convention, which *technically* distinguishes (H) from this special case of (J): the null vector $\mathfrak{x} = 0$, which is always a solution of (H) (the so-called *identical solution*), shall *not* be counted as a solution of (H). In particular, therefore, we say that (H) *cannot be solved* if the null vector is its only solution. However, we regard the null vector as an admissible solution for the mentioned special case of (J).

By the *matrix of* (J) *and* (H) we understand the (m, n)-rowed matrix $A = (a_{ik})$.

By means of the concepts developed in Section 10 the existence of (J) and (H) for a system $x_1, \ldots, x_n$ can also be expressed as follows: The linear combination of the columns of A with the coefficients $x_1, \ldots, x_n$ yields the vector $\mathfrak{a}$ formed by the right-hand sides of (J), or the null vector, respectively. By this convention the solvability of (H) becomes equivalent, in particular, to the linear dependence of the columns of A. (Cf. formulae, Section 10, (4), (5), [84], which refer, however, in this sense to the system of equations with the matrix A'.) The problem of linear algebra Section 5, (1) can accordingly be formulated in this case as follows: Find all possible linear combinations of a given system of vectors which yield a particular vector; in particular, find all linear dependences of a given system of vectors. It is important to keep this interpretation in mind, since it will be frequently used in the following.

Finally, besides (J) and (H) we will also have to take into consideration the *transpose system of homogeneous equations* formed with the transpose matrix $A' = (a_{ki})$:

$$(\mathrm{H}')\ f_k(x_1', \ldots, x_m') \equiv \sum_{i=1}^{m} a_{ik} x_i' \doteq 0 \text{ [5]} \qquad (k = 1, \ldots, n).$$

Originally (J) alone was to be investigated. The independent consideration of (H) is justified by the following theorem:

Theorem 46. *If* (J) *can be solved, then all remaining solutions* $\mathfrak{x}_J$ *of* (J) *are obtained by adding to any fixed solution* $\mathfrak{x}_J^{(0)}$ *of* (J) *all solutions* $\mathfrak{x}_H$ *of* (H); *therefore, they have the form* $\mathfrak{x}_J = \mathfrak{x}_J^{(0)} + \mathfrak{x}_H$.

Proof: a) By Theorem 44 [86] it follows from $f_i(\mathfrak{x}_J^{(0)}) = a_i$, $f_i(\mathfrak{x}_H) = 0$, that $f_i(\mathfrak{x}_J^{(0)} + \mathfrak{x}_H) = f_i(\mathfrak{x}_J^{(0)}) + f_i(\mathfrak{x}_H) = a_i + 0 = a_i$; therefore, all $\mathfrak{x}_J = \mathfrak{x}_J^{(0)} + \mathfrak{x}_H$ are solutions of (J).

b) If $f_i(\mathfrak{x}_J) = a_i$, $f_i(\mathfrak{x}_J^{(0)}) = a_i$, then it likewise follows that $f_i(\mathfrak{x}_J - \mathfrak{x}_J^{(0)}) = 0$. Therefore, if $\mathfrak{x}_J \neq \mathfrak{x}_J^{(0)}$, then $\mathfrak{x}_J - \mathfrak{x}_J^{(0)} = \mathfrak{x}_H$ is a solution of (H). This means that any solution $\mathfrak{x}_J$ of (J) distinct from $\mathfrak{x}_J^{(0)}$ can actually be written as $\mathfrak{x}_J = \mathfrak{x}_J^{(0)} + \mathfrak{x}_H$.

Theorem 46 reduces the problem of linear algebra to the following two subproblems:

J) Determination of *one* solution of (J);

H) Determination of *all* solutions of (H).

On the one hand, in the case of (H) we have

Theorem 47. *If* $\mathfrak{x}_1, \ldots, \mathfrak{x}_s$ *are solutions of* (H), *so also are all their linear combinations.*

Proof: By Theorem 44 [86] $f_i(\mathfrak{x}_j) = 0$ $(j = 1, \ldots, s)$ implies

$$f_i\left(\sum_{j=1}^{s} c_j \mathfrak{x}_j\right) = \sum_{j=1}^{s} c_j f_i(\mathfrak{x}_j) = \sum_{j=1}^{s} c_j 0 = 0 \qquad (i = 1, \ldots, m).$$

---

[5] On writing out the proposed system of equations it actually turns out that it is the coefficient a_{ki} which is in the i-th row and k-th column and *not* a_{ik}, as one might believe at a first glance. — It is worth while in the following to visualize the equations of (H′) as written *side by side* with each individual equation running *downwards*, to show the generation of (H′) from the matrix A.

We now state

Definition 29. *A system* $\mathfrak{x}_1, \ldots, \mathfrak{x}_s$ *of linearly independent solutions of* (H) *is called a* ***system of fundamental solutions of*** (H) *if every solution of* (H) *is a linear combination of* $\mathfrak{x}_1, \ldots, \mathfrak{x}_s$.

By Theorem 47 and Def. 29 the totality of solutions of (H) is identical with the totality of linear combinations of a system of fundamental solutions of (H); moreover by Theorem 41 [81] the representations of the solutions in terms of the fundamental solutions are unique. Consequently, problem H) reduces to the problem of determining a system of fundamental solutions of (H).

Whether such a system actually exists in all cases remains undecided for the time being;[6] it will be decided affirmatively only later (Theorem 50 [104]). If (H) cannot be solved, that is, if there exist no linearly independent solutions of (H) (cf. the remark to Def. 24 [80]), then we say, so as to conform with our convention, that (H) has a system of fundamental solutions consisting of 0 solutions. That the latter case actually occurs can be illustrated by the system of equations $a_{11}x_1 = 0$, where $m = n = 1$ with $a_{11} \neq 0$.

On the other hand, in the case of J) the following necessary condition for solvability exists. Later (Theorem 49 [102]) it will be shown that this condition is also sufficient.

Theorem 48. *A necessary condition for the solvability of* (J) *is the following: If any linear dependence* $\sum_{i=1}^{m} x_i' f_i = 0$ *exists between the linear forms on the left, then the corresponding relation* $\sum_{i=1}^{m} x_i' a_i = 0$ *must also be valid for the right sides.*

---

[6] It could very well be that to any system of linearly independent solutions of (H) there would still exist another solution of (H) linearly independent of these.

Proof: Let us assume that (J) can be solved. Then a vector $\mathfrak{x}$ exists such that the function values are $f_i(\mathfrak{x}) = a_i$. Hence by the principle of substitution $\sum_{i=1}^{m} x'_i f_i = 0$ implies that $\sum_{i=1}^{m} x'_i a_i = 0$ is also valid.

Now, by Section 10 a linear dependence $\sum_{i=1}^{m} x'_i f_i = 0$ of the linear forms f_i is equivalent to the linear dependence $\sum_{i=1}^{m} x'_i \mathfrak{a}_i = 0$ between the corresponding vectors $\mathfrak{a}_i$, i. e., the rows of A. Since this amounts to saying that $\mathfrak{x}'$ is a solution of (H′), we have

Corollary 1. *The condition of Theorem* 48 *can also be expressed as follows: For every solution* $\mathfrak{x}'$ *of* (H′), $\mathfrak{x}'\mathfrak{a} = 0$ *must be valid.*

If we assume the existence of a system of fundamental solutions of (H′), then by Theorem 43 [85] we also have in addition:

Corollary 2. *The condition of Theorem* 48 *can also be expressed as follows: For the solutions* $\mathfrak{x}'_l$ *of a system of fundamental solutions of* (H′) $\mathfrak{x}'_l\,\mathfrak{a} = 0$ *must be valid.*

These corollaries justify the introduction of (H′) within the range of our considerations, since they show that (J) is not only related to (H) as shown in Theorem 46 but also to (H′).

The problems J) and H) under discussion can next be subdivided into a *theoretical* and a *practical* part as formulated below:

J_{th}) *to prove that the necessary condition given in Theorem* 48 *for the existence of a solution of* (J) *is also sufficient*;

J_{pr}) *to determine a solution of* (J) *if it can be solved*;

H_{th}) *to prove the existence of a system of fundamental solutions of* (H);

H_{pr}) *to determine a system of fundamental solutions of* (H).

We have seen that in the case of (J) we are only concerned with *one* solution; while in the case of (H), with *all* solutions. Hence the investigations and results relative to (H) will naturally take up more space in the following than those relative to (J), which was originally to be our only object of study. Due to limitations of space we will not always be able to express according to Theorems 46 and 48 the meaning of the results to be found for (H) in terms of (J). The reader should not fail to realize this meaning clearly in every individual case.

12. The Toeplitz Process

The theoretical parts J_{th}) and H_{th}) of the problems specified at the end of the previous section can be completely solved by a process given by *Toeplitz*,[7] which we will explain in this section.

For this purpose we set up the following three definitions:

Definition 30. *Two systems of linear equations are said to be* ***equivalent*** *if they have the same totality of solutions.*

This is naturally an equivalence relation in the sense of Section 2, (I). However, we have no need of the partition thereby determined. This partition is significant only in the calculus of matrices, where the equivalence itself can be described in terms of relations between the matrices of the systems of equations.

Definition 31. *The* ***length*** *of a linear form* $f(x_1, \ldots, x_n)$ *is defined as* 1) *the number* 0 *if* $f = 0$; 2) *the index of its last coefficient (taking the natural ordering* $x_1, \ldots, x_n$ *as a basis) different from zero if* $f \neq 0$.

This implies that the length k of a linear form $f(x_1, \ldots, x_n)$ is always $0 \leqq k \leqq n$, and that $k = 0$ is equivalent to $f = 0$.

Definition 32. *A linear form of length* $k \geqq 1$ *is said to be* ***normalized*** *if its k-th coefficient is e.*

[7] Cf. O. Toeplitz, *Über die Auflösung unendlich vieler linearer Gleichungen mit unendlich vielen Unbekannten (On the Solution of an Infinite Number of Linear Equations with an Infinite Number of Unknowns)*, Rendiconti del Circolo Matematico di Palermo 28 (1909). The process is developed there so as to apply to the more general problem introduced in point 2 of footnote 13 [55] to Section 5.

The objective of the Toeplitz process is to find a system of equations equivalent to (J) or (H) whose totality of solutions is especially simple to survey.

It will be assumed that (J) satisfies the necessary condition for solvability of Theorem 48 [92]. Since this condition is always valid if $\mathfrak{a} = 0$, there will be no loss of generality, from the point of view of the process mentioned, if (H) is regarded as the special case $\mathfrak{a} = 0$ of (J). Consequently, it is sufficient to subject (J) alone to the process. We will again consider (H) separately from (J) only for the theorems dealing with the solvability and the solutions of systems of linear equations to be derived from this process in the next section.

The proof of the following existence statement forms the *content* of the Toeplitz process.

Theorem of Toeplitz. *If* (J) *satisfies the necessary condition for solvability of Theorem* 48 [92] *and not all linear forms* $f_i = 0$, *then there is a system of equations equivalent to* (J)

$$(\mathrm{J}_0)\begin{cases} g_1(\mathfrak{x}) \equiv b_{11}x_1 + \cdots + b_{1,k_1-1}x_{k_1-1} + x_{k_1} {}^{8} & \doteq b_1 \\ g_2(\mathfrak{x}) \equiv b_{21}x_1 + \cdots + b_{2,k_2-1}x_{k_2-1} + x_{k_2} & \doteq b_2 \\ \dots\dots\dots\dots\dots\dots\dots\dots\dots\dots\dots\dots & \\ g_r(\mathfrak{x}) \equiv b_{r1}x_1 + \cdots\cdots + b_{r,k_r-1}x_{k_r-1} + x_{k_r} & \doteq b_r \end{cases}$$

with the properties:

(1) *r is the maximal number of linearly independent* f_i,

(2) $g_1, \dots, g_r$ *are linearly independent*,

(3) $g_1, \dots, g_r$ *are normalized*,

(4) *The lengths* $k_1, \dots, k_r$ *of* $g_1, \dots, g_r$ *satisfy the relations*

[8] In order to bring out the structure of (J_0) clearly we avoid, here and at similar places in the following, using the summation symbol even though it may be possible to do so. — The awkward notation for the case $k_1 = 1$ cannot be readily avoided. We make the convention that a sum $u_1 + \cdots + u_{k-1}$ for $k = 1$ is to be considered as nonexistent, and eventually replaced by 0; also, that statements about $u_1, \dots, u_{k-1}$ for $k = 1$ are to be considered as void.

$$1 \leqq k_1 < k_2 < \cdots < k_r \leqq n.$$

Proof: The proof will be handled in two steps. In the first step, which is of a preliminary nature, we will prove the existence of a system of equations ($\bar{J}_0$) equivalent to (J) with the properties (1), (2). In the second step we will give the proper existence proof for a system of equations (J_0) equivalent to ($\bar{J}_0$), and consequently also to (J), with all properties (1) to (4) specified in the theorem.

First Step

The first step consists in the application of the following lemma to the linear forms f_i on the left in (J):

Lemma 1. *To any [finite*[9]*] system of linear forms f_i, which are not all* 0, *there exists a* ***maximal system of linearly independent*** f_i, *that is, a subsystem containing the greatest possible number of linearly independent f_i, the so-called* ***maximal number of linearly independent*** f_i.

Proof: Let $f_1, \ldots, f_m$ be a system of linear forms in which not all $f_i = 0$. We now apply the fact that every non-empty set of natural numbers $\leqq m$ contains a greatest number, to the set of numbers obtained by counting all linearly independent subsystems of the system $f_1, \ldots, f_m$. Since by assumption this set of natural numbers $\leqq m$ is not empty — (according to Def. 24 [80] the number 1 surely belongs to this set) — there must be a greatest possible number in this set. The corresponding subsystem must contain the greatest possible number of linearly independent forms. This completes the proof of Lemma 1.

It should be noted that in order to formulate later results uniformly it is convenient to say in the case excluded in Lemma 1,

---

[9] Cf. Section 13, Lemma 2 [104].

where all $f_i = 0$, just as with respect to Def. 29 [92], that the maximal number of linearly independent f_i is 0, and that a maximal system of 0 linearly independent f_i exists.

Lemma 1 will be used to prove the equivalence of the system $(\overline{J}_0)$, set up below, to (J). This application depends on the following lemma, which we formulate especially because of its frequent use in the following.

Lemma 2. *The totality of linear combinations of a [finite*[10]*] system of linear forms f_i, which are not all 0, is identical with the totality of linear combinations of a maximal system of linearly independent f_i.*

Proof: Let $f_{i_1}, \ldots, f_{i_r}$ be a maximal system of linearly independent linear forms of the system $f_1, \ldots, f_m$. By Theorem 42 [82] the proof rests on the following facts:

a) Every f_{i_ν} $(\nu = 1, \ldots, r)$ is a linear combination of $f_1, \ldots, f_m$. — This is clear since f_{i_ν} occurs among $f_1, \ldots, f_m$.

b) Every f_i $(i = 1, \ldots, m)$ is a linear combination of $f_{i_1}, \ldots, f_{i_r}$. — If i is an i_ν, then, as above, this is clear. If i is not an i_ν, then $f_i, f_{i_1}, \ldots, f_{i_r}$ is a subsystem of $f_1, \ldots, f_m$ with a greater number $r + 1$ of linearly independent f_i than the maximal number r. Therefore, $f_i, f_{i_1}, \ldots, f_{i_r}$ are linearly dependent. By a′) in Theorem 38 [80] the linear independence of $f_{i_1}, \ldots, f_{i_r}$ then implies that f_i is linearly dependent on $f_{i_1}, \ldots, f_{i_r}$.

This completes the proof of Lemma 2.

The hypothesis of the Theorem of Toeplitz enables us to apply Lemma 1 to the linear forms $f_1, \ldots, f_m$ on the left in (J). Now, the totality of solutions of (J) is independent of the ordering of the equations; in other words, any rearrangement

[10] Cf. Section 13, Lemma 2 [104].

of the equations of (J) takes (J) into an equivalent system of equations. Hence we are permitted to assume without loss of generality[11] that $f_1, \ldots, f_r$ is a maximal system of linearly independent f_i. From the linear forms of this maximal system we form the system of equations

$$(\overline{\mathrm{J}_0}) \qquad f_i(x) \doteq a_i \quad (i = 1, \ldots, r).$$

$(\overline{\mathrm{J}_0})$ has then the properties (1) and (2) of the Theorem of Toeplitz.

Moreover, $(\overline{\mathrm{J}_0})$ is equivalent to (J). This is clear if $r = m$, since in this case $(\overline{\mathrm{J}_0})$ is the same as (J). Let $r < m$. Then, on the one hand, any solution of (J) is a fortiori also a solution of $(\overline{\mathrm{J}_0})$. On the other hand, by Lemma 2 there exist relations of the form

$$(5) \qquad f_j = \sum_{i=1}^{r} c_{ji} f_i \quad (j = r+1, \ldots, m),$$

and by Theorem 48 [92], which by the assumption of the Theorem of Toeplitz is valid for (J), there exist at the same time the relations

$$(6) \qquad a_j = \sum_{i=1}^{r} c_{ji} a_i \quad (j = r+1, \ldots, m).$$

By the principle of substitution (5) and (6) yield that any solution of $(\overline{\mathrm{J}_0})$ is also conversely a solution of (J).

Second Step

The *basic idea of the second step* consists in the repeated application of the following lemma to subsystems of linear forms on the left in $(\overline{\mathrm{J}_0})$:

[11] This is only a matter of notation.

Lemma 3. *Every system*[12] *of linearly independent linear forms contains one and only one normalized linear combination of smallest positive length.*

Proof: Let $f_1, \ldots, f_\nu$ be linearly independent linear forms. Now, in any set of non-negative integers which does not consist of the number 0 alone there is a uniquely determined smallest positive number. We apply this fact to the set of lengths of all linear combinations of $f_1, \ldots, f_\nu$. Since this set of non-negative integers does not consist of the number 0 alone, due to the linear independence of the $f_1, \ldots, f_\nu$, there is a linear combination

$$\bar{g} = \bar{c}_1 f_1 + \cdots + \bar{c}_\nu f_\nu \equiv \bar{b}_1 x_1 + \cdots + \bar{b}_k x_k. \ (\bar{b}_k \neq 0)$$

of $f_1, \ldots, f_\nu$ with smallest positive length k, and k is hereby uniquely determined. If we set

$$\frac{e}{\bar{b}_k}\bar{g} = g, \quad \frac{\bar{c}_i}{\bar{b}_k} = c_i, \quad \frac{\bar{b}_l}{\bar{b}_k} = b_l, \text{ then}$$

$$g = c_1 f_1 + \cdots + c_\nu f_\nu \equiv b_1 x_1 + \cdots + b_{k-1} x_{k-1} + x_k$$

is a normalized linear combination of $f_1, \ldots, f_\nu$ of smallest positive length. Now, if

$$g' = c'_1 f_1 + \cdots + c'_\nu f_\nu \equiv b'_1 x_1 + \cdots + b'_{k-1} x_{k-1} + x_k$$

is another one of this kind (by the remarks, its length must again be k), then by subtraction it follows that

$$g - g' = (c_1 - c'_1) f_1 + \cdots + (c_\nu - c'_\nu) f_\nu$$
$$\equiv (b_1 - b'_1) x_1 + \cdots + (b_{k-1} - b'_{k-1}) x_{k-1}.$$

Therefore $g - g'$ is a linear combination of $f_1, \ldots, f_\nu$ with a length $< k$. Due to the choice of k this length must be 0. Therefore $g - g' = 0$, that is, $g = g'$. This completes the proof of Lemma 3.

---

[12] Naturally "finite". Infinite systems of linearly independent linear forms are not defined. Moreover, due to Lemma 1 [103] to be given in Section 13 they cannot on principle be meaningfully defined so as to make sense.

By means of Lemma 3 we next prove the following lemma. The crucial point *of the second step* consists in its application to the linear forms on the left in $(\overline{J}_0)$.

Lemma 4. *Let $f_1, \ldots, f_r$ be a system of linearly independent linear forms of $x_1, \ldots, x_n$. It is possible to order $f_1, \ldots, f_r$ so that there exists a system of linear forms $g_1, \ldots, g_r$ with the properties* (2), (3), (4) *of the Theorem of Toeplitz which are the following linear combinations of the $f_1, \ldots, f_r$.*

$$(7)\quad \begin{cases} g_1 = c_{11} f_1 + \cdots\cdots\cdots\cdots + c_{1r} f_r \\ g_2 = c_{21} f_1 + \cdots + c_{2,r-1} f_{r-1} \\ \cdots\cdots\cdots \\ g_r = c_{r1} f_1 \end{cases}$$

$$(8)\quad c_{1r}, c_{2,r-1}, \ldots, c_{r1} \neq 0.$$

Proof: We apply Lemma 3 in r steps, 1) to r), to certain r subsystems of the system $f_1, \ldots, f_r$. This is possible, since by Theorem 39 [81] any such subsystem is linearly independent.

1) a) Let

$$g_1 = c_{11} f_1 + \cdots + c_{1r} f_r \equiv b_{11} x_1 + \cdots + b_{1,k_1-1} x_{k_1-1} + x_{k_1}$$

be the normalized linear combination of $f_1, \ldots, f_r$ of smallest positive length k_1. Naturally $k_1 \geqq 1$.

b) Since $g_1 \neq 0$, it is naturally linearly independent.

c) Since $g_1 \neq 0$, not all $c_{1i} = 0$. We can assume, therefore, that the ordering of the $f_1, \ldots, f_r$ is chosen so that $c_{1r} \neq 0$.

2) a) Let
$$\begin{aligned} g_2 &= c_{21} f_1 + \cdots + c_{2,r-1} f_{r-1} \\ &\equiv b_{21} x_1 + \cdots + b_{2,k_2-1} x_{k_2-1} + x_{k_2} \end{aligned}$$

be the normalized linear combination of $f_1, \ldots, f_{r-1}$ of smallest positive length k_2. Then $k_2 > k_1$. First of all, since the linear combinations of $f_1, \ldots, f_{r-1}$ are contained among those of $f_1, \ldots, f_{r-1}, f_r$, the definition of k_1 precludes that $k_2 < k_1$. But, if $k_2 = k_1$ were valid, then g_2 could be regarded as a linear combination of $f_1, \ldots, f_r$ identical with g_1 on account of the unique determination of g_1. By Theorem 41 [81] and the fact that $c_{1r} \neq 0$, this result would contradict the linear independence of $f_1, \ldots, f_r$.

b) g_1, g_2 are linearly independent. For otherwise, on account of 1) b) and a′) in Theorem 38 [80], g_2 would be a linear combination of g_1, which obviously contradicts $k_2 > k_1$.

c) Since $g_2 \neq 0$, not all $c_{2i} = 0$. Since the assumption made under 1) c) regarding the ordering refers only to the position of f_r, we can assume the ordering of $f_1, \ldots, f_{r-1}$ as chosen so that $c_{2,r-1} \neq 0$.

3) to $(r-1)$) As above.

r) a) As above. Naturally, $k_r \leq n$.

b) As above.

c) Since $g_r \neq 0$, $c_{r1} \neq 0$.

The system $g_1, \ldots, g_r$ resulting from 1) to r) has the properties (2) to (4), (7), (8). This completes the proof of Lemma 4.

We next apply Lemma 4 to the linearly independent system of linear forms $f_1, \ldots, f_r$ on the left in $(\overline{\mathrm{J}}_0)$. As above there is no loss in generality if we assume[13] that the equations of $(\overline{\mathrm{J}}_0)$ are arranged in accord with Lemma 4. We now adopt the notation introduced in Lemma 4; in addition we set

$$(9)\quad \begin{cases} b_1 = c_{11} a_1 + \cdots\cdots\cdots\cdots\cdots + c_{1r} a_r \\ b_2 = c_{21} a_1 + \cdots + c_{2,r-1} a_{r-1} \\ \quad\cdots\cdots \\ b_r = c_{r1} a_1 \end{cases}$$

and form the system of equations with these $b_1, \ldots, b_r$ as the right sides and $g_1, \ldots, g_r$ as the left sides, namely,

$$(\mathrm{J}_0) \qquad g_i(\mathfrak{x}) = b_i \quad (i = 1, \ldots, r).$$

By the preceding this system has then the properties (1) to (4) of the Theorem of Toeplitz.

---

[13] This is only a matter of notation.

In order to complete the proof we only have to show in addition that (J_0) is equivalent to $(\bar{J}_0)$ and consequently also to (J). Now, on the one hand, any solution $\mathfrak{x}$ of $(\bar{J}_0)$ is also a solution of (J_0), since by (7), (9) and the principle of substitution $f_i(\mathfrak{x}) = a_i$ implies $g_i(\mathfrak{x}) = b_i$ $(i = 1, \ldots, r)$. On the other hand, by (7), (9) and the principle of substitution $g_i(\mathfrak{x}) = b_i$ $(i = 1, \ldots, r)$ implies, above all, that

$$\begin{aligned}
c_{11} f_1(\mathfrak{x}) + \cdots\cdots + c_{1r} f_r(\mathfrak{x}) &= c_{11} a_1 + \cdots\cdots + c_{1r} a_r \\
c_{21} f_1(\mathfrak{x}) + \cdots + c_{2,r-1} f_{r-1}(\mathfrak{x}) &= c_{21} a_1 + \cdots + c_{2,r-1} a_{r-1} \\
\cdots\cdots\cdots & \cdots\cdots\cdots \\
c_{r1} f_1(\mathfrak{x}) \qquad\qquad &= c_{r1} a_1 .
\end{aligned}$$

By (8), however, it can be deduced by proceeding successively upwards through this system that $f_i(\mathfrak{x}) = a_i$ $(i = 1, \ldots, r)$. Hence every solution of (J_0) is conversely also a solution of $(\bar{J}_0)$.

This completes the proof of the Theorem of Toeplitz.

For the application to (H) in the next section we further add:

Corollary. *The* (H) *associated to* (J) *is equivalent to the* (H_0) *associated to* (J_0).

Proof: If $\mathfrak{a} = 0$, then by (9) we also have $\mathfrak{b} = 0$, that is, (J_0) goes over into its associated homogeneous system (H_0).

13. Solvability and Solutions of Systems of Linear Equations

We will now use the Theorem of Toeplitz to solve the two problems J_{th}) and H_{th}) formulated at the end of Section 11, as well as to deduce some results concerning the solutions of (H), going beyond H_{th}).

J_{th}) is solved through the proof of the following theorem:

Theorem 49. *For the solvability of* (J) *the necessary condition of Theorem* 48 [92] *is also sufficient.*

Proof: a) The statement is trivial if all $f_i = 0$. Namely, since in this case the special linear dependences $f_i = 0$ exist between the f_i, the condition of Theorem 48 says that it must also be true that all $a_i = 0$. This means, however, that every $\mathfrak{x}$ is a solution of (J).

b) If not all $f_i = 0$, then by the Theorem of Toeplitz [95] it is sufficient to show that the (J_0), appearing there, always has a solution $\mathfrak{x}$. This, however, is easily established by means of condition (4) of that theorem. First of all, $x_1, \ldots, x_{k_1-1}$ [14] are arbitrarily chosen; then x_{k_1} can be (uniquely) determined such that the first equation exists no matter how the remaining x_k may be chosen. Next, $x_{k_1+1}, \ldots, x_{k_2-1}$ [14] are arbitrarily chosen; then x_{k_2} can be (uniquely) determined such that not only the first but also the second equation exists no matter how the remaining x_k may be chosen, etc. After the determination of x_{k_r} the $x_{k_r+1}, \ldots, x_n$ are still to be chosen arbitrarily. Then the $\mathfrak{x}$ so determined is a solution of (J_0), therefore also of (J).

For the solution of H_{th}) we first prove the following two lemmas:

Lemma 1. *There are at most n linearly independent linear forms in n indeterminates.*

Proof: If $f_1, \ldots, f_r$ is a system of r linearly independent linear forms, then by Section 12, Lemma 4 [100] there exist, in particular, r integers $k_1, \ldots, k_r$ satisfying condition (4) of the Theorem of Toeplitz. Obviously the number of these can be at most n. Therefore $r \leqq n$.

That the maximal number n is actually attained is shown by the n linearly independent linear forms $x_1, \ldots, x_n$.

[14] In regard to the cases $k_1 = 1, k_2 = k_1 + 1, \ldots$ cf. footnote 8 [95] in Section 12 to the Theorem of Toeplitz.

Lemma 1 immediately yields the following facts regarding the number r occurring in the Theorem of Toeplitz. This number is important for the later development of the theory of (J), (H), (H′).

Corollary. *The maximal number r of linearly independent forms among* $\begin{Bmatrix} m \text{ linear forms of } n \text{ indeterminates} \\ \text{the rows of an } (m, n)\text{-rowed matrix} \end{Bmatrix}$ *satisfies not only the self-evident inequality* $0 \leqq r \leqq m$ *but also the inequality* $0 \leqq r \leqq n$.

Lemma 2. *Lemmas* 1 [96] *and* 2 | [97] *of Section* 12 *are also valid for an infinite system of linear forms which do not all vanish, that is, for any such system there exists a subsystem*[15] *consisting of the greatest possible number of linearly independent linear forms, and the totality of all linear combinations of the forms of such a subsystem is identical with the totality of all linear combinations (each combination containing only a finite number*[15]*) of linear forms of the entire system.*

Proof: By Lemma 1 proved above the number of linearly independent linear forms in a subsystem picked at random from the infinite system of linear forms is $\leqq n$. The proof of Section 12, Lemma 1, can then be completely transferred if the number n is used instead of the number m appearing there. Furthermore, the proof of Section 12, Lemma 2 immediately carries over.

By the methods then at our command we would not have been able to prove Lemma 2, since it would not have been established whether the number of linearly independent linear forms in every subsystem is *bounded* (cf. footnote 6 [92] after Def. 29).

H_{th}) itself can now be solved by the proof of the following theorem:

Theorem 50. *There exists a system of fundamental solutions of* (H).

---

[15] Cf. footnote 12 [99] to Section 12, Lemma 3.

Proof: a) If (H) cannot be solved, the theorem is trivial (cf. the remark regarding this after Def. 29 [92]).

b) If (H) can be solved, then the totality of its solutions forms a finite or infinite system of vectors which do not all vanish. By Lemma 2, expressed in terms of vectors, there exists a linearly independent subsystem of this system such that all vectors of the entire system are linear combinations of the vectors of this subsystem. By Def. 29 [92] this means that there exists a system of fundamental solutions of (H).

By Lemma 1 we can, for the present, only say that the number s of fundamental solutions of (H) satisfies the inequality $0 \leqq s \leqq n$. But, in the meantime, we are unable to say which of these possible values s has and, above all, whether this number s is an *invariant* for all systems of fundamental solutions of (H). That the latter is actually the case can now be inferred from Lemma 1:

Theorem 51. *All systems of fundamental solutions of (H) have exactly the same number of solutions.*

Proof: a) If (H) cannot be solved, the theorem is trivial.

b) If (H) can be solved, let $\mathfrak{x}_1, \ldots, \mathfrak{x}_s$ and $\mathfrak{x}'_1, \ldots, \mathfrak{x}'_{s'}$ be two systems of fundamental solutions of (H). Then there exist representations of $\mathfrak{x}_i$ in terms of the $\mathfrak{x}'_k$ of the form

$$\mathfrak{x}_i = \sum_{k=1}^{s'} c_{ik} \mathfrak{x}'_k \quad (i = 1, \ldots, s).$$

Now, if $s' < s$, then by Lemma 1 the s rows of the (s, s')-rowed matrix (c_{ik}) would be linearly dependent as s'-termed vectors; consequently, the corresponding linear dependence would also be valid for the $\mathfrak{x}_i$. By Def. 29 [92], however, the $\mathfrak{x}_i$ are linearly independent. Hence $s' < s$ cannot be valid. Similarly, the representations of the $\mathfrak{x}'_k$ in terms of the $\mathfrak{x}_i$ imply that $s < s'$ cannot be valid. Consequently, $s' = s$.

The conclusion of Theorem 51 already goes beyond problem H_{th}) even though its proof did not take advantage of the Theorem of Toeplitz to the same extent as the solution of J_{th}) in the proof of Theorem 49. Through the full use of the Theorem of Toeplitz we now can go beyond Theorem 51 and actually determine the exact number of fundamental solutions of (H). We prove

Theorem 52. *The number of fundamental solutions of* (H) *is $n - r$, where r is the maximal number of linearly independent f_i, i. e., the maximal number of linearly independent rows of the* (m, n)*-rowed matrix of* (H).

Proof: The number $n - r$ will turn out to be the number of indeterminates $x_1, \ldots, x_n$ different from the $x_{k_1}, \ldots, x_{k_r}$ specified in the Theorem of Toeplitz.

a) If all $f_i = 0$, therefore $r = 0$ (cf. the remark to Section 12, Lemma 1 [96]), the theorem is trivial. For, in this case all $\mathfrak{x}$ are solutions of (H), therefore by Def. 29 [92] the $n - 0 = n$ linearly independent unit vectors $\mathfrak{e}_1, \ldots, \mathfrak{e}_n$ form a system of fundamental solutions of (H).

b)If not all $f_i = 0$, then by the Theorem of Toeplitz (and its corollary [102]) it is sufficient to show that the number of fundamental solutions of the system (H_0) of homogeneous equations associated to the (J_0), appearing there, is $n - r$. We can now form the totality of solutions of (H_0) on the basis of condition (4) of the Theorem of Toeplitz [95] in exactly the same way as we have indicated a solution of (J_0) in the proof to Theorem 49.

1) First of all, in order to satisfy the first equation of (H_0) with respect to any given $x_1 = \xi_1, \ldots, x_{k_1 - 1} = \xi_{k_1 - 1}$[16] we must

[16] Regarding the cases $k_1 = 1, k_2 = k_1 + 1, \ldots$ cf. footnote 8 [95] in Section 12 to the Theorem of Toeplitz.

replace x_{k_1} by the linear homogeneous expression in $\xi_1, \ldots, \xi_{k_1-1}$

$$x_{k_1} = (-b_{11})\,\xi_1 + \cdots + (-b_{1,k_1-1})\,\xi_{k_1-1};$$

the first equation will be satisfied by such $x_1, \ldots, x_{k_1}$ no matter how the remaining x_k may be chosen.

2) Next, in order to satisfy the second equation of (H_0) with respect to any given $x_{k_1+1} = \xi_{k_1}, \ldots, x_{k_2-1} = \xi_{k_2-2}$[16] we must replace x_{k_2} by the linear homogeneous expression in $\xi_1, \ldots, \xi_{k_2-2}$

$$\begin{aligned} x_{k_2} &= (-b_{21})\,\xi_1 + \cdots + (-b_{2,k_1-1})\,\xi_{k_1-1} \\ &\quad + (-b_{2k_1})\,[(-b_{11})\,\xi_1 + \cdots + (-b_{1,k_1-1})\,\xi_{k_1-1}] \\ &\quad + (-b_{2,k_1+1})\,\xi_{k_1} + \cdots + (-b_{2,k_2-1})\,\xi_{k_2-2} \\ &= (-b_{21} + b_{2k_1}b_{11})\,\xi_1 + \cdots + (-b_{2,k_1-1} + b_{2k_1}b_{1,k_1-1})\,\xi_{k_1-1} \\ &\quad + (-b_{2,k_1+1})\,\xi_{k_1} + \cdots + (-b_{2,k_2-1})\,\xi_{k_2-2}. \end{aligned}$$

The second equation as well as the first will be satisfied by such $x_1, \ldots, x_{k_2}$, no matter how the remaining x_k may be chosen.

3) to r) As above.

After the r-th step $x_{k_r+1} = \xi_{k_r-r+1}, \ldots;\ x_n = \xi_{n-r}$[17] can still be arbitrarily chosen. The $x_1, \ldots, x_n$ so determined will satisfy all equations of (H_0).

To recapitulate: Let those of the indeterminates $x_1, \ldots, x_n$ different from $x_{k_1}, \ldots, x_{k_r}$ be designated by $x_{k_{r+1}}, \ldots, x_{k_n}$. Then (H_0) is satisfied with respect to any given

$$\begin{matrix} x_{k_{r+1}} = \xi_1 \\ \vdots \qquad \ddots \\ x_{k_n} = \xi_{n-r} \end{matrix}$$

by substituting for $x_{k_1}, \ldots, x_{k_r}$ certain linear homogeneous expressions in $\xi_1, \ldots, \xi_{n-r}$

---

[17] In case these do not appear the last ξ which does occur has at any rate the index $n - r$. The limiting case $r = n$, namely, where no ξ appears, will be considered by itself under c).

$$x_{k_1} = \alpha_{11}\xi_1 + \cdots\cdots + \alpha_{n-r,1}\xi_{n-r}$$
$$\cdots\cdots\cdots\cdots\cdots\cdots\cdots$$
$$x_{k_r} = \alpha_{1r}\xi_1 + \cdots\cdots + \alpha_{n-r,r}\xi_{n-r}$$

(whose coefficients α_{ki} are uniquely determined by the coefficients b_{ik} of (H_0)); conversely, the system (H_0) will be satisfied in this way in the case of any given $\xi_1, \ldots, \xi_{n-r}$. This means that the totality of solutions of (H_0) is generated by the $n-r$ special solutions

$$\begin{array}{ll} \mathfrak{x}_1 = (e, 0, \ldots, 0; & \alpha_{11}, \ldots, \alpha_{1r}) \\ \vdots & \vdots \\ \mathfrak{x}_{n-r} = (0, \ldots, 0, e; & \alpha_{n-r,1}, \ldots, \alpha_{n-r,r}) \end{array}$$

through arbitrary linear combinations (with the $\xi_1, \ldots, \xi_{n-r}$ as coefficients), whereby the x_k are to be thought of as arranged as above. Now, by Theorem 40 [81] the linear independence of the $(n-r)$-termed unit vectors implies that $\mathfrak{x}_1, \ldots, \mathfrak{x}_{n-r}$ are also linearly independent. Hence the latter form a system of fundamental solutions of (H_0) of $n-r$ solutions, as stated.

c) The proof carried through under b) must be supplemented for the limiting case $r = n$. In this case $\xi_1, \ldots, \xi_{n-r}$ do not appear at all, and by condition (4) of the Theorem of Toeplitz the set of numbers $k_1, \ldots, k_r$ is identical with the sequence $1, \ldots, n$. Consequently, the r steps under b) yield that $x_{k_1}, \ldots, x_{k_r}$, i. e., $x_1, \ldots, x_n$ are all to be set $= 0$ in order to satisfy (H_0). This means that (H_0) cannot be solved; in other words, it possesses a system of fundamental solutions of $0 = n - n = n - r$ solutions, as stated in the theorem.

Theorem 52 says that the number of fundamental solutions of the system of equations (H) increases as the number of linearly independent rows of its matrix A decreases. Hence the more linear dependences there are between these rows, or, since a linear dependence between the rows of A is equivalent to a solution of (H′), the greater the totality of solutions of (H′). It is, therefore, to be expected that a relation exists between the number of fundamental solutions of (H) and (H′). By Theorem 52 this relation must also be expressible as one between the maximal numbers of linearly independent rows and columns of A. We now prove in this regard the following two facts:

Theorem 53. *The maximal number of linearly independent rows of a matrix A is equal to the maximal number of linearly independent columns of A.*

Theorem 54. *Let s be the number of fundamental solutions of a system of homogeneous equations* (H) *consisting of m equations, and s' the number of fundamental solutions of its transpose* (H′) *consisting of m' equations. Then the following relation is valid:*

$$m + s = m' + s'.$$

Here, for once, we have written m' for the number designated otherwise by n, for the sake of symmetry.

Proofs: 1) (Theorem 53.) Let r and r' be the maximal numbers specified in the theorem for the (m, m')-rowed matrix A.

a) For $A = 0$ the theorem is trivial, since in this case $r = 0$, $r' = 0$ (cf. the remark to Section 12, Lemma 1 [96]).

b) For $A \neq 0$ we can apply Section 12, Lemmas 1, 2 [96, 97] to the rows $\mathfrak{a}_1, \ldots, \mathfrak{a}_m$ of A. Since the rearrangement of the rows will in no way alter any linear dependences which may exist either between the rows or between the columns, we are permitted to assume[18] without loss of generality that the rows are arranged so that $\mathfrak{a}_1, \ldots, \mathfrak{a}_r$ is a maximal system of linearly independent rows. Now, to start with, let $r < m$. Then by Section 12, Lemma 2, there exist corresponding to Section 12,

[18] This is only a matter of notation.

(5) $m-r$ relations between the rows of the form

$$\mathfrak{a}_j = \sum_{i=1}^{r} c_{ji}\mathfrak{a}_i \quad (j = r+1, \ldots, m).$$

These say that the $m-r$ vectors

$$\begin{array}{l} (-c_{r+1,1}, \ldots, -c_{r+1,r};\ e, 0, \ldots, 0) \\ \vdots \\ (-c_{m1}\quad, \ldots, -c_{mr}\quad;\ 0, \ldots, 0, e), \end{array}$$

which are linearly independent by Theorem 40 [81], are solutions of the (H′) belonging to A. On applying Theorems 50 to 52 to (H′) the number of fundamental solutions $m-r'$ of (H′) is at least $m-r$, that is, $m-r' \geqq m-r, r' \leqq r$. In case $r=m$ this is also valid by Lemma 1. On applying analogous considerations to the columns of A it likewise follows that $r \leqq r'$. Consequently, $r=r'$.

2) (Theorem 54.) By Theorems 52, 53 we have $s = m' - r$, $s' = m - r$, that is, $m + s = m' + s'$ $(= m + m' - r)$.

Theorem 53 clarifies the fact established above in the Corollary to Lemma 1. For, by Theorem 53 the "non-self-evident" inequality $0 \leqq r \leqq m'$ between a *row*-number and a *column*-number goes over into the "self-evident" inequality $0 \leqq r' \leqq m'$ between two *column*-numbers.

By Theorem 54 the "circle" of our considerations regarding (J), (H), (H′) is closed: By Theorem 46 [91] (J) is linked with (H), by Theorem 54 (H) with (H′), and by Theorems 48 [92], 49 (H′) with (J).

14. The Case $m = n$

It is of interest for the investigations in Chapter IV and also for the applications to specialize the results obtained in Theorems 46 to 54 [91 to 109], regarding the solvability and solutions of systems of linear equations, to the case where the number m of equations is the same as the number n of unknowns, namely, to the case where A is an (n, n)-rowed matrix. Now, in the previous section we have seen that the numbers m and n alone say practically nothing about the totality of solutions of (H) (and also of (J), as seen by Theorem 46 [91]); on the contrary, we had to include the above number r to determine this totality. Hence special results are not be expected here unless a definite assumption is made regarding r. We will therefore introduce another specialization besides $m = n$, which will distinguish *only* between the limiting case $r = m = n$ and the case $0 \leqq r < m = n$ (*without* further distinction in the latter case).[19]

Accordingly we make the following convention whose full significance will become clear only through the developments in Chapter IV; for the time being it is made only to make our terminology briefer.

Definition 33. *An (n, n)-rowed matrix A is said to be* ***regular*** *or* ***singular*** *according as $r = n$ or $0 \leqq r < n$, where r has the significance of Sections* 12, 13.

The facts contained in Theorems 52 to 54 [106 to 109] about (H) can now be summarized as follows:

Theorem (52, 53, 54) a. *If A is an (n, n)-rowed matrix, then either its rows as well as its columns are linearly independent or its rows as well as its columns are linearly dependent; that is, either both systems of equations* (H) *and* (H′) *belonging to A cannot be solved or both can be solved. The former or the latter is valid according as A is regular or singular.*

The facts contained in Theorems 46 [91], 48 [92], 49 [102] about (J) yield the further result:

Theorem (46, 48, 49) a. *The system of equations* (J) *with (n, n)-rowed matrix A can be uniquely solved for any arbitrary vector $\mathfrak{a}$ on the right if and only if A is regular.*

Proof: a) Let A be regular.

1. Then by Theorem 49 [102] (J) can be solved for arbitrary $\mathfrak{a}$, since by Theorem (52, 53, 54) a (H′) cannot be solved; therefore, the restrictive condition of Theorem 48 (Corollary) [93] with regard to $\mathfrak{a}$ does not exist.

---

[19] The other limiting case $r = 0$ is too trivial to warrant a special consideration.

2. Furthermore, by Theorem 46 [91] (J) can be uniquely solved in this case, since by Theorem (52, 53, 54) a (H) cannot be solved.

b) Let A be singular.

1. Then by Theorem (52, 53, 54)a there exists a solution $\mathfrak{x}'$ ($\neq 0$) of (H′). If $x_i \neq 0$ is in this solution, therefore $\mathfrak{x}'\mathfrak{e}_i = x'_i \neq 0$, then by Theorem 48 [92] (J) cannot be solved for the vector $\mathfrak{a} = \mathfrak{e}_i$; therefore, it cannot be solved for any arbitrary vector $\mathfrak{a}$.

2. Furthermore, by Theorem 46 [91] (J) can then, if at all, not be uniquely solved, since by Theorem (52, 53, 54)a (H) can be solved.

These two theorems further yield through the elimination of the *alternative* (that is, the *contradictory* opposed statements) "A is regular" or "A is singular":

Corollary. *There exists the* ***alternative:*** *Either* (J) *can be solved without restriction and uniquely, or* (H) *and* (H′) *can be solved.*

Finally, for the first case of this alternative, that is, for regular A, we can make an elegant statement concerning the dependence of the solution $\mathfrak{x}$ of (J) (which always exists in this case and is uniquely determined) on the vector $\mathfrak{a}$ on the right. This statement will go beyond the results of Section 13. In this connection we designate $\mathfrak{a}$ by $\mathfrak{x}^*$ and prove:

Theorem 55. Let $A = (a_{ik})$ *be an (n, n)-rowed regular matrix. Then a uniquely determined (n, n)-rowed matrix A^* exists such that if $\mathfrak{x}$ is a solution (which always exists and is uniquely determined) of the system of equations*

$$\text{(J)} \qquad \sum_{k=1}^{n} a_{ik} x_k = x_i^* \quad (i = 1, \ldots, n)$$

with the matrix A the dependence of the solution on the x_i^* on the right is given by the formulae

$$(\mathfrak{J}^*) \qquad \sum_{k=1}^{n} a_{ik}^* x_k^* = x_i \quad (i = 1, \ldots, n)$$

with the matrix A^*. A^* too is regular and $(A^*)^* = A$, *that is, the system of equations corresponding to the formulae* $(\mathfrak{J}^*)$

$$\text{(J*)} \qquad \sum_{k=1}^{n} a_{ik}^* x_k^* = x_i \quad (i = 1, \ldots, n),$$

which has A^* as its matrix, x_k^* as its unknowns and x_i on the right *side, is solved by the formulae corresponding to the system of equations (J)*

$$(\mathfrak{J}) \qquad \sum_{k=1}^{n} a_{ik} x_k = x_i^* \qquad (i = 1, \ldots, n)$$

with the matrix A.

Proof:[20] a) Let the n vectors $\mathfrak{a}^*_{..k} = (a^*_{1k}, \ldots, a^*_{nk})$ be the solutions of (J) in the case where the right-hand sides are $\mathfrak{e}_k (k = 1, \ldots, n)$. Then Theorem 44 [86] immediately implies that the linear combination $\mathfrak{x} = \sum_{k=1}^{n} x_k^* \mathfrak{a}^*_{..k}$ is a solution of (J), and therefore *the* solution, corresponding to the linear combination $\mathfrak{x}^* = \sum_{k=1}^{n} x_k^* \mathfrak{e}_k$. But, on writing it out, the representation of $\mathfrak{x}$ in terms of the $\mathfrak{a}^*_{..k}$ goes over into ($\mathfrak{J}^*$). Therefore, there exists an (n, n)-rowed A^* with the property specified in the first part of the theorem.

b) Let $\bar{A}^* = (\bar{a}^*_{ik})$ be another matrix with this property, so that ($\mathfrak{J}^*$) and the ($\mathfrak{J}^*$) formed with $\bar{A}^*$ always yield the same $\mathfrak{x}$ on the right for all $\mathfrak{x}^*$. Then for the special case $\mathfrak{x}^* = \mathfrak{e}_k$ the k-th columns $\bar{\mathfrak{a}}^*_{..k}$ and $\mathfrak{a}^*_{..k}$ of $\bar{A}^*$ and A^* coincide $(k = 1, \ldots, n)$, and therefore $\bar{A}^* = A^*$. This means that A^* is uniquely determined by the property specified in the first part of the theorem.

c) Conversely, if $\mathfrak{x}$ is arbitrarily chosen and, in addition, $\mathfrak{x}^*$ determined so that ($\mathfrak{J}$) exists, then by a) ($\mathfrak{J}^*$) also must exist (since in this very case $\mathfrak{x}$ is *the* solution of (J) for the $\mathfrak{x}^*$ thereby determined). In other words, ($\mathfrak{J}$) yields a solution of (J*) for any arbitrary $\mathfrak{x}$. Hence by Theorem (46, 48, 49) a its matrix A^* is regular, and further $(A^*)^* = A$.

In view of the property given in Theorem 55 which characterizes the matrix A^* we define in addition:

Definition 34. *The matrix A^* uniquely determined by Theorem 54 through an (n, n)-rowed regular matrix A is called the* ***resolvent matrix*** *of A.*

---

[20] For a better understanding of the connection in this proof the reader should set, as is done in the theorem, the phrase *system of equations* before each (J), (J*) and the word *formulae* before each ($\mathfrak{J}$), ($\mathfrak{J}^*$).

15. Importance of Linear Algebra without Determinants

Through the results of Sections 11, 13 the problem of linear algebra Section 5, (1) is completely solved from a *theoretical* point of view. This follows from the fact that we have obtained for the system of equations (J) a necessary and sufficient condition for solvability (Theorems 48 [92] , 49 [102]) as well as precise information regarding the structure of the totality of solutions (Theorem 46 [91] | together with Theorems 50 to 52 [104 to 106]). From a *practical* point of view, however, we have made very little progress. That is to say, the specified results make it possible neither to decide whether an explicitly given system of equations (J) can be solved nor to determine in the solvability case the totality of solutions, because the application of these results requires in general, that is, for infinite ground fields, infinitely many trials.

By Theorem 48 (Corollary 2) [93], Theorem 49 [102] and Theorem 46 [91] these two points could be effected by a finite process if only the two problems J_{pr}) and H_{pr}) cited at the end of Section 11 could be solved by a finite process. Now, at a first glance this seems actually possible by means of the Toeplitz process; for in the proof to Theorem 49 [102, 103] and Theorem 52 [106, 107] this process yielded obviously finite constructions of a solution of (J) and of a system of fundamental solutions of (H). For this, however, it is assumed that the coefficients b_{ik} of (J_0) are known, and the process of Section 12, the Toeplitz process itself, leading to their determination, is in general infinite in the first as well as in the second step. Thus, in the first step (Lemma 1 [96]) the decision whether a subsystem selected from the f_i is linearly independent (a decision that must actually be made finitely often for the determination of a maximal system of linearly independent f_i and the associated maximal number r) requires the testing of all possible, in general infinitely many, existing linear combinations of the f_i; this is also true in regard to making a decision in the second step (Lemma 3 [99]) as to which linear combination of the f_i has the minimal length.

In particular, this means that even the number r and consequently the number of fundamental solutions of (H) cannot in general be determined by finitely many trials. From a practical standpoint the results of Theorem 52 [106] are not to be regarded as a *determination* of the number of fundamental solutions of (H), since to know r is equivalent to knowing all linear dependences between the rows of A, that is, all solutions of (H′). Hence from a practical point of view only a *circular connection* is given, such as is expressed in Theorem 54 [109] which ties (H) to (H′) (cf. also the remark at the end of Section 13).

Naturally, the preceding remarks also apply to the results obtained in the special case of Section 14. In particular, Theorem 55 [112] is on this account not applicable form a practical viewpoint; for, though the existence of the resolvent matrix A^* is established, no finite process is given for its construction.

In spite of the extremely important theoretical insights arising from Theorems 46 to 54, for the practical applications direct methods must still be developed for deciding in finitely many steps whether (J) can be solved, and in the solvability case for constructing the totality of solutions. Only in this way would the complex of facts obtained so far receive its desired conclusion from a practical (and naturally also theoretical) standpoint. Such methods are developed by the *theory of determinants*, starting from the special case dealt with in Section 14, and then passing on to the decision of solvability and the construction of solutions in the most general case.

As a rule, the foregoing results are derived by means of the theory of determinants. We have not used this approach here for two reasons. On the one hand, if the concept of determinant were put at the fore of the above investigations, it would look rather extraneous, having nothing to do with the problem to be solved. Thus the results obtained through this approach would appear surprising and loosened from their context. Instead, the methods we have used are adapted throughout to the problem and the connective thread between Theorems 46 to 54 stands out very clearly. On the other hand, however, the *complex of theorems of linear algebra* developed *without determinants* has received special attention in modern times, since it is only these theorems, with all their proofs, which can be transferred nearly word for word to the corresponding problems in the case of *infinitely many equations with infinitely many unknowns* and to the theory of *linear integral equations* closely connected with this. For such problems the concept of determinant, except for special cases, proves to be too narrow. Besides, the beauty and completeness of the theory without determinants, as developed in the preceding, is enough to justify its separate treatment.

IV. Linear Algebra with Determinants

16. Permutation Groups

In the proofs of the preceding chapter we have frequently made rearrangements of the rows or columns of a matrix *merely for reasons of notation.* The concept of determinant to be introduced in this chapter is now based *in a factual manner* on such rearrangements or, to be more exact, on certain relations connected with them. Before developing the theory of determinants we must, therefore, first of all become familiar with these relations.

The concept of *rearrangement* or *permutation* is a pure set-theoretic concept. It arises from the fact that every set is equipotent to itself [Section 2, (II)], so that every set corresponds biuniquely to itself in at least one way (namely, the correspondence which maps every element onto itself). A permutation is formed by considering *any arbitrary* correspondence of this kind.

Definition 35. *A* ***permutation*** *of a set* M *is any one-to-one correspondence of* M *onto itself with a definite mapping rule;* ***to carry out*** *or* ***apply*** *the permutation means to replace each element of* M *by the element corresponding to it.*

Def. 35 implies that to distinguish permutations according to the correspondences based on them we should consider the mapping rule. Therefore, we call two permutations equal if and only if to each element there corresponds the same element under both permutations. In order to describe a permutation uniquely we could naturally give all the mappings as well as all the substitutions (transitions) to be made in carrying them out; these are merely two different ways of looking at one and the same formal fact. Obviously, the permutation is independent of the order in which the individual correspondences are given.

Regarding the permutations of a set we now prove:

Theorem 56. *The totality of permutations of a set form a group, if the product of two permutations is defined as the permutation generated by applying one after the other. The unity element of this group is the permutation which takes every element into itself; the reciprocal of a permutation is obtained by reversing the mapping rule.*

Proof: Section 6, (a) is satisfied in the sense of the previous remarks.

We will now prove that Section 6, (b) is satisfied. Let a be mapped on a' by the first permutation and a' on a'' by the second. Then the successive application of these two permutations, that is, the actual replacement of a by a'', is again a permutation. This is valid for every pair of permutations that may be chosen.

Section 6, (1) is valid, since (logical) substitutions satisfy the associative law; Section 6, (2 a) und (2 b) are obviously satisfied in the way stated in the theorem.

Theorem 57. *If* M *and* $\overline{\mathsf{M}}$ *are equipotent sets, then the groups of permutations of* M *and* $\overline{\mathsf{M}}$ *are isomorphic.*

Proof: If every permutation of M is associated to that permutation of $\overline{\mathsf{M}}$ which is generated by carrying out a biunique transition from M to $\overline{\mathsf{M}}$, then this correspondence satisfies condition (2) of Theorem 23 [65]. Since it is easy to work out the details, it is left to the reader.

On the basis of Theorem 57 the type of the permutation group of M is determined only by the cardinal number of M (see Section 2, (II) and Def. 17 [65]). In particular, for finite M the type is determined only by the number of elements of M. If isomorphic groups are not to be distinguished, we can then define:

Definition 36. *The group of all permutations of a finite set of n distinct elements is called the* ***symmetric group***[1] *of n elements. It is denoted by $\mathfrak{S}_n$.*

Here, we will be occupied exclusively with this group $\mathfrak{S}_n$. Since every set of n elements can be associated biuniquely to the particular set of n numerals $1, \ldots, n$, by Theorem 57 it is sufficient to base the study of $\mathfrak{S}_n$ on this set of numerals. We designate by

$$\begin{pmatrix} 1 \ldots n \\ p_1 \ldots p_n \end{pmatrix}, \text{ briefly } \begin{pmatrix} i \\ p_i \end{pmatrix} \qquad (i = 1, \ldots, n),$$

that permutation of the numerals $1, \ldots, n$ which takes the numeral i into p_i $(i = 1, \ldots, n)$. If $a_1, \ldots, a_n$ is any set of n elements which through the numbering of its elements corresponds biuniquely to the set of numerals $1, \ldots, n$, then the above permutation can also be regarded as a permutation of the n elements $a_1, \ldots, a_n$, namely, as that permutation by which a_i goes into a_{p_i} $(i = 1, \ldots, n)$.

The biuniqueness imposed on permutations in Def. 35 [conditions Section 2, (δ), (δ'), (ε), (ε')], applied to the above notation $\begin{pmatrix} i \\ p_i \end{pmatrix}$ $(i = 1, \ldots, n)$, is the precise formulation of the following statement: $p_1, \ldots, p_n$ are the numerals $1, \ldots, n$ *apart from their arrangement* or *in any arrangement*. This will frequently be used. The totality of arrangements of $1, \ldots, n$

[1] The designation *symmetric group* is to be understood as meaning that "something" is symmetric, in the usual sense of the word, relative to n elements if it remains unchanged by the application of all permutations of these elements. For example, in Section 4 it was in this sense that we called $[x_1, \ldots, x_n]$ symmetric in $x_1, \ldots, x_n$. Cf. also Theorem 131 [329] (Theorem of symmetric functions).

corresponds biuniquely to the totality of permutations of $1, \ldots, n$.[2]

By the remark to Def. 35 a permutation is completely indifferent to the order in which its individual transitions are given. Hence in giving the above permutation we could just as well use

$$\begin{pmatrix} q_1 \ldots q_n \\ p_{q_1} \ldots p_{q_n} \end{pmatrix}, \text{ briefly } \begin{pmatrix} q_i \\ p_{q_i} \end{pmatrix} \quad (i = 1, \ldots, n),$$

where $q_1, \ldots, q_n$ is any arrangement of $1, \ldots, n$. By means of this remark the multiplication rule of Theorem 56 for permutations in $\mathfrak{S}_n$ can be expressed by the formula

$$\begin{pmatrix} i \\ q_i \end{pmatrix} \begin{pmatrix} i \\ p_i \end{pmatrix} = \begin{pmatrix} i \\ p_{q_i} \end{pmatrix} \quad (i = 1, \ldots, n),$$

and similarly the reciprocal of $\begin{pmatrix} i \\ p_i \end{pmatrix}$ can be given as $\begin{pmatrix} p_i \\ i \end{pmatrix}$.

$\mathfrak{S}_1$ is naturally the identity group $\mathfrak{E}$. $\mathfrak{S}_2$ is the Abelian group consisting of the two elements $E = \begin{pmatrix} 1\,2 \\ 1\,2 \end{pmatrix}$, $P = \begin{pmatrix} 1\,2 \\ 2\,1 \end{pmatrix}$ (with $P^2 = E$) (cf. Section 6, Example 3). For $n \geqq 3$, on the contrary, $\mathfrak{S}_n$ is surely not Abelian; for example, we have

$$\begin{pmatrix} 1\,2\,3 \ldots \\ 2\,1\,3 \ldots \end{pmatrix} \begin{pmatrix} 1\,2\,3 \ldots \\ 3\,2\,1 \ldots \end{pmatrix} = \begin{pmatrix} 1\,2\,3 \ldots \\ 2\,3\,1 \ldots \end{pmatrix},$$
$$\begin{pmatrix} 1\,2\,3 \ldots \\ 3\,2\,1 \ldots \end{pmatrix} \begin{pmatrix} 1\,2\,3 \ldots \\ 2\,1\,3 \ldots \end{pmatrix} = \begin{pmatrix} 1\,2\,3 \ldots \\ 3\,1\,2 \ldots \end{pmatrix}.$$

Incidentally, $\mathfrak{S}_3$ is isomorphic to the group of 6 elements considered in Sections 6, 7, Example 4, as can be seen by mapping the rotations, appearing there, onto the permutations of the vertices of the triangle generated by the rotations.

---

[2] In elementary mathematics it is usually the *arrangements* themselves not the *process of their derivation* which are called permutations of $1, \ldots, n$. Even though, after the above remarks, this amounts to the same thing, it would, on the one hand, certainly be inconvenient for the formulation of the rule of combination of Theorem 56, and, on the other hand, it would not agree with the literal meaning of *permutation* (*interchange*) as an operation.

We can assume as known from the elements of arithmetic:

Theorem 58. *$\mathfrak{S}_n$ is finite and has the order $n! = 1 \cdot 2 \cdots n$.*

In the following we actually need only the finiteness, not the order of $\mathfrak{S}_n$.

We next separate the permutations of $\mathfrak{S}_n$ into two categories, a distinction which is basic for the definition of determinants.

For this purpose, and also in other connections to arise later, we must consider *subsets* of the set of numerals $1, \ldots, n$ on which the permutations of $\mathfrak{S}_n$ are based. In accordance with the terminology used in the elements of arithmetic, such subsets are called *combinations* of the numerals $1, \ldots, n$; if they contain ν numerals, they are said to be *of ν-th order*. We designate the combination consisting of the numerals $i_1, \ldots, i_\nu$ by $\{i_1, \ldots, i_\nu\}$. This notation implies that 1) $i_1, \ldots, i_\nu$ are *different* numerals of the sequence $1, \ldots, n$, 2) $\{i_1, \ldots, i_\nu\} = \{i'_1, \ldots, i'_\nu\}$ if and only if the numerals $i'_1, \ldots, i'_\nu$ are the numerals $i_1, \ldots, i_\nu$ *except for the order*, therefore can be derived by a permutation of these. This means that a combination does not depend on the arrangement of the numerals. Two mutually exclusive combinations of $1, \ldots, n$ whose union is the entire set $1, \ldots, n$ are called *complementary*. The combination complementary to $\{i_1, \ldots, i_\nu\}$ $(1 \leqq \nu \leqq n-1)$ is usually designated by $\{i_{\nu+1}, \ldots, i_n\}$. The number of different combinations of ν-th order of $1, \ldots, n$ is designated, as usual, by $\binom{n}{\nu}$; its value, which, incidentally, will follow from the proof of Theorem 66 [183], is not important for us.

First of all we have:

Theorem 59. *Let $1 \leqq \nu \leqq n$. If a permutation $P = \begin{pmatrix} i \\ p_i \end{pmatrix}$ of the numerals $1, \ldots, n$ is applied to the totality of $\binom{n}{\nu}$ combinations of ν-th order of these numerals, that is, if each such combination $\{i_1, \ldots, i_\nu\}$ is replaced by $\{p_{i_1}, \ldots, p_{i_\nu}\}$, then this totality of $\binom{n}{\nu}$ combinations is again generated. In other words,*

P will effect a permutation of the set of these combinations.

Proof: Obviously, through the application of P we can generate all the $\binom{n}{\nu}$ combinations of ν-th order of the set $p_1, \ldots, p_n$, which is identical with the set $1, \ldots, n$.

We now consider, in particular, the combinations of 2nd order of $1, \ldots, n$. If in any such combination $\{i, k\}$ we think of the two numerals i and k as written in their natural order (namely, $i < k$ is assumed), then this ordering relation will not necessarily be preserved under the application of a permutation, since there could exist very many pairs of numerals i, k with $i < k$ but $p_i > p_k$. This situation is the occasion for separating the permutations of $\mathfrak{S}_n$ into two categories; this distinction, as already mentioned, is important for the definition of determinants.

Definition 37. *Let* $n > 1$ *and* $P = \binom{i}{p_i}$ *be a permutation of* $1, \ldots, n$. *The appearance of a pair of numerals* i, k *with* $i < k$ *but* $p_i > p_k$ *is called an* ***inversion*** *of* P. P *is said to be* ***even*** *or* ***odd*** *according as the number* ν *of its inversions is even or odd. We set* $\operatorname{sgn} P = (-1)^\nu$, *therefore* $= 1$ or $= -1$, *according as* P *is even or odd.*[3]

For $n = 1$, *where only the permutation* $E = \binom{1}{1}$ *exists, we will set* $\operatorname{sgn} E = 1$.

sgn is an abbreviation for the Latin word signum (sign). For real numbers $p \neq 0$ we set, as is well known, $\operatorname{sgn} p = 1$ or -1 according as $p > 0$ or < 0.

For $n > 1$ it is easy to see that there actually are even and

[3] This is just as in the case of Section 9, Example 4 (footnote 6) [77].

odd permutations. For example, $E=\begin{pmatrix}1\ldots n\\1\ldots n\end{pmatrix}$ is even and $\begin{pmatrix}1\,2\,3\ldots n\\2\,1\,3\ldots n\end{pmatrix}$ is odd.

We now prove a property basic for our application:

Theorem 60. *For two permutations P and Q of $1,\ldots,n$ we have*

$$\operatorname{sgn}(PQ)=\operatorname{sgn}P\operatorname{sgn}Q.$$

Proof: *For* $n=1$, the statement is trivial. Let $n>1$. Then Def. 37 says that in counting the inversions of a permutation $P=\begin{pmatrix}i\\p_i\end{pmatrix}$ $(i=1,\ldots,n)$ we must consider all pairs of numerals i,k of the sequence $1,\ldots,n$ with $i<k$, that is, all combinations of 2nd order $\{i,k\}$ with the ordering rule $i<k$ for its numerals. If this ordering rule is left out, then a combination $\{i,k\}$ yields an inversion of P if and only if the integers (different from zero) $i-k$ and p_i-p_k have different signs, that is, if $\frac{i-k}{p_i-p_k}<0$. Accordingly sgn P can also be defined by the formula

$$\operatorname{sgn}P=\prod_{\{i,k\}}\operatorname{sgn}\frac{i-k}{p_i-p_k},$$

where the product on the right is to extend over all different combinations of 2-nd order of $1,\ldots,n$ (without regard to the order in which the two numerals are taken). For, by the remarks, the number of times the factor -1 appears in this product is exactly the number ν of inversions of P. Now, if $Q=\begin{pmatrix}i\\q_i\end{pmatrix}$ $(i=1,\ldots,n)$, then we have

$$\operatorname{sgn}Q=\prod_{\{i,k\}}\operatorname{sgn}\frac{i-k}{q_i-q_k}=\prod_{\{i,k\}}\operatorname{sgn}\frac{p_i-p_k}{q_{p_i}-q_{p_k}};$$

the latter is valid, since by Theorem 59 $\{p_i, p_k\}$ runs through the totality of different combinations of 2nd order of $1, \ldots, n$ if $\{i, k\}$ does, and because the product is indifferent to the order of the factors. Now, as is well known, the rule $\operatorname{sgn}(p\, q) = \operatorname{sgn} p \operatorname{sgn} q$ is valid for real numbers $p,\ q \neq 0$. Hence, by termwise multiplication of both products it is also true for $\operatorname{sgn} P$ and $\operatorname{sgn} Q$ that

$$\operatorname{sgn} P \operatorname{sgn} Q = \prod_{\{i,k\}} \left[\operatorname{sgn} \frac{i-k}{p_i - p_k} \operatorname{sgn} \frac{p_i - p_k}{q_{p_i} - q_{p_k}}\right] = \prod_{\{i,k\}} \operatorname{sgn} \frac{i-k}{q_{p_i} - q_{p_k}}.$$

The product on the right-hand side, however, is $\operatorname{sgn}(PQ)$, since

$$PQ = \begin{pmatrix} i \\ q_{p_i} \end{pmatrix} \quad (i = 1, \ldots, n).$$

As an immediate consequence of Theorem 60, which is to be used later, we have:

Theorem 61. $\operatorname{sgn} P = \operatorname{sgn} P^{-1}$.

Proof: By Theorem 60 $\operatorname{sgn} P \operatorname{sgn} P^{-1} = \operatorname{sgn}(PP^{-1}) = \operatorname{sgn} E = 1$, since $E = \begin{pmatrix} 1 \ldots n \\ 1 \ldots n \end{pmatrix}$ obviously has no inversions.

The concept of inversion defined in Def. 37 and the explanation of $\operatorname{sgn} P$ based on this is not determined by *the permutation P of the set* $1, \ldots, n$ alone; in addition, it refers to a definite *basic order* of this set, namely, the natural order $1, \ldots, n$.

This reference to the natural order $1, \ldots, n$ as the basic order becomes especially clear if the rule of Def. 37 for counting the inversions of $P = \begin{pmatrix} 1 \ldots n \\ p_1 \ldots p_n \end{pmatrix}$ is formulated as follows: Let the upper row of P be written in the natural order. Then the number of inversions is the number of those pairs of numerals of the lower row whose order is opposite to that in the upper row. If this rule were to be applied in the case of any other ordering of the upper row of P, then, in general, another number of such pairs of numerals of the lower row would be obtained. For example, if we write $\begin{pmatrix} 1\,2\,3\,4 \\ 4\,1\,3\,2 \end{pmatrix}$

there are in the lower row 4 pairs of numerals {41}, {43}, {42}, {32} whose orders are opposite to that in the upper row; while in $\begin{pmatrix}3142\\3421\end{pmatrix}$ there are 2 pairs of numerals {41}, {21} whose orders are opposite to that in the upper row. However, for the determination of sgn P these are not to be distinguished, since both numbers are even. The following theorem shows that this is generally valid.

Theorem 62. sgn P *defined in Def. 37 is independent, in the following sense, of the natural order of the numerals* $1, \ldots, n$ *on which its definition is based: If* $q_1, \ldots, q_n$ *is any ordering of* $1, \ldots, n$, *and*

$$P = \begin{pmatrix}1 \ldots . n\\ p_1 \ldots p_n\end{pmatrix} = \begin{pmatrix}q_1 \ldots . q_n\\ p_{q_1} \ldots p_{q_n}\end{pmatrix} = \begin{pmatrix}q_1 \ldots q_n\\ q_{r_1} \ldots q_{r_n}\end{pmatrix},$$

therefore $$p_{q_i} = q_{r_i} \quad (i = 1, \ldots, n),$$

so that the permutation $R = \begin{pmatrix}1 \ldots . n\\ r_1 \ldots r_n\end{pmatrix}$ *thereby introduced specifies how P changes the order of* $q_1, \ldots, q_n$, *then*

$$\operatorname{sgn} P = \operatorname{sgn} R.$$

Proof: Let $Q = \begin{pmatrix}1 \ldots . n\\ q_1 \ldots q_n\end{pmatrix}$. Then if the equation of permutations given in the theorem is multiplied on the left by Q, we obtain

$$QP = \begin{pmatrix}1 \ldots . n\\ p_{q_1} \ldots p_{q_n}\end{pmatrix} = \begin{pmatrix}1 \ldots . n\\ q_{r_1} \ldots q_{r_n}\end{pmatrix} = RQ.$$

Consequently, by Theorem 60 $\operatorname{sgn} Q \operatorname{sgn} P = \operatorname{sgn} R \operatorname{sgn} Q$ ($=$ $\operatorname{sgn} Q \operatorname{sgn} R$); this implies the statement of the theorem, since $\operatorname{sgn} Q \neq 0$.

The inversions of the permutation R introduced in the theorem are obviously to be understood as those pairs of numerals in the lower row of P whose order is opposite to that in the upper row if the numerals of the upper row are written in the sequence $q_1, \ldots, q_n$; therefore, Theorem 62 proves the statement made beforehand in the remark. — We point to the fact that the permutation R

of Theorem 62 is generated from P by transformation with Q^{-1} (cf. the remark to Theorem 28 [70]). — By Theorem 62 it now makes sense to speak of *even and odd permutations of n elements* without specifying a basic order as a reference system for the "evenness" or "oddness."

In conclusion we call attention to the following additional facts, even though we have no need of them here, because they give us a deeper insight into our classification of the permutations of n elements into even and odd.

Theorem 63. *The totality of even permutations of n elements* $(n > 1)$ *form a normal divisor* $\mathfrak{A}_n$ *of* $\mathfrak{S}_n$ *of index 2, the so-called* ***alternating group*** *of n elements. One of the two cosets into which* $\mathfrak{S}_n$ *decomposes relative to* $\mathfrak{A}_n$ *consists of all the even and the other of all the odd permutations. Consequently, there are just as many permutations of one kind as the other* $\left(\textit{namely, exactly } \frac{n!}{2}\right)$.

Proof: This immediately follows from Theorem 35 [75], since the relation $P \equiv Q$, if $\operatorname{sgn} P = \operatorname{sgn} Q$, obviously represents a congruence relation in the group $\mathfrak{S}_n$. The partition of $\mathfrak{S}_n$, thereby determined, corresponds to the classification into even and odd permutations.

That $\mathfrak{A}_n$ is a normal divisor also follows from Theorem 62. In the proof of this theorem we used $QP = RQ$. On writing this relation in the form $QPQ^{-1} = R$, it says in conjunction with the result $\operatorname{sgn} P = \operatorname{sgn} R$ that if P is even so also are all its conjugates R (Theorem 32 [73]). Conversely, Theorem 62 can also be inferred from the result of Theorem 63 that $\mathfrak{A}_n$ is a normal divisor of index 2 (Theorem 32).

17. Determinants

In the space of this presentation we must forego a *genetic* introduction of determinants[4] based on the methods of Chapter III. Instead we immediately make the following definition:

Definition 38. *The **determinant** of the* (n, n)*-rowed matrix* $A = (a_{ik})$ *is defined as the expression*

$$|A| = |a_{ik}| = \begin{vmatrix} a_{11} & \dots & a_{1n} \\ \dots & \dots & \dots \\ a_{n1} & \dots & a_{nn} \end{vmatrix} = \sum_{P \text{ in } \mathfrak{S}_n} \operatorname{sgn} P\, a_{1p_1} \dots a_{np_n},^{5}$$

where the summation extends over all permutations $P = \begin{pmatrix} i \\ p_i \end{pmatrix}$ *of the column indices* $1, \dots, n$.

Written out in detail, this means that the determinant $|A|$ of A is formed as follows: While holding the first (row) index fixed, apply all permutations $P = \begin{pmatrix} i \\ p_i \end{pmatrix}$ to the second (column) indices in the product $a_{11} \dots a_{nn}$ of the n terms standing in the so-called *principal diagonal* of A. Thereby products of the form $a_{1p_1} \dots a_{np_n}$ (there are $n!$ of these) are generated. The determinant is obtained from these by forming the difference

$$\sum_{P \text{ in } \mathfrak{A}_n} a_{1p_1} \dots a_{np_n} - \sum_{P \text{ not in } \mathfrak{A}_n} a_{1p_1} \dots a_{np_n} = \sum_{P \text{ in } \mathfrak{S}_n} \operatorname{sgn} P\, a_{1p_1} \dots a_{np_n}$$

of the sum of all such products corresponding to the even permutations and the sum of all those corresponding to the odd permutations.

---

[4] Through such an introduction starting from the Toeplitz process the concept of determinant would no longer appear out of phase with the concept formations and methods of Chapter III, and thereby we would obtain a deeper understanding as to why our present course leads to the same results.

[5] See the end of Section 1 for the significance of sgn $P = \pm 1$ as a "factor" before a field element.

In particular we have

for $n = 1$: $|a_{11}| = a_{11}$, for $n = 2$: $\begin{vmatrix} a_{11} a_{12} \\ a_{21} a_{22} \end{vmatrix} = a_{11}a_{22} - a_{12}a_{21}$,

for $n = 3$: $\begin{vmatrix} a_{11}a_{12}a_{13} \\ a_{21}a_{22}a_{23} \\ a_{31}a_{32}a_{33} \end{vmatrix} = \begin{cases} a_{11}a_{22}a_{33} + a_{12}a_{23}a_{31} + a_{13}a_{21}a_{32} \\ - a_{11}a_{23}a_{32} - a_{13}a_{22}a_{31} - a_{12}a_{21}a_{33}. \end{cases}$

For $n = 3$ the determinant can also be formed by the following rule:

Let the first two columns be adjoined to A once more on the right, then form products according to the 6 lines drawn parallel to the two diagonals of A and subtract from the sum of the products in the direction $\diagdown$ (principal diagonal) the sum of the products in the direction $\diagup$ (secondary diagonal).

For $n = 2$ a corresponding rule is obviously valid; on the contrary, such a rule is not valid for $n > 3$.

In addition, we cite the following formulae for arbitrary n since they will be frequently used:

$$\begin{vmatrix} a_1 & 0 & \cdots & 0 \\ 0 & a_2 & \cdots & 0 \\ \vdots & \vdots & \ddots & \vdots \\ 0 & 0 & \cdots & a_n \end{vmatrix} = a_1 a_2 \ldots a_n; \text{ in particular, } \begin{vmatrix} e & 0 & \cdots & 0 \\ 0 & e & \cdots & 0 \\ \vdots & \vdots & \ddots & \vdots \\ 0 & 0 & \cdots & e \end{vmatrix} = e.$$

These follow directly from Def. 38.

Historically, (*Leibniz*, *Cramer*, etc.) the concept of determinant arose somewhat as follows: In the case of 2 linear equations in 2 unknowns

$$a_{11}x_1 + a_{12}x_2 \doteq a_1$$
$$a_{21}x_1 + a_{22}x_2 \doteq a_2$$

the so-called *method of multiplication* leads to the conditions

$$(a_{11}a_{22} - a_{12}a_{21})x_1 \doteq a_{22}a_1 - a_{12}a_2$$
$$(a_{11}a_{22} - a_{12}a_{21})x_2 \doteq a_{11}a_2 - a_{21}a_1,$$

from which it is easy to show the unique solvability for arbitrary a_1, a_2 if the expression $a_{11}a_{22} - a_{12}a_{21} = \begin{vmatrix} a_{11}a_{12} \\ a_{21}a_{22} \end{vmatrix} \neq 0$. Similarly, for $n = 3, 4, \ldots$ we obtain by the method of multiplication the determinants $|a_{ik}|$ as coefficients if we linearly combine the linear forms on the left in a single step with only *one* indeterminate x_k. The expressions, which are easily formed for $n = 2, 3, 4$, enable us to read off the general rule of formation (if we wish, even to *derive* them by induction from n to $n+1$) and lead to the definition given above. Here we must forego such an *inductive* approach to determinants. Instead, in a strictly *deductive* manner we will derive the indicated connection with the problem of solving equations in linear algebra for the case $m = n$ (Sections 20, 21) after developing in Sections 17 to 19 the most important properties of determinants as defined above.

In Def. 38 the rows and columns of A play a different role. This is however only an apparent difference, since we have

Theorem 64. *An (n, n)-rowed matrix A and its transpose A' have equal determinants: $|A| = |A'|$. The determinant of A depends, therefore, on the rows of A in the same way as on the columns of A, and it can be defined not only by the formula of Def. 38 but also by the formula*

$$|A| = \sum_{P \text{ in } \mathfrak{S}_n} \operatorname{sgn} P \, a_{p_1 1} \ldots a_{p_n n},$$

where the summation extends over all permutations $P = \begin{pmatrix} i \\ p_i \end{pmatrix}$ of the row indices.

Proof: By Def. 38 we have

$$|A'| = \sum_{P \text{ in } \mathfrak{S}_n} \operatorname{sgn} P \, a_{p_1 1} \ldots a_{p_n n}.$$

Since the ordering of the factors of a product is arbitrary, we may always apply the permutation P^{-1} in each summand to the n factors. If $P^{-1} = \begin{pmatrix} p_i \\ i \end{pmatrix} = \begin{pmatrix} i \\ q_i \end{pmatrix} = Q$, then we obtain

$$|A'| = \sum_{P \text{ in } \mathfrak{S}_n} \operatorname{sgn} P \, a_{1 q_1} \ldots a_{n q_n}.$$

On the one hand, $\operatorname{sgn} P = \operatorname{sgn} Q$ (Theorem 61 [124]); on the other hand, Q runs through the whole group $\mathfrak{S}_n$ if P does, every element once (Theorem 17 [60]). Hence we also have

$$|A'| = \sum_{Q \text{ in } \mathfrak{S}_n} \operatorname{sgn} Q \, a_{1 q_1} \ldots a_{n q_n} = |A|.$$

From the earlier standpoint the symmetry relative to the rows and columns in Theorems 53, 54 [109] and Theorem (52, 53, 54)a

[111] was not very plausible. From the standpoint of the theory of determinants it is finally brought back to the symmetry of the determinant $|A|$ relative to the rows and columns of A exhibited in Theorem 64. This will be brought out even more clearly in the following.

While Theorem 64 compares the dependence of the determinant $|A|$ on the rows of A with that on the columns, the following theorem states something about the dependence of the determinant $|A|$ on the ordering of the rows or columns of A.

Theorem 65. *If A_1 is generated from the (n, n)-rowed matrix A by a permutation R of the rows (columns), then*

$$|A_1| = \operatorname{sgn} R\,|A|,$$

therefore, $|A_1| = |A|$ or $|A_1| = -|A|$, according as R is even or odd.

Proof: By Theorem 64 it is sufficient to carry out the proof for the case in which A_1 is generated from A by a permutation $R = \begin{pmatrix} i \\ r_i \end{pmatrix}$ of the *rows*. By Def. 38 we have in this case

$$|A_1| = \sum_{P \text{ in } \mathfrak{S}_n} \operatorname{sgn} P\, a_{r_1 p_1} \ldots a_{r_n p_n},$$

since the $a_{r_1 1}, \ldots, a_{r_n n}$ are the n terms contained in the principal diagonal of A_1. By applying the permutation $R^{-1} = \begin{pmatrix} r_i \\ i \end{pmatrix} = \begin{pmatrix} i \\ s_i \end{pmatrix} = S$ to the n factors of each summand and using the fact that $\operatorname{sgn} R \operatorname{sgn} S = 1$ (Theorem 61 [124]) we obtain

$$|A_1| = \operatorname{sgn} R \sum_{P \text{ in } \mathfrak{S}_n} \operatorname{sgn} S \operatorname{sgn} P\, a_{1 p_{s_1}} \ldots a_{n p_{s_n}},$$

where each time the column indices are generated from $1, \ldots, n$ by the permutation $\begin{pmatrix} i \\ p_{s_i} \end{pmatrix} = SP = Q = \begin{pmatrix} i \\ q_i \end{pmatrix}$. Then, on the one hand, $\operatorname{sgn} S \operatorname{sgn} P = \operatorname{sgn} Q$ (Theorem 60 [123]); on the other hand, Q runs through the entire group $\mathfrak{S}_n$ if P does, every element once (Theorem 16 [60]). Hence we also have

$$|A_\iota| = \operatorname{sgn} R \sum_{Q \text{ in } \mathfrak{S}_n} \operatorname{sgn} Q\, a_{1q_1} \ldots a_{nq_n} = \operatorname{sgn} R\, |A|.$$

The two facts in Theorem 64 and Theorem 65 imply that all general theorems about determinants have a symmetric form, on the one hand, relative to the words row and column, on the other hand, (except for possibly distinct signs) relative to the individual rows as well as the individual columns. In the following we will make use of this in our proofs, just as already in the proof to Theorem 65.

18. Minors and Cofactors. The Laplace Expansion Theorem

In this section and the following we will give theorems which go beyond both Theorems 64 and 65 of the previous section and which penetrate deeper into the structure of determinants. Two objectives will thereby be realized. On the one hand, the way will be prepared for applying determinants to systems of linear equations; on the other hand, methods will be developed more suitable for the evaluation of determinants than the formula used to define them. For this purpose we define:

Definition 39. *Let A be an (n, n)-rowed matrix, $1 \leqq \nu \leqq n-1$, $\{i_1, \ldots, i_\nu\}$, and $\{k_1, \ldots, k_\nu\}$ a combination of ν-th order of its rows and its columns,*[6] *respectively, $\{i_{\nu+1}, \ldots, i_n\}$ and $\{k_{\nu+1}, \ldots, k_n\}$ the associated complementary combinations. Then we write, set up, or designate:*

$$A_{\{i_1, \ldots, i_\nu\}, \{k_1, \ldots, k_\nu\}}$$

the (ν, ν)-rowed matrix generated by striking out the rows $i_{\nu+1}, \ldots, i_n$ and the columns $k_{\nu+1}, \ldots, k_n$ in A;

$$\mathsf{A}_{\{i_1, \ldots, i_\nu\}, \{k_1, \ldots, k_\nu\}} = A_{\{i_{\nu+1}, \ldots, i_n\}, \{k_{\nu+1}, \ldots, k_n\}},$$

---

[6] For the sake of simplicity the rows and columns are merely indicated by their indices.

that is, the $(n-\nu, n-\nu)$-rowed matrix generated by striking out the rows $i_1, \ldots, i_\nu$ and the columns $k_1, \ldots, k_\nu$ in A;

$$a_{\{i_1,\ldots,i_\nu\},\{k_1,\ldots,k_\nu\}} = | A_{\{i_1,\ldots,i_\nu\},\{k_1,\ldots,k_\nu\}} |$$

the ***subdeterminant or minor of ν-th degree*** or ***$(n-\nu)$-th order*** *of A;*

$$\begin{aligned}\alpha_{\{i_1,\ldots,i_\nu\},\{k_1,\ldots,k_\nu\}} &= (-1)^{i_1+\cdots+i_\nu+k_1+\cdots+k_\nu} | \mathsf{A}_{\{i_1,\ldots,i_\nu\},\{k_1,\ldots,k_\nu\}} | \\ &= (-1)^{i_1+\cdots+i_\nu+k_1+\cdots+k_\nu}\ a_{\{i_{\nu+1},\ldots,i_n\},\ \{k_{\nu+1},\ldots,k_n\}}\end{aligned}$$

the ***cofactor of $(n-\nu)$-th degree*** or ***ν-th order*** *of A;* ***complementary determinant, algebraic complement*** or ***cofactor*** *of*

$$a_{\{i_1,\ldots,i_\nu\},\{k_1,\ldots,k_\nu\}}.$$

For the limiting cases $\nu = 0$, and $\nu = n$, we consider e and $A|$ as the only minors and cofactors of 0-th and n-th degree, respectively.

Therefore, the *capital letters* denote *matrices*; the corresponding *small* letters, their *determinants*. The *Latin* letters indicate that only the intersections of the rows and columns specified by their indices are *retained*; the *Greek* letters, that these rows and columns are *deleted*, therefore, that only the intersections of their complements are retained. The *degree* indicates the number of sequences *still left*; the *order*, the number of sequences *deleted*. For the especially important limiting case $\nu = 1$, we simply write A_{ik}, a_{ik}, A_{ik}, α_{ik} for the $A_{\{i\},\{k\}}$, ... This is admissible for the a_{ik} since the A_{ik}, and consequently also their determinants, are actually the elements a_{ik} of A.

Furthermore we stipulate:

Definition 40. *Let the assumptions of Def. 39 be valid and the $\binom{n}{\nu}$ combinations of ν-th order of the numerals $1, \ldots, n$ be set somehow in a definite order. With respect to one and the same such ordering $\{i_1, \ldots, i_\nu\}$ is regarded as a row index and $\{k_1, \ldots, k_\nu\}$ as a column index and accordingly the $\binom{n}{\nu}$ $\binom{n}{\nu}$*

minors of ν-th degree $a_{\{i_1,\ldots,i_\nu\},\{k_1,\ldots,k_\nu\}}$ *of* A *are combined into an* $\left(\binom{n}{\nu}, \binom{n}{\nu}\right)$*-rowed matrix* $A^{(\nu)}$, *and similarly the* $\binom{n}{\nu}\binom{n}{\nu}$ *cofactors of ν-th order* $\alpha_{\{i_1,\ldots,i_\nu\},\{k_1,\ldots,k_\nu\}}$ *of* A *into an* $\left(\binom{n}{\nu}, \binom{n}{\nu}\right)$*-rowed matrix* $\mathsf{A}^{(\nu)}$. *Then* $A^{(\nu)}$ *is called the* ***ν-th derived matrix*** *and* $\mathsf{A}^{(\nu)}$ *the* ***ν-th complementary matrix of*** A *or the* ***complementary matrix of*** $A^{(\nu)}$; *the latter refers to the fact that the terms of* $\mathsf{A}^{(\nu)}$ *were also called the complementary determinants of the corresponding terms of* $A^{(\nu)}$.

In the case $\nu = 1$, where the $\binom{n}{1}$ combinations of 1st order are simply the n numerals $1, \ldots, n$, let their natural order be taken as a basis for the formation of $A^{(1)}$ and $\mathsf{A}^{(1)}$. Then $A^{(1)}$ becomes the matrix A itself. Similarly, we write for $\mathsf{A}^{(1)}$ simply A. The formation of this 1st complementary matrix of A, or, simply, complementary matrix of A, is arrived at by the following rule:

Let every element a_{ik} of A be replaced by the determinant of that $(n-1, n-1)$-rowed matrix A_{ik} which is obtained by striking out the i-th row and k-th column from A, and affix to this the sign factor $(-1)^{i+k}$. The distribution of the sign factors 1 and -1 can be visualized by covering the square array of A with 1 and -1, just as a chessboard with black and white squares, starting with 1 at the upper left corner (at the position of a_{11}).

For the limiting cases $\nu = 0$ and $\nu = n$, according to the convention agreed upon in Def. 39, we set $A^{(0)} = \mathsf{A}^{(n)} = (e)$, $A^{(n)} = \mathsf{A}^{(0)} = (|A|)$. This means, in particular, that $\mathsf{A} = (e)$ is the complementary matrix of a $(1, 1)$-rowed matrix $A = (a_{11})$.

These concept formations, which seem very complicated at first, are introduced in order to be able to express as simply as possible the following theorem known as the **Laplace Expansion Theorem.**

Theorem 66. *Under the assumptions of Def. 39, 40 the formulae*

$$\sum_{\{k_1,\ldots,k_\nu\}} a_{\{i_1,\ldots,i_\nu\},\{k_1,\ldots,k_\nu\}}\,\alpha_{\{i_1,\ldots,i_\nu\},\{k_1,\ldots,k_\nu\}} = |A|,$$

$$\sum_{\{i_1,\ldots,i_\nu\}} a_{\{i_1,\ldots,i_\nu\},\{k_1,\ldots,k_\nu\}}\,\alpha_{\{i_1,\ldots,i_\nu\},\{k_1,\ldots,k_\nu\}} = |A|$$

are valid, in which the summations extend over all $\binom{n}{\nu}$ *combinations* $\{k_1, \ldots, k_\nu\}$ and $\{i_1, \ldots, i_\nu\}$, *respectively, while* $\{i_1, \ldots, i_\nu\}$ *and* $\{k_1, \ldots, k_\nu\}$ *each indicate a fixed combination. In words, the determinant* $|A|$ *is equal to the inner product of a row (column) of the* ν*-th derived matrix* $A^{(\nu)}$ *and the corresponding row (column) of the* ν*-th complementary matrix* $\mathsf{A}^{(\nu)}$ *of* A.

This implies that the $\alpha_{\{i_1,\ldots,i_\nu\},\{k_1,\ldots,k_\nu\}}$ are linked to the $a_{\{i_1,\ldots,i_\nu\},\{k_1,\ldots,k_\nu\}}$. This is the reason for calling the former the complementary determinant of the latter and $\mathsf{A}^{(\nu)}$ the complementary matrix of $A^{(\nu)}$.

Proof: For the limiting cases $\nu = 0$ and $\nu = n$ the theorem is trivial in view of the conventions agreed upon. Therefore, let $1 \leqq \nu \leqq n-1$, that is, in particular, $n > 1$. It is then sufficient to prove the first formula of the theorem. For, the second formula follows from the first formula formed for the matrix A' through the application of Theorem 64 [129] to the determinants on the left and right.

The proof of the first formula is based on a definite grouping of the summands in the formula used to define the determinant:

$$|A| = \sum_{P \text{ in } \mathfrak{S}_n} \operatorname{sgn} P\, a_{1p_1} \ldots a_{np_n}.$$

For this purpose we decompose the group $\mathfrak{S}_n$ into right cosets $\mathfrak{R}_1, \ldots, \mathfrak{R}_{\binom{n}{\nu}}$ relative to a subgroup $\mathfrak{C}_{\{i_1,\ldots,i_\nu\}}$ of index $\binom{n}{\nu}$ determined by the combination $\{i_1, \ldots, i_\nu\}$ and then carry out the required summation $\sum\limits_{P \text{ in } \mathfrak{S}_n}$ in the grouping

$$\sum_{P \text{ in } \mathfrak{S}_n} = \sum_{P \text{ in } \mathfrak{R}_1} + \cdots + \sum_{P \text{ in } \mathfrak{R}_{\binom{n}{\nu}}}.$$

Each such sum, extended over a coset, is then just one of the summands from the left side of the formula to be proved, the number of which is likewise $\binom{n}{\nu}$.

The subgroup $\mathfrak{C}_{\{i_1,\ldots,i_\nu\}}$ of $\mathfrak{S}_n$ of index $\binom{n}{\nu}$ to be used is the totality of all those permutations of $1,\ldots,n$ in which the numerals $i_1,\ldots,i_\nu$ (and therefore also the remaining numerals $i_{\nu+1},\ldots,i_n$) are permuted only among themselves. By Theorem 20 [64] this is surely a subgroup of $\mathfrak{S}_n$. Its permutations can be written in the form

$$C_{R,S}=\left(\begin{array}{ccc|ccc} i_1 & \ldots & i_\nu & i_{\nu+1} & \ldots & i_n \\ i_{r_1} & \ldots & i_{r_\nu} & i_{s_{\nu+1}} & \ldots & i_{s_n}\end{array}\right),^{7}$$

where

$$R=\binom{\iota}{r_\iota}\ (\iota=1,\ldots,\nu)\ \text{and}\ S=\binom{\iota}{s_\iota}\ (\iota=\nu+1,\ldots,n)$$

run through all permutations of the numerals $1,\ldots,\nu$ and $\nu+1,\ldots,n$, respectively, independently of one another, namely, the groups $\mathfrak{S}_\nu$ and $\mathfrak{S}_{n-\nu}$ (the former for the elements $1,\ldots,\nu$, the latter for the elements $\nu+1,\ldots,n$).

The right cosets relative to $\mathfrak{C}_{\{i_1,\ldots,i_\nu\}}$, and thereby the index of $\mathfrak{C}_{\{i_1,\ldots,i_\nu\}}$ are determined as follows: Let P_0 be any permutation in $\mathfrak{S}_n$. We can think of it as written in the form

$$P_0=\begin{pmatrix} i_1 & \ldots & i_\nu\, i_{\nu+1} & \ldots & i_n \\ k_1 & \ldots & k_\nu\, k_{\nu+1} & \ldots & k_n\end{pmatrix}.$$

Then the right coset $\mathfrak{C}_{\{i_1,\ldots,i_\nu\}}P_0$ generated by P_0 consists of the totality of permutations

$$\begin{aligned} P=C_{R,S}P_0&=\left(\begin{array}{ccc|ccc} i_1 & \ldots & i_\nu & i_{\nu+1} & \ldots & i_n \\ i_{r_1} & \ldots & i_{r_\nu} & i_{s_{\nu+1}} & \ldots & i_{s_n}\end{array}\right)\begin{pmatrix} i_1 & \ldots & i_\nu\, i_{\nu+1} & \ldots & i_n \\ k_1 & \ldots & k_\nu\, k_{\nu+1} & \ldots & k_n\end{pmatrix}\\ &=\begin{pmatrix} i_1 & \ldots & i_\nu & i_{\nu+1} & \ldots & i_n \\ k_{r_1} & \ldots & k_{r_\nu} & k_{s_{\nu+1}} & \ldots & k_{s_n}\end{pmatrix},\end{aligned}$$

[7] The vertical line indicates that the left and the right parts are permutations in themselves.

that is, of all and only those permutations for which the numerals of $\{i_1, \ldots, i_\nu\}$ go over in some order into those of $\{k_1, \ldots, k_\nu\}$ (and consequently the permutations of $\{i_{\nu+1}, \ldots, i_n\}$ into those of $\{k_{\nu+1}, \ldots, k_n\}$). This means that each combination $\{k_1, \ldots, k_\nu\}$ corresponds biuniquely to a right coset $\mathfrak{K}_{\{k_1, \ldots, k_\nu\}}$ relative to $\mathfrak{C}_{\{i_1, \ldots, i_\nu\}}$; therefore, in particular, the index of $\mathfrak{C}_{\{i_1, \ldots, i_\nu\}}$ is equal to the number $\binom{n}{\nu}$ of combinations of ν-th order of $1, \ldots, n$.

This partition of $\mathfrak{S}_n$ relative to $\mathfrak{C}_{\{i_1, \ldots, i_\nu\}}$ is nothing but the group-theoretic form of the inferences familiar from the elements of arithmetic for determining the number $\binom{n}{\nu}$. In fact, by the above the order of $\mathfrak{C}_{\{i_1, \ldots, i_\nu\}}$ is $\nu!(n-\nu)!$, so that by Theorem 25 [68] the well-known formula $\binom{n}{\nu} = \frac{n!}{\nu!\,(n-\nu)!}$ follows.

We now consider that part of the sum $\sum\limits_{P \text{ in } \mathfrak{S}_n}$, representing $|A|$ which corresponds to such a right coset $\mathfrak{K}_{\{k_1, \ldots, k_\nu\}}$. By the above this can be written in the form

$$\sum_{P \text{ in } \mathfrak{K}_{\{k_1, \ldots, k_\nu\}}} = \sum_{C_{R,S} \text{ in } \mathfrak{C}_{\{i_1, \ldots, i_\nu\}}} \operatorname{sgn}(C_{R,S} P_0)\, a_{i_1 k_{r_1}} \cdots a_{i_\nu k_{r_\nu}} a_{i_{\nu+1} k_{s_{\nu+1}}} \cdots a_{i_n k_{s_n}},$$

or by Theorem 60 [123], and since P_0 is fixed in this sum,

$$\sum_{P \text{ in } \mathfrak{K}_{\{k_1, \ldots, k_\nu\}}} = \operatorname{sgn} P_0 \sum_{R \text{ in } \mathfrak{S}_\nu,\, S \text{ in } \mathfrak{S}_{n-\nu}} \operatorname{sgn} C_{R,S}\, a_{i_1 k_{r_1}} \cdots a_{i_\nu k_{r_\nu}} a_{i_{\nu+1} k_{s_{\nu+1}}} \cdots a_{i_n k_{s_n}},$$

whereby corresponding to the structure of $\mathfrak{C}_{\{i_1, \ldots, i_\nu\}}$, explained above, the summation over all $C_{R,S}$ is written as the summation over all R and S of the kind indicated above. Now, everything depends on the computation of sgn P_0 and a suitable splitting up of sgn $C_{R,S}$ into two factors corresponding to the two parts of $C_{R,S}$. Here and in the following we can assume without loss of generality that the numerals of the four combinations $\{i_1, \ldots, i_\nu\}$, $\{i_{\nu+1}, \ldots, i_n\}$, $\{k_1, \ldots, k_\nu\}$, $\{k_{\nu+1}, \ldots, k_n\}$ are in their natural order.

On the one hand, the ordering of the numerals of these combinations does not enter at all into the formula to be proved. For, by Def. 39, it merely dictates the order in which the rows and columns are to be deleted in forming the minors and cofactors; whereas, the rows and columns of their underlying matrices always remain in the natural order. On the other hand, $\mathfrak{C}_{\{i_1,\ldots,i_\nu\}}$ is independent of the order of the numerals $i_1,\ldots,i_\nu$ and $i_{\nu+1},\ldots,i_n$, just as the classes $\mathfrak{K}_{\{k_1,\ldots,k_\nu\}}$ are independent of the ordering of these numerals and also of the numerals $k_1,\ldots,k_\nu$ and $k_{\nu+1},\ldots,k_n$, and in any such class the representative P_0 can be chosen so that $k_1,\ldots,k_\nu$ and $k_{\nu+1},\ldots,k_n$ are in natural order.

1.) *Computation of* sgn P_0

We decompose

$$P_0 = \begin{pmatrix} i_1 \ldots i_\nu\, i_{\nu+1} \ldots i_n \\ k_1 \ldots k_\nu\, k_{\nu+1} \ldots k_n \end{pmatrix}$$
$$= \begin{pmatrix} i_1 \ldots i_\nu\, i_{\nu+1} \ldots i_n \\ 1 \ldots \nu\;\; \nu+1 \ldots n \end{pmatrix} \begin{pmatrix} 1 \ldots \nu\;\; \nu+1 \ldots n \\ k_1 \ldots k_\nu k_{\nu+1} \ldots k_n \end{pmatrix} = I^{-1} K$$

and then by Theorems 60, 61 [123, 124] we have

$$\operatorname{sgn} P_0 = \operatorname{sgn} I^{-1} \operatorname{sgn} K = \operatorname{sgn} I \operatorname{sgn} K.$$

Since $i_1,\ldots,i_\nu$ and $i_{\nu+1},\ldots,i_n$ are in natural order, inversions of $I = \begin{pmatrix} 1 \ldots \nu\;\; \nu+1 \ldots n \\ i_1 \ldots i_\nu\, i_{\nu+1} \ldots i_n \end{pmatrix}$ can take place only between a numeral of $\{i_1,\ldots,i_\nu\}$ and one from $\{i_{\nu+1},\ldots,i_n\}$. These inversions can be enumerated by counting for each of the ν numerals $i_1,\ldots,i_\nu$ the number of numerals $i_{\nu+1},\ldots,i_n$ with which they form inversions. It is now obvious that i_1 leads to inversions with the i_1-1 numerals $1,\ldots,i_1-1$[8] belonging to the second row and only with these; similarly, i_2 with the i_2-2 numerals $1,\ldots,i_2-1$ except i_1 belonging to the second row and only with these, ...; finally, i_ν with the $i_\nu-\nu$ nume-

[8] In regard to the cases $i_1 = 1$, $i_2 = i_1 + 1, \ldots$ cf. footnote 8 [95] in Section 12 to the Theorem of Toeplitz.

rals $1, \ldots, i_\nu - 1$ except $i_1, \ldots, i_{\nu-1}$ belonging to the second row. Consequently,

$$\operatorname{sgn} I = (-1)^{i_1-1+i_2-2+\cdots+i_\nu-\nu} = (-1)^{i_1+\cdots+i_\nu-(1+\cdots+\nu)}.$$

Similarly, it follows that

$$\operatorname{sgn} K = (-1)^{k_1+\cdots+k_\nu-(1+\cdots+\nu)}.$$

We have thereby shown that

$$\operatorname{sgn} P_0 = \operatorname{sgn} I \operatorname{sgn} K = (-1)^{i_1+\cdots+i_\nu+k_1+\cdots+k_\nu} = (-1)^{(i,k)},$$

where (i, k) is an abbreviation for $i_1 + \cdots + i_\nu + k_1 + \cdots + k_\nu$.

2.) *Splitting up of* sgn $C_{R,S}$

Since the two parts of $C_{R,S}$ are permutations in themselves, $C_{R,S}$ permits the following splitting:

$$C_{R,S} = \left(\begin{array}{ccc|ccc} i_1 & \ldots & i_\nu & i_{\nu+1} & \ldots & i_n \\ i_{r_1} & \ldots & i_{r_\nu} & i_{s_{\nu+1}} & \ldots & i_{s_n} \end{array}\right)$$

$$= \left(\begin{array}{ccc|ccc} i_1 & \ldots & i_\nu & i_{\nu+1} & \ldots & i_n \\ i_{r_1} & \ldots & i_{r_\nu} & i_{\nu+1} & \ldots & i_n \end{array}\right) \left(\begin{array}{ccc|ccc} i_1 & \ldots & i_\nu & i_{\nu+1} & \ldots & i_n \\ i_1 & \ldots & i_\nu & i_{s_{\nu+1}} & \ldots & i_{s_n} \end{array}\right) = C_R C_S.$$

By Theorem 60 [123] we then have

$$\operatorname{sgn} C_{R,S} = \operatorname{sgn} C_R \operatorname{sgn} C_S;$$

furthermore, by Theorem 62 [125]

$$\operatorname{sgn} C_R = \operatorname{sgn} \begin{pmatrix} 1 & \ldots & \nu & \nu+1 & \ldots & n \\ r_1 & \ldots & r_\nu & \nu+1 & \ldots & n \end{pmatrix},$$

$$\operatorname{sgn} C_S = \operatorname{sgn} \begin{pmatrix} 1 & \ldots & \nu & \nu+1 & \ldots & \nu \\ 1 & \ldots & \nu & s_{\nu+1} & \ldots & s_n \end{pmatrix}.$$

Now, it is obvious that inversions of the permutations on the right-hand side occur only between pairs of numerals from the sequence $r_1, \ldots, r_\nu$ or pairs of numerals from the sequence $s_{\nu-1}, \ldots, s_n$. Hence it is further valid that

$$\operatorname{sgn} C_R = \operatorname{sgn} \begin{pmatrix} 1 & \ldots & \nu \\ r_1 & \ldots & r_\nu \end{pmatrix} = \operatorname{sgn} R,$$

$$\operatorname{sgn} C_S = \operatorname{sgn} \begin{pmatrix} \nu+1 & \ldots & n \\ s_{\nu+1} & \ldots & s_n \end{pmatrix} = \operatorname{sgn} S,$$

therefore,

$$\operatorname{sgn} C_{R,S} = \operatorname{sgn} R \operatorname{sgn} S.$$

Together with the results of 1) and 2) this now implies

$$\sum_{P \text{ in } \mathfrak{K}_{k_1,\dots,k_\nu\}}} = (-1)^{(i,k)} \sum_{R \text{ in } \mathfrak{S}_\nu,\, S \text{ in } \mathfrak{S}_{n-\nu}} \operatorname{sgn} R\, a_{i_1 k_{r_1}} \dots a_{i_\nu k_{r_\nu}} \operatorname{sgn} S\, a_{i_{\nu+1} k_{s_{\nu+1}}} \dots a_{i_n k_{s_n}}$$

$$= \sum_{R \text{ in } \mathfrak{S}_\nu} \operatorname{sgn} R\, a_{i_1 k_{r_1}} \dots a_{i_\nu k_{r_\nu}} (-1)^{(i,k)} \sum_{S \text{ in } \mathfrak{S}_{n-\nu}} \operatorname{sgn} S\, a_{i_{\nu+1} k_{s_{\nu+1}}} \dots a_{i_n k_{s_n}};$$

for, the termwise expansion and multiplication of the two $\sum_{R \text{ in } \mathfrak{S}_\nu}$, $\sum_{S \text{ in } \mathfrak{S}_{n-\nu}}$ yields the double sum $\sum_{R \text{ in } \mathfrak{S}_\nu,\, S \text{ in } \mathfrak{S}_{n-\nu}}$ first written, since the summations over R and S are independent. The two factors $\sum_{R \text{ in } \mathfrak{S}_\nu}$ and $(-1)^{(i,k)} \sum_{S \text{ in } \mathfrak{S}_{n-\nu}}$ appearing in the last formula are now the determinants $a_{\{i_1,\dots,i_\nu\},\{k_1,\dots,k_\nu\}}$ and $\alpha_{\{i_1,\dots,i_\nu\},\{k_1,\dots,k_\nu\}}$ of the formula to proved.

For, on account of the assumption regarding the ordering of the numerals of our combinations, $a_{i_1 k_1} \dots a_{i_\nu k_\nu}$ and $a_{i_{\nu+1} k_{\nu+1}} \dots a_{i_n k_n}$ are the products of the terms in the principal diagonals of the matrices $A_{\{i_1,\dots,i_\nu\},\{k_1,\dots,k_\nu\}}$ and $\mathsf{A}_{\{i_1,\dots,i_\nu\},\{k_1,\dots,k_\nu\}}$. Furthermore, the summations extend over all permutations R and S of the column indices $k_1, \dots, k_\nu$ and $k_{\nu+1}, \dots, k_n$ in these products, where in every case the proper sign factors sgn R and sgn S are attached. Finally, the proper sign factor $(-1)^{(i,k)} = (-1)^{i_1+\dots+i_\nu+k_1+\dots+k_\nu}$ stands before the second sum.

Consequently, we finally have

$$\sum_{P \text{ in } \mathfrak{K}_{\{k_1,\dots,k_\nu\}}} = a_{\{i_1,\dots,i_\nu\},\{k_1,\dots,k_\nu\}}\, \alpha_{\{i_1,\dots,i_\nu\},\{k_1,\dots,k_\nu\}},$$

and this implies the formula to be proved, because by the above remarks about the cosets we have

$$|A| = \sum_{P \text{ in } \mathfrak{S}_n} = \sum_{\{k_1,\dots,k_\nu\}} \sum_{P \text{ in } \mathfrak{K}_{\{k_1,\dots,k_\nu\}}}$$

The first formula of Theorem 66 can also be expressed as follows: Let a fixed row combination $\{i_1, \dots, i_\nu\}$ of the matrix A be chosen. From these ν rows we can then cut out, corresponding to the $\binom{n}{\nu}$ combinations $\{k_1, \dots, k_\nu\}$ of the columns, $\binom{n}{\nu}$ (ν, ν)-rowed matrices $A_{\{i_1,\dots,i_\nu\},\{k_1,\dots,k_\nu\}}$ with the determinants $a_{\{i_1,\dots,i_\nu\},\{k_1,\dots,k_\nu\}}$. To every such matrix there corresponds a complementary $\mathsf{A}_{\{i_1,\dots,i_\nu\},\{k_1,\dots,k_\nu\}}$, which is cut out from the complementary row combination by using the complementary column combination, or can also be obtained by striking out the rows and columns of A occurring in $A_{\{i_1,\ldots,i_\nu\},\{k_1,\ldots,k_\nu\}}$ and whose determinant, to which the sign factor $(-1)^{i_1+\cdots+i_\nu+k_1+\cdots+k_\nu}$ is attached, is the algebraic complement $\alpha_{\{i_1,\ldots,i_\nu\},\{k_1,\ldots,k_\nu\}}$ to $a_{\{i_1,\ldots,i_\nu\},\{k_1,\ldots,k_\nu\}}$. Now, by running through the system of rows $\{i_1,\ldots,i_\nu\}$ with $a_{\{i_1,\ldots,i_\nu\},\{k_1,\ldots,k_\nu\}}$ and adding all products of the minors $a_{\ldots,\ldots}$ with their algebraic complements $\alpha_{\ldots,\ldots}$, we obtain the determinant $|A|$. Similarly, if the roles of rows and columns are interchanged in this rule, the second formula of Theorem 66 is obtained. These formulae are also called, in this sense, the *expansions of the determinant* $|A|$ *by the minors of the system of rows* $\{i_1,\ldots,i_\nu\}$, *or of the system of columns* $\{k_1,\ldots,k_\nu\}$, *respectively.*

In the particularly important case $\nu = 1$ the formulae of Theorem 66 become

$$(1)\qquad |A| = \sum_{k=1}^{n} a_{ik}\alpha_{ik} \quad (i = 1,\ldots,n),$$

$$(2)\qquad |A| = \sum_{i=1}^{n} a_{ik}\alpha_{ik} \quad (k = 1,\ldots,n).$$

(*Expansion of* $|A|$ *by the elements of a row or column, respectively.*) By (1) or (2) the evaluation of a determinant $|A|$ of n-th degree is reduced to the evaluation of n determinants of $(n-1)$-th degree (say $\alpha_{11},\ldots,\alpha_{1n}$). The implied recursive process for computing determinants can occasionally be used in applications.

19. Further Theorems on Determinants

First of all we will derive some conclusions from the special case $\nu = 1$ of the Laplace Expansion Theorem. Namely, this theorem immediately yields the following fact, which can also be immediately read, by the way, from the formula used to define the determinant (Def. 38 [127]).

Theorem 67. *The determinant* $|A|$ *of an* (n, n)*-rowed matrix* A $(n > 1)$ *is linear and homogeneous in the elements of each row (column) of* A, *that is, to be more exact, it is a linear form* *of the elements of any one row (column), whose coefficients are determined only by the elements standing in the remaining rows (columns).*

By applying Theorem 44 [86] this immediately yields the rule used frequently:

Theorem 68. *If the (n, n)-rowed matrices $A, A_1, \ldots, A_m$ $(n > 1)$ coincide in $n-1$ corresponding rows (columns), while the remaining row (column) $\mathfrak{a}$ of A is the linear combination*

$$\mathfrak{a} = \sum_{i=1}^{m} c_i \mathfrak{a}_i$$

of the corresponding rows (columns) $\mathfrak{a}_1, \ldots, \mathfrak{a}_m$ of $A_1, \ldots, A_m$, then the determinant $|A|$ is the same linear combination

$$|A| = \sum_{i=1}^{m} c_i |A_i|$$

of the determinants $|A_1|, \ldots, |A_m|$.

In particular, we frequently need the special case $m = 1$ of this theorem which says that $|A|$ itself is multiplied by c if the elements of a row (column) of A are multiplied by c. Accordingly, it further follows that [cf. Section 10, c), (3')] $|cA| = c^n |A|$, that is, $|ca_{ik}| = c^n |a_{ik}|$ $(i, k = 1, \ldots, n)$.

Finally, for $m = 1$, $c_1 = 0$ we call special attention to the theorem (naturally also valid for $n = 1$) following either directly from Theorem 67 or from Theorem 68.

Theorem 69. *If all elements of a row (column) of A are zero, then $|A| = 0$.*

All these facts can also be read directly from the formula used to define the determinant (Def. 38 [127]).

Further, in the special case $\nu = 2$ of the Laplace Expansion Theorem we next derive the important result:

Theorem 70. *If two rows (columns) of an (n, n)-rowed matrix A $(n > 1)$ are the same, then $|A| = 0$.*

Proof: By the Laplace Expansion Theorem the determinant $|A|$ is also linear and homogeneous in the minors of a pair of rows or columns. Hence it is sufficient to show that all determinants of second degree are zero if they are formed from a pair of rows or columns which are alike. This immediately follows from the formula used to define determinants, for according to this any determinant of the form $\begin{vmatrix} a\,b \\ a\,b \end{vmatrix}$ or $\begin{vmatrix} a\,a \\ b\,b \end{vmatrix}$ is equal to $ab - ab = 0$.

As a rule the proof given for Theorem 70 is based on Theorem 65 [130]. It runs as follows: By Theorem 62 [125] a permutation of $1, \ldots, n$ interchanging only two numerals, namely, one which can be written in the form $\begin{pmatrix} i_1\, i_2\, i_3 \ldots i_n \\ i_2\, i_1\, i_3 \ldots i_n \end{pmatrix}$, is odd. Hence by interchanging the two rows (columns) that are alike it follows by Theorem 65 [130] that $|A| = -|A|$, that is, $|A| + |A| = 2\,|A| = 0$. In general, however, this does not imply that $|A| = 0$, since, for example, in the field of Section 1, Example 4 (and also in any of its extension fields) $e + e = 2\,e = 0$ but still $e \neq 0$. This simpler proof usually answers the purpose only because we restrict the ground field to *numbers*, for which this conclusion is admissible. The proof given above, by means of the Laplace Expansion Theorem, is theoretically more exact, since it is valid without restriction. (See, however, also Vol. 3, Exer. 11 to Vol. 2, Section 4.)

By means of Theorems 68 and 70 we next prove the following theorem which is basic for the application of determinants to systems of linear equations:

Theorem 71. *If the rows or the columns of an (n, n)-rowed matrix A are linearly dependent, then $|A| = 0$.*

Proof: For $n = 1$ the theorem is trivial. Let $n > 1$. Then, by a′) in Theorem 38 [80] at least one row (column) is a linear combination of the remaining rows (columns). Hence by

Theorem 68 the determinant $|A|$ is a linear combination of those $n-1$ determinants which arise if the row (column) of A in question is replaced successively by one of the remaining $n-1$ rows (columns). But, by Theorem 70, these $n-1$ determinants are zero; therefore, their linear combination $|A|$ is also.

For the practical applications (evaluation of determinants) it is convenient to state Theorem 71 also in the following form:

Corollary. *If the matrix B is formed from the (n, n)-rowed matrix A $(n > 1)$ by adding to a row (column) of A a linear combination of the remaining rows (columns), then* $|B| = |A|$.

Proof: $|B|$ is then the linear combination $|A| + c_1 |A_1| + \cdots + c_{n-1} |A_{n-1}|$, where $|A_1|, \ldots, |A_{n-1}|$ designate the determinants occurring in the proof of Theorem 71, which are all zero.

Finally, we apply Theorem 70 in order to prove the following **extension of the Laplace Expansion Theorem:**

Theorem 72. *Under the assumptions of Def.* 39, 40 [131, 132] *the formulae*

$$\sum_{\{k_1, \ldots, k_\nu\}} a_{\{i_1, \ldots, i_\nu\}, \{k_1, \ldots, k_\nu\}} \alpha_{\{i'_1, \ldots, i'_\nu\}, \{k_1, \ldots, k_\nu\}} = \begin{cases} |A|, & \text{if } \{i_1, \ldots, i_\nu\} = \{i'_1, \ldots, i'_\nu\} \\ 0, & \text{if } \{i_1, \ldots, i_\nu\} \neq \{i'_1, \ldots, i'_\nu\} \end{cases},$$

$$\sum_{\{i_1, \ldots, i_\nu\}} a_{\{i_1, \ldots, i_\nu\}, \{k_1, \ldots, k_\nu\}} \alpha_{\{i_1, \ldots, k_\nu\}, \{k'_1, \ldots, k'_\nu\}} = \begin{cases} |A|, & \text{if } \{k_1, \ldots, k_\nu\} = \{k'_1, \ldots, k'_\nu\} \\ 0, & \text{if } \{k_1, \ldots, k_\nu\} \neq \{k'_1, \ldots, k'_\nu\} \end{cases}$$

are valid. In words: The inner product of a row (column) of the ν-th derived matrix $A^{(\nu)}$ and a row (column) of the ν-th complementary matrix $\mathsf{A}^{(\nu)}$ of A is $|A|$ or 0 according as the two rows (columns) occupy corresponding or different positions in the matrices $A^{(\nu)}$ and $\mathsf{A}^{(\nu)}$.

Proof: We only have to prove the second half of the two formulae as the rest is already contained in Theorem 66

[133]. Furthermore, by Theorem 64 [129] we can restrict ourselves to the first formula. By the Laplace Expansion Theorem (Theorem 66), already proved, the sum on the left-hand side in the first formula of Theorem 72 can be regarded as the expansion of the matrix A_1 by the row combination $\{i_1, \ldots, i_\nu\}$, where A_1 is formed from A by substituting for the $n-\nu$ complementary rows $i_{\nu+1}, \ldots, i_n$ the $n-\nu$ rows of A from which the cofactors $\alpha_{\{i'_1,\ldots,i'_\nu\},\{k_1,\ldots,k_\nu\}}$ are formed, namely, the row combination $\{i'_{\nu+1}, \ldots, i'_n\}$. However, since $\{i_1, \ldots, i_\nu\} \neq \{i'_1, \ldots, i'_\nu\}$ implies that at least one of the $i_1, \ldots, i_\nu$ differs from all $i'_1, \ldots, i'_\nu$, namely, is equal to one of the $i'_{\nu+1}, \ldots, i'_n$, A_1 contains at least two rows which are alike. Therefore, by Theorem 70 $|A_1| = 0$, which implies the first formula.

We note here the corresponding extension of the formulae Section 18, (1) and (2) relative to the special case $\nu = 1$:

$$(1) \quad \sum_{k=1}^{n} a_{ik}\alpha_{i'k} = \begin{Bmatrix} |A|, & \text{if } i = i' \\ 0, & \text{if } i \neq i' \end{Bmatrix},$$

$$(2) \quad \sum_{i=1}^{n} a_{ik}\alpha_{ik'} = \begin{Bmatrix} |A|, & \text{if } k = k' \\ 0, & \text{if } k \neq k' \end{Bmatrix}.$$

20. Application of the Theory of Determinants to Systems of Linear Equations in the Case $m = n$

The theorems developed in the preceding will now be used to derive anew the complex of theorems of Chapter III about systems of linear equations and, besides this, to fill up the gaps in the linear algebra without determinants which were called to our attention in Section 15. In so doing we will, for technical reasons, make no use of the theorems of Sections 13, 14 obtained by means of the Toeplitz process. However, the developments of Sections 10, 11 preceding this process are regarded as facts based on elementary proofs, and shall serve as a basis for the following expositions.

We begin with the consideration of systems of linear equations (J) and (H) with an (n, n)-rowed matrix A, since this case naturally adapts itself to the methods of determinants. The results of this section relative to this case are indispensable for the derivation of the results in the general case considered in the following two sections. This is the reverse of the treatment in Chapter III, where the case $m=n$ could be handled only by specializing from the general case.

First of all the result contained in Theorem 71 [142] immediately says:

Theorem 73. (*Theorem* (52, 53, 54) a [111]). *The system of equations* (H) *with an* (n, n)*-rowed matrix* A *and its transpose* (H′) *cannot be solved if the determinant* $|A| \neq 0$.

Theorem 71 [142] or 73 state the following in regard to the concept *regular* introduced in Section 14:

Corollary. (*Def.* 33 [111]). *If* $|A| \neq 0$, A *is regular.*

One of the principal results of the theory of determinants is that if A is regular, then conversely $|A| \neq 0$. Therefore, the *alternative* of Section 14, which was at that time reducible only to the inapplicable, from a practical point of view, disjunction *A regular or A singular,* can be decided in a practical way by means of the equivalent disjunction $|A| \neq 0$ *or* $|A| = 0$. However, to prove this converse we need the general theory of the following section.

Furthermore, by means of the special case $\nu=1$ of the extended Laplace Expansion Theorem (Theorem 72 [142]) we can prove relative to (J):

Theorem 74. (*Theorem* (46, 48, 49) a [111] , *Theorem* 55 [112] *and Def.* 34). *The system of equations* (J) *with an* (n, n)*-rowed matrix* A *can be solved uniquely for any vector* $\mathfrak{x}^*$

on the right if $|A| \neq 0$. *In such a case the system has a uniquely determined resolvent matrix* A^*, namely.

$$A^* = |A|^{-1}\mathsf{A}' = \left(\frac{\alpha_{ki}}{|A|}\right) \quad (i, k = 1, \ldots, n),$$

where A *is the complementary matrix of* A.

Proof: The theorem is trivial for $n = 1$ (cf. the remark in connection with Def. 40 [132]). Therefore let $n > 1$.

a) The matrix A^* specified in the theorem, which can actually be formed since $|A| \neq 0$, *is* the resolvent matrix of A. Namely, if it is used with the x_i^* to form the elements

$$x_k = \sum_{i=1}^{n} \frac{\alpha_{ik}}{|A|} x_i^* \quad (k = 1, \ldots, n),$$ [9]

then by substituting these x_k in the left sides of (J) and interchanging the order of summation we obtain

$$\sum_{k=1}^{n} a_{i'k} x_k = \sum_{k=1}^{n} a_{i'k} \sum_{i=1}^{n} \frac{\alpha_{ik}}{|A|} x_i^* = \sum_{i=1}^{n} x_i^* \frac{\sum_{k=1}^{n} a_{i'k}\alpha_{ik}}{|A|} \quad (i' = 1, \ldots, n).$$

By Section 19, (1), however, $\sum_{k=1}^{n} = |A|$ or $= 0$ according as $i' = i$ or $i' \neq i$. Therefore, it follows that

$$\sum_{k=1}^{n} a_{i'k} x_k = x_{i'}^* \quad (i' = 1, \ldots, n),$$

hence, (J) exists for the above x_k.

b) The solution of (J) indicated under a) is the *only one*. Namely, if $\mathfrak{x}$ is a solution of (J), therefore,

$$\sum_{k=1}^{n} a_{ik} x_k = x_i^* \quad (i = 1, \ldots, n),$$

[9] Cf. footnote 5 [91] to (H′) in Section 11. The way of indexing chosen here is more convenient for the following substitution than the one used in Section 14 (x_i, x_k^* and accordingly α_{ki}), which immediately calls attention to the fact that it is the *transpose* matrix $\mathsf{A}' = (\alpha_{ki})$ with which we are operating, and not $\mathsf{A} = (\alpha_{ik})$.

then on multiplying the i-th equation by the cofactor of 1-st order $\alpha_{ik'}$ and summing over i we obtain

$$\sum_{i=1}^{n} \alpha_{ik'} \sum_{k=1}^{n} a_{ik} x_k = \sum_{i=1}^{n} \alpha_{ik'} x_i^* \quad (k' = 1, \ldots, n),$$

therefore, by interchanging the order of summation

$$\sum_{k=1}^{n} x_k \sum_{i=1}^{n} a_{ik} \alpha_{ik'} = \sum_{i=1}^{n} \alpha_{ik'} x_i^* \quad (k' = 1, \ldots, n).$$

But, by Section 19, (2) the $\sum_{i=1}^{n} \cdot$ on the left $= |A|$ or $= 0$ according as $k = k'$ or $k \neq k'$. Hence this system of equations simply says

$$|A| \, x_{k'} = \sum_{i=1}^{n} \alpha_{ik'} x_i^* \quad (k' = 1, \ldots, n)$$

or, since $|A| \neq 0$,

$$x_{k'} = \sum_{i=1}^{n} \frac{\alpha_{ik'}}{|A|} x_i^* \quad (k' = 1, \ldots, n),$$

therefore, $\mathfrak{x}$ is identical with the solution under a).

c) That A^* is uniquely determined follows as in the proof to Theorem 55 [112].

Point b) of this proof could have been settled just as in the proof to Theorem (46, 48, 49)a [111]. Namely, we could have used the fact that if $|A| \neq 0$ then by Theorem 73 the associated (H) cannot be solved and consequently by Theorem 46 [91] (J) can be solved uniquely. However, the course chosen here is significant for the actual construction of the solution $\mathfrak{x}$. It amounts to the *method of multiplication* already mentioned in Section 17 [128]. Indeed, by b) the cofactors α_{ik} $(i = 1, \ldots, n)$ of the elements of the k-th column of A are precisely the quantities by which the n left-hand linear forms f_i must be multiplied in order that the linear combination $\sum_{i=1}^{n} \alpha_{ik} f_i \equiv |A| \, x_k$ should contain only one indeterminate x_k. Moreover, it should be pointed out that the *calculation* of the solution $\mathfrak{x}$ by means of the method of multiplication b) does not yet say theoretically that $\mathfrak{x}$ is actually a solution; instead, it says that *if a solution exists,* then $\mathfrak{x}$ is the unique solution. Point a) of the proof is therefore theoretically indispensable.[10]

If $|A| \neq 0$, the solution of (J) always exists and is uniquely determined. In this case a general system of formulae can be established for the solution of (J) on the basis of Theorem 74. It is known as **Cramer's Rule**:

Theorem 75. *Let* (J) *be a system of equations with* (n, n)-*rowed matrix* A *and* $|A| \neq 0$. *Then for any vector* $\mathfrak{x}^*$ *on the right there exists a uniquely determined solution* $\mathfrak{x}$ *of* (J) *given by the quotient of determinants*

$$x_k = \frac{|A^{(k)}|}{|A|} \qquad (k = 1, \ldots, n),$$

where the matrix $A^{(k)}$ *arises from* A *by replacing the* k-*th column of* A *by the vector* $\mathfrak{x}^*$.

Proof: The theorem is trivial for $n = 1$. Therefore, let $n > 1$. Then by Theorem 74 this solution is

$$x_k = \frac{\sum_{i=1}^{n} \alpha_{ik} x_i^*}{|A|} \qquad (k = 1, \ldots, n).$$

By Theorem 66 [133] (Section 18, (2)) the $\sum_i$ appearing in this expression is simply the expansion of the determinant $|A^{(k)}|$ of the matrix $A^{(k)}$, specified in the theorem, by the elements of its k-th column.

By Theorems 73 to 75 only a half of the results of Section 14 have been regained. Our exposition still lacks the converse statements. First, we have not yet shown that for $|A| = 0$, on the one hand, (H) and (H′) can be solved and, on the other hand, (J) cannot be solved unconditionally and uniquely; secondly, we have not established the further statements of Theorem 55 [112]

[10] Unfortunately this fact is too often overlooked or not sufficiently stressed when solving equations in elementary mathematics.

about the resolvent matrix A^*. All this will be established also from the present standpoint by the literal transfer of the proofs in question of Section 14 as soon as the converse of the above corollary has been proved, that is, the equivalence of the statements "A is regular" and "$|A| \neq 0$." At first it could appear that this converse, as all previous statements,[11] could be deduced from the *special case* $\nu = 1$ of the extended Laplace Expansion Theorem by saying: If $|A| = 0$, then the formulae Section 19, (1), (2) represent linear dependences between the rows and columns of A, and therefore A must be singular. However, this is not possible; for, as it is easy to verify by examples, the coefficients α_{ik} in each formula could all be zero, so that in such a case these formulae would not yield linear dependences. The developments of the following sections will show that the converse in question lies deeper, namely, that its proof must take into account the *general case* of the extended Laplace Expansion Theorem.

21. The Rank of a Matrix

The developments (and announcements) of Section 20 show that it is not the determinant $|A|$ itself but only the alternative $|A| \neq 0$ or $|A| = 0$ which is significant for the solvability of systems of linear equations with the (n, n)-rowed matrix A. Therefore, for the application to general systems of linear equations it does not seem necessary to extend the definition of determinants (Def. 38 [127]) to (m, n)-rowed matrices A. Instead, it seems to be a question of finding the proper generalization of this alternative. Now, the alternative in Section 14, in fact equivalent to it, arises from the disjunction $0 \leq r < n$ or $0 < r = n$ made there, therefore, from an "$(n+1)$-ative" in which n possibilities are collected together. Consequently, here we will have to try to split up the alternative $|A| \neq 0$ or $|A| = 0$ into an $(n+1)$-ative expressible for any matrix A. This is accomplished by defining the above number r in terms of determinants.

---

[11] Except for the application of the case $\nu = 2$ in the proof to Theorem 70 [141].

In order to obtain a more convenient nomenclature we first generalize Def. 39 [131]:

Definition 41. *By a* ***minor of ν-th degree*** *of an (m, n)-rowed matrix A, where $0 < \nu \leqq m$ and $0 < \nu \leqq n$, we understand the determinant of an (ν, ν)-rowed matrix obtained by striking out $m - \nu$ rows and $n - \nu$ columns from A.*

As in Section 12, Lemma 1 [96], corresponding to the existence of the maximal number r of linearly independent rows of A we now introduce here the existence of a *maximal degree ϱ for the minors of A different from zero.*

Definition 42. *By the* ***rank*** *ϱ of a matrix A we understand 1) the number 0 if $A = 0$; 2) the greatest number among the degrees of the minors of A different from zero if $A \neq 0$.*

In order to prove that the rank ϱ of A so defined coincides with the number r occurring in Chapter III, we first establish three lemmas about ϱ. Through these a series of self-evident properties of the maximal numbers r and r' of linearly independent rows and columns of A will turn out to be also valid for ϱ. The numbers r and r' are in fact equal to each other.

Def. 41, 42 immediately imply

Lemma 1. *For the rank ϱ of an (m, n)-rowed matrix A the relations*

$$0 \leqq \varrho \leqq m, \quad 0 \leqq \varrho \leqq n,$$
$$\varrho = 0 \quad \text{is equivalent to} \quad A = 0,$$

are valid.

Furthermore, by applying Theorems 64, 65 [129, 130] to all minors of A we immediately obtain:

Lemma 2. *If the matrix A has rank ϱ, then the transpose A', as well as all matrices deducible from A by row and column permutations, have the rank ϱ.*

Finally we have:

Lemma 3. *If the (m, n)-rowed matrix A arises from the $(m+1, n)$-rowed $[(m, n+1)$-rowed$]$ matrix A_1 by striking out a row (column) linearly dependent on the remaining, then A and A_1 have the same rank.*

Proof: By Lemma 2 it is sufficient to prove the theorem for the rows. Let $\mathfrak{a}_1, \ldots, \mathfrak{a}_m$ be the rows of A and $\mathfrak{a}$ the surplus row of A_1 whose deletion gives rise to A, and which is by assumption a linear combination of $\mathfrak{a}_1, \ldots, \mathfrak{a}_m$. Furthermore, let ϱ be the rank of A, ϱ_1 that of A_1. If $\varrho = 0$, by Lemma 1 it also follows that $\varrho_1 = 0$, since it must then be valid that all $\mathfrak{a}_i = 0$, and consequently $\mathfrak{a} = 0$. If $\varrho > 0$, A has a minor of ϱ-th degree different from zero. Since this is also a minor of A_1, it must also be true that $\varrho_1 \geqq \varrho$. Now, if $\varrho_1 > \varrho$, there would then exist a (ϱ_1, ϱ_1)-rowed matrix $\bar{A}_1$ obtained by striking out rows and columns from A_1 such that $|\bar{A}_1| \neq 0$. We will show that this is impossible.

Either, we have $\varrho = n$, so that the possibility of cutting out a (ϱ_1, ϱ_1)-rowed $\bar{A}_1$ from the $(m+1, n)$-rowed A_1 is irreconcilable with the assumption $\varrho_1 > \varrho\ (= n)$ (Lemma 1);

Or $\varrho < n$, so that a (ϱ_1, ϱ_1)-rowed matrix $\bar{A}_1$ can at any rate be cut out of A_1 with $\varrho_1 > \varrho$. In this case there are only two possibilities:

a) $\bar{A}_1$ contains no part of the row $\mathfrak{a}$. Then $\bar{A}_1$ can even be cut out of A; therefore $|\bar{A}_1| = 0$, since it would be a minor of A of degree $\varrho_1 > \varrho$.

b) $\bar{A}_1$ contains a part of the row $\mathfrak{a}$. Then, by Theorem 40 [81] the part in A is a linear combination of the corresponding parts of $\mathfrak{a}_1, \ldots, \mathfrak{a}_m$. Now, by Theorem 68 [141] $|\bar{A}_1|$ can be linearly composed from the determinants of such (ϱ_1, ϱ_1)-rowed matrices as consist of the corresponding parts of the rows of A. However, these determinants, and consequently $|\bar{A}_1|$, are zero, since their matrices either have two identical rows or, if this is not the case, are minors of A of degree $\varrho_1 > \varrho$.

This shows that a (ϱ_1, ϱ_1)-rowed $\bar{A}_1$ with $\varrho_1 > \varrho$ and $|\bar{A}_1| \neq 0$ cannot exist. Therefore, $\varrho_1 > \varrho$ cannot be valid, that is, $\varrho_1 = \varrho$.

We now prove that ϱ is equal to r and r'.

Theorem 76. (*Theorem* 53 [109]). *The rank ϱ of a matrix A is equal to the maximal number r of linearly independent rows and equal to the maximal number r' of linearly independent columns of A. In particular, therefore, $r = r'$.*

Proof: By means of our Lemmas 1 to 3 we first reduce the statement to be proved to its bare essentials by making the following four statements:

1. It is sufficient to prove the theorem for the rows (Lemma 2).

2. It is sufficient to assume $A \neq 0$, therefore, $r > 0, \varrho > 0$ (Lemma 1).

3. It is sufficient to assume[12] that the minor of A of ϱ-th degree different from zero, which exists on account of 2, is the minor formed from the first ϱ rows and columns of A (Lemma 2).

4. It is sufficient to assume that the rows of A are linearly independent (Lemma 3).

For, if A_0 is the matrix consisting of a maximal system of r linearly independent rows of A, which exists on account of 2 and Section 12, Lemma 1 [96] , then by Section 12, Lemma 2 [97] all remaining rows of A are linearly dependent on the rows of A_0. But, by Lemma 3 (and Theorem 42 [82]) the successive deletion of the remaining rows of A leaves the rank unchanged. Hence the statement amounts to proving $\varrho = r$ for A_0.

---

[12] This is only a matter of notation.

Accordingly, let $A=(a_{ik})$ be an (r,n)-rowed matrix with linearly independent rows of rank ϱ for which the minor $\alpha=|a_{ik}|$ $(i,k=1,\ldots,\varrho)$ formed from the first ϱ rows and columns is different from zero. Then we make the first ϱ rows of A into an (n,n)-rowed matrix by the addition of $n-\varrho\geqq 0$ (Lemma 1) rows as follows:

$$\bar{A}=\begin{pmatrix} a_{11} \cdots a_{1\varrho} & a_{1,\varrho+1} \cdots a_{1n} \\ \vdots \quad\;\; \vdots & \vdots \qquad\quad \vdots \\ a_{\varrho 1} \cdots a_{\varrho\varrho} & a_{\varrho,\varrho+1} \cdots a_{\varrho n} \\ 0 \cdots 0 & e \cdots\cdots 0 \\ \vdots \quad\;\; \vdots & \vdots \;\;\ddots\;\; \vdots \\ 0 \cdots 0 & 0 \cdots\cdots e \end{pmatrix}.$$

Regarding the determinant of $\bar{A}$ we have that $|\bar{A}|\neq 0$. For, if $\varrho=n$, therefore $\bar{A}=A$, then we obviously have $|\bar{A}|=\alpha\neq 0$. However, if $\varrho<n$, then on expanding $\bar{A}$ by the minors of the last $n-\varrho$ rows it also follows that $|A|=\alpha\neq 0$, since by Theorem 69 [141] only the minor corresponding to the last $n-\varrho$ columns (with the cofactor α) is different from zero, namely $=e$.

Now, by Lemma 1 we have at any rate $\varrho\leqq r$. If $\varrho<r$ were true, therefore A would contain $r-\varrho$ rows $(a_{i1},\ldots,a_{in})$ $(i=\varrho+1,\ldots,r)$ not in $\bar{A}$, then by Theorem 74 [145] and Theorem 64 [129] each of the $r-\varrho$ systems of linear equations

$$\begin{array}{l} a_{11}x_1+\cdots+a_{\varrho 1}x_\varrho+0x_{\varrho+1}\;+\cdots+0x_n \doteq a_{i1} \\ \quad\vdots \\ a_{1\varrho}x_1+\cdots+a_{\varrho\varrho}x_\varrho+0x_{\varrho+1}\;+\cdots+0x_n \doteq a_{i\varrho} \\ a_{1,\varrho+1}x_1+\cdots+a_{\varrho,\varrho+1}x_\varrho+x_{\varrho+1}+\cdots+0x_n \doteq a_{i,\varrho+1} \\ \quad\vdots \\ a_{1n}x_1+\cdots+a_{\varrho n}x_\varrho+0x_{\varrho+1}\;+\cdots+x_n \doteq a_{in} \end{array}$$
$$(i=\varrho+1,\ldots,r)$$

with the matrix $\bar{A}'$ could be solved, that is, each of these $r-\varrho$ rows would be a linear combination of the n rows of $\bar{A}$.

Now, in case $\varrho = n$ (which is compatible with the assumption $\varrho < r$ only in the case $r > n$) the existence of these $r - \varrho$ systems of equations would indicate that the last $r - \varrho$ rows of A were linear combinations of the first ϱ, which contradicts the assumption that the rows of A are linearly independent. We arrive at the same conclusion for $\varrho < n$ by proving that in the solutions $(x_{i1}, \ldots, x_{in})$ $(i = \varrho + 1, \ldots, r)$ of these systems of equations the last $n - \varrho$ unknowns $x_{i, \varrho + 1}, \ldots, x_{in}$ are equal to zero.

In order to show this we think of the solutions $(x_{i1}, \ldots, x_{in})$ $(i = \varrho + 1, \ldots, r)$, which are uniquely determined by Theorem 74 [145] and can be obtained by Cramer's rule (Theorem 75 [148]), as written in the form

$$x_{ij} = \frac{|\bar{A}_i^{(j)}|}{|\bar{A}'|} = \frac{|\bar{A}_i^{(j)}|}{|\bar{A}|} \qquad \begin{pmatrix} i = \varrho + 1, \ldots, r \\ j = 1, \ldots, n \end{pmatrix}.$$

The matrices $\bar{A}_i^{(j)}$ arise from $\bar{A}$ by replacing the j-th row in $\bar{A}$ by $(a_{i1}, \ldots, a_{in})$. Now, if j is one of the indices $\varrho + 1, \ldots, n$ in question, then $\bar{A}_i^{(j)}$ accordingly contains $\varrho + 1$ different rows of A. If $\bar{A}_i^{(j)}$ is then expanded in terms of these $\varrho + 1$ rows and it is borne in mind that all its minors, as minors of $(\varrho + 1)$-th degree of A, are zero, it follows that $|\bar{A}_i^{(j)}| = 0$; therefore $x_{ij} = 0$ $(i = \varrho + 1, \ldots, r;\ j = \varrho + 1, \ldots, n)$. In accordance with what has already been said this means that the impossibility of $\varrho < r$ is proved. Consequently, we have $\varrho = r$ as stated.

Theorem 76 just proved immediately yields the part still missing of the results of Section 14, cited at the end of the previous section, in regard to the special system of equations with $m = n$. Namely, we can next easily prove the following *converse of Theorem* 71 [142]:

Theorem 77. *If A is an (n, n)-rowed matrix with* $|A| = 0$, *then the rows as well as the columns of A are linearly dependent.*

Proof: If $|A|=0$, then the rank $\varrho<n$, since $|A|$ is the only minor of n-th degree of A. Hence by Theorem 76 the n rows and the n columns of A are linearly dependent.

Theorem 77 also says as a *converse to Theorem* 73 [145]:

Theorem 78. (Theorem (52, 53, 54) a [111]). *The system of equations* (H) *with* (n, n)*-rowed matrix A and its transpose* (H′) *can be solved if* $|A|=0$.

Finally, Theorem 77 or 78 give the *converse of the Corollary to Theorem* 73 [145] mentioned in Section 20:

Corollary. (*Def.* 33 [111]). *If A is regular, then* $|A| \neq 0$.

Consequently we have

Theorem 79. (*Def.* 33 [111]). *The alternatives "A regular or A singular" and "$|A| \neq 0$ or $|A|=0$" are equivalent.*

As already stated at the end of Section 20, the following *converse to Theorem* 74 [145] as well as the further statements based on it can now be regarded as proved from the present standpoint:

Theorem 80. (*Theorem* (46, 48, 49) a [111]). *The condition* $|A| \neq 0$ *is also necessary in order that the system of equations* (J) *with* (n, n)*-rowed matrix A have an unconditional and unique solution.*

Theorem 81. (*Theorem* 55 [112]). *If* $|A| \neq 0$, *so also is the determinant* $|A^*|$ *of the resolvent matrix* $A^*=|\mathsf{A}|^{-1}\mathsf{A}'$, *that is, the determinant* $|\mathsf{A}|=|A|^n|A^*|$[13] *of the complementary matrix of A is also different from zero and* $(A^*)^*=A$.

This easily yields that the complementary matrix $\hat{A}$ of the complementary A of A differs from A only by a factor, namely, that $\hat{A}=\frac{|\mathsf{A}|}{|A|}A$. The determination of this factor, that is, the

[13] Cf. the remark after Theorem 68 [141].

evaluation of $|\mathsf{A}|$, can be carried out, however, only by means of the calculus of matrices. It turns out that A^* is simply the *inverse* A^{-1} of A, so that $|A^*| = |A|^{-1}$. Hence for $\mathsf{A}' = |A|\,A^{-1}$ we get $|\mathsf{A}| = |A|^n\,|A|^{-1} = |A|^{n-1}$. Moreover, the determinants of all derived and complementary matrices $A^{(\nu)}$, $\mathsf{A}^{(\nu)}$ are also powers of $|A|$. (Cf. for this Vol. 3, Section 14, Exer. 4; Section 19, Exer. 13; Vol. 2, Section 2, Exer. 30 to 32.)

We have thereby established from the point of view of determinants all the results of Section 14 for the special case $m = n$. In addition to this, according to Theorem 79 we are now able to come to a decision in a practical way regarding the *alternative* appearing there, that is, regarding the solvability of (H) or the unconditional, unique solvability of (J). Furthermore, Theorems 74, 75 [145, 148] provide us with a simple process for determining the solution of (J) in the "regular" case ($|A| \neq 0$).

In Sections 11, 13 the *decision regarding the solvability of* (H) and the *delineation of the totality of solutions of* (H) *and* (J) was made to depend only on the number r to be determined. Our Theorem 76 says for the general case that this number r can be found as the rank ϱ of A in finitely many steps, namely, by the evaluation of all minors of A. Moreover, this means that a *maximal system of linearly independent rows* (*columns*) of A can also be determined in finitely many steps, that is, the application of the first step of the Toeplitz process now becomes practical. Hence we can immediately deduce from Theorem 76 the following fact, which is to be applied in the following sections:

Lemma 4. *If A is a matrix of rank $\varrho > 0$, then every pair of combinations of ϱ rows and ϱ columns of A to which corresponds a minor of ϱ-th degree different from zero yields a maximal system of linearly independent rows and columns of A.*

Proof: By Theorem 71 [142] the parts of the ϱ rows (columns) of A under consideration going into any minor of ϱ-th degree are linearly independent; by Theorem 40 [81], therefore, all the ϱ rows (columns) are also; and by Theorem 76 they form in this case a maximal system of linearly independent rows (columns).

Furthermore, Theorem 76 can also be thought of as establishing from a determinantal point of view Lemmas 1, 2 [103, 104] proved in Section 13 by means of the partial application of the second step of the Toeplitz process. Consequently, this theorem also implies all inferences deduced from these lemmas in Section 13, that is, the *existence of a system of fundamental solutions of* (H) (*Theorem* 50 [104]) and the *invariance of the number of fundamental solutions* (*Theorem* 51 [105]). Hence, in order to completely reproduce the earlier results all that is left for us to do is to prove from the determinantal point of view *Theorems* 49 [102] *and* 52 [106] about (J) and (H), which were deduced in Section 13 by using the second step of the Toeplitz process in its entirety. We will do this in the next section. We will then be immediately able to conclude that *Theorem* 54 [109] of Section 13 regarding (H) and (H′), which is the only one still not cited, is naturally also a consequence of Theorem 76.

22. Application of the Theory of Determinants to Systems of Linear Equations in the General Case

The proof of Theorems 49 [102] and 52 [106] to be given using determinants will yield, besides the statements contained in these theorems, the *explicit determination of the totality of solutions of* (J) *and* (H), therefore the complete solution of both *problems* J_{pr}) and H_{pr}) cited at the end of Section 11, which the developments of Chapter III were unable to do. For technical reasons it is advisable to consider (H) before (J).

1. *Solution of* H_{pr})

The complete solution of H_{pr}) is obviously contained in the following theorem:

Theorem 82. (*Theorem* 52 [106]). *The system of equations* (H) *with* (m, n)*-rowed matrix* A *of rank* ϱ *possesses a system of fundamental solutions of* $n-\varrho$ *solutions. If* $0<\varrho<n$ *and, as can be assumed without loss of generality,*[14] *the ordering of the equations and unknowns is chosen so that the minor formed from the first* ϱ *rows and columns of* A *is different from zero, then such a system will be formed by the last* $n-\varrho$ *rows of the complementary matrix* $\overline{\mathsf{A}}$ *of the* (n, n)*-rowed matrix* $\bar{A}$ *from the proof of Theorem* 76 [152] , *therefore by the* $n-\varrho$ *vectors*

$$(\bar{\alpha}_{i1}, \ldots, \bar{\alpha}_{in}) \quad (i=\varrho+1, \ldots, n)$$

from the cofactors of 1-st order of that matrix $\bar{A}$.

Proof: For $\varrho=0$, namely, $A=0$, the theorem is trivial (cf. proof to Theorem 52 [106]). Therefore, let $\varrho>0$, so that $A \neq 0$. By the assumption made in the theorem the first ϱ rows form in this case a maximal system of linearly independent rows of A (Section 21, Lemma 4 [156]). As in Section 12 (first step) the system of equations (H_0) with the (ϱ, n)-rowed matrix A_0 formed from the first ϱ equations of (H) is equivalent to (H), so that for the proof it is sufficient to use (H_0) instead of (H).

Now, on the one hand, let $\varrho=n$, so that A_0 is a (ϱ, n)-rowed matrix for which $|A_0| \neq 0$ by assumption. Then by Theorem 73

[14] This is only a matter of notation.

[145] (H_0) cannot be solved and therefore has a system of fundamental solutions of $0 = \varrho - \varrho = n - \varrho$ solutions, as stated.

On the other hand, let $0 < \varrho < n$. Then we have:

a) The specified $n - \varrho$ vectors *are* solutions of (H_0). For, by the extended Laplace Expansion Theorem [Section 19, (1)], applied to the matrix $\bar{A}$, we have

$$\sum_{k=1}^{n} a_{ik}\bar{\alpha}_{i'k} = 0 \qquad (i = 1, \ldots, \varrho;\ i' = \varrho + 1, \ldots, n).$$

b) These $n - \varrho$ solutions of (H_0) are *linearly independent.* For, by Theorem 81 [155], since $|\bar{A}| \neq 0$, we also have $|\bar{\mathsf{A}}| \neq 0$. Hence by Theorem 71 [142] the n rows of $\bar{\mathsf{A}}$ are linearly independent; therefore by Theorem 39 [81] so also are the last $n - \varrho$ rows.

c) *Any solution* $\mathfrak{x}$ of (H_0) is a *linear combination* of these $n - \varrho$ solutions of (H_0). For, the system of equations

$$\sum_{i=1}^{n} \frac{\bar{\alpha}_{ik}}{|\bar{A}|} x_i^* = x_k \qquad (k = 1, \ldots, n),$$

whose matrix is the resolvent matrix $\bar{A}^*$ of $\bar{A}$, has, since $|\bar{A}| \neq 0$, by Theorems 74 [145], 81 [155] the uniquely determined solution

$$\begin{aligned} x_i^* &= \sum_{k=1}^{n} a_{ik} x_k \qquad &(i = 1, \ldots, \varrho) \\ x_i^* &= \quad x_i &(i = \varrho + 1, \ldots, n) \end{aligned}$$

with the matrix $(\bar{A}^*)^* = \bar{A}$. Since, however, $\mathfrak{x}$ should be a solution of (H_0), we have $x_1^*, \ldots, x_\varrho^* = 0$, that is, the formulae

$$\sum_{i=\varrho+1}^{n} \frac{x_i^*}{|\bar{A}|} \bar{\alpha}_{ik} \left(= \sum_{i=\varrho+1}^{n} \frac{x_i}{|\bar{A}|} \bar{\alpha}_{ik} \right) = x_k \qquad (k = 1, \ldots, n)$$

are valid. This means that $\mathfrak{x}$ is a linear combination of our $n - \varrho$ solutions from a), b).

a) to c) imply that the $n - \varrho$ vectors specified in the theorem form a system of fundamental solutions of (H_0), therefore also of (H).

2. *Solution of* J_{pr})

The complete solution of J_{pr}) is obviously contained in the following theorem:

Theorem 83. (*Theorem* 48 [92]). *Let* (J) *be a system of equations with* (m, n)*-rowed matrix* A *of rank* ϱ. *If the necessary solvability condition of Theorem* 48 *is satisfied, then* (J) *can be solved. If* $\varrho > 0$ *and the assumption of Theorem* 82 *is again made about the ordering of the equations and unknowns, then a solution of* (J) *is obtained by setting the unknowns* $x_{\varrho+1}, \ldots, x_n = 0$ *in the system of equations* (J_0) *formed from the first* ϱ *equations of* (J) (*in case* $\varrho < n$), *and then determining* $x_1, \ldots, x_\varrho$ *by solving the system of equations thereby obtained with a* (ϱ, ϱ)*-rowed matrix whose determinant is different from zero. The solution of the latter system may be obtained by using Theorems* 74, 75 [145, 148].

Proof: The theorem is trivial in case $\varrho = 0$ (cf. the proof to Theorem 49 [102]). Therefore, let $\varrho > 0$. By the assumption made in the theorem it again follows in this case by Section 21, Lemma 4 [156], as in Section 12 (first step), that the system (J_0) is equivalent to (J). That the process described in the theorem yields a solution of (J_0), and consequently of (J), is immediately clear.

By the remarks in Section 11 it follows that Theorems 82 and 83 completely solve the problem Section 5, (1) of linear algebra.

In conclusion we will deduce two further rules which supplement Theorem 83 and are useful in practical applications. These will also enable us, on the one hand, to *determine the totality of solutions of* (J) directly, that is, without having to compute according to Theorem 46 [91] a system of fundamental solutions of (H) by Theorem 82, and, on the other hand, to come to a *decision regarding the solvability of* (J) directly, that is, without having to compute according to Theorem 48, Corollary 2 [93] a system of fundamental solutions of (H′) by Theorem 82.

Without further discussion it is clear:

Corollary 1. *Under the assumptions of Theorem* 83 *the totality of solutions of* (J) *in the case* $\varrho > 0$ *can be found as follows: In the system of equations* (J_0) *appearing there replace the unknowns* $x_{\varrho+1}, \ldots, x_n$ *by any elements* $\xi_{\varrho+1}, \ldots, \xi_n$ *whatever (in case* $\varrho < n$*); then by Theorems* 74, 75 [145, 148] *determine* $x_1, \ldots, x_\varrho$ *by solving the resulting system of equations*

$$\sum_{k=1}^{\varrho} a_{ik} x_k = a_i + \sum_{k=\varrho+1}^{n} (-a_{ik})\, \xi_k \text{ [15]} \qquad (i = 1, \ldots, \varrho)$$

with a (ϱ, ϱ)*-rowed matrix, whose determinant is different from zero. To any arbitrary system* $\xi_{\varrho+1}, \ldots, \xi_n$ *there is thereby obtained one and only one solution of* (J).

Incidentally, if α_{ik} designate the cofactors of the elements a_{ik} in that (ϱ, ϱ)-rowed matrix (a_{ik}) $(i, k = 1, \ldots, \varrho)$ and $a = |a_{ik}|$ its determinant, then by Theorem 74 [145] on interchanging the order of summation

$$x_k = \sum_{i=1}^{\varrho} \frac{\alpha_{ik}}{a} a_i + \sum_{l=\varrho+1}^{n} \xi_l \sum_{i=1}^{\varrho} \frac{\alpha_{ik}}{a} (-a_{il}) = a_k^* + \sum_{l=\varrho+1}^{n} a_{kl}^* \xi_l$$
$$(k = 1, \ldots, \varrho)$$

becomes the solution of the system of equations in question, which together with

$$x_k = 0 + \xi_k \qquad (k = \varrho + 1, \ldots, n)$$

yields the general solution $\mathfrak{x}_J$ of (J). Here the solution $\mathfrak{x}_J$ turns out to be automatically decomposed into two summands $\mathfrak{x}_J^{(0)}$ and $\mathfrak{x}_H$ according to Theorem 46 [91]. The first $\mathfrak{x}_J^{(0)} = (a_1^*, \ldots, a_\varrho^*, 0, \ldots, 0)$ is obviously the particular solution of (J), corresponding to $\xi_{\varrho+1}, \ldots, \xi_n = 0$, specified in Theorem 83; while the second $\mathfrak{x}_H$ must accordingly represent the general solution of the associated (H). In fact the second summand seems to be a linear combination of $n - \varrho$ fundamental solutions as was the case in the proof to Theorem 52 [106].

---

[15] For the limiting case $\varrho = n$ cf. the statement in footnote 8 [95] to the Theorem of Toeplitz in Section 12.

Furthermore we prove:

Corollary 2. *The system of equations* (J) *can be solved if and only if its* (m, n)*-rowed matrix* A *has the same rank as the* $(m, n+1)$*-rowed matrix* A_1 *arising from it by adjoining the column formed from the right side* $(a_1, \ldots, a_m)$ *of* (J).

Proof: a) If (J) can be solved, then the column $(a_1, \ldots, a_m)$ is linearly dependent on the columns of A. But, by Section 21, Lemma 3 [151] A_1 has then the same rank as A.

b) If (J) cannot be solved, then the column $(a_1, \ldots, a_m)$ is linearly independent of the columns of A. If $A = 0$, then this column is different from zero, that is, the rank of A_1 is equal to 1 while that of A is equal to 0. However, if $A \neq 0$, then by b) in Theorem 38 [80] this column together with a maximal system of ϱ linearly independent columns forms a system of $\varrho + 1$ linearly independent columns. By Theorem 76 [152] the rank of A_1 is therefore greater than the rank ϱ of A. Consequently, if A and A_1 have the same rank, (J) can be solved.

Conclusion

Dependence on the Ground Field

To wind up our developments we ask one further question: Are the results of Chapter III and IV to be altered if we no longer, as has been done throughout the foregoing, require that the solutions $x_1, \ldots, x_n$ of the given system of linear equations (J) belong to the field K but instead demand that they merely belong to any extension field $\overline{\mathsf{K}}$ of K? Since the system of equations (J) can in this case also be regarded as a system with coefficients in $\overline{\mathsf{K}}$, our entire theory can also be carried out using $\overline{\mathsf{K}}$ as ground field. In doing so, the totality of solutions of (J) is in general larger than in the case of K, since the freely disposable elements of K, occurring in the general solution of (J), can now be freely taken from the more extensive $\overline{\mathsf{K}}$. Nevertheless, we have:

Theorem 84. *In regard to a system of linear equations* (J) *in* K, *the solvability or nonsolvability, the unique solvability as well as the number* $n-r$ *of the elements freely disposable in the general solution are invariant with respect to the passage from* K *to any extension field* $\overline{\mathsf{K}}$ *of* K *as ground field.*

Proof: If A is the matrix of (J), A_1 the matrix specified in Theorem 83, Corollary 2 [162], and r and r_1 are the ranks of A and A_1, then by Theorem 83, Corollary 2 the solvability or nonsolvability of (J) is equivalent to the relation

$$r = r_1 \text{ or } r < r_1, \text{ respectively,}$$

and by Theorem 83, Corollary 1 [161] the unique solvability of (J) is equivalent to the relation

$$r = r_1 = n.$$

But, the property of a determinant being zero or different from zero is independent of whether its terms are regarded as elements of K or $\overline{K}$. Hence according to Def. 42 [150] the rank of a matrix is invariant with respect to the passage from K to $\overline{K}$; therefore, on account of the self-evident invariance of n the above relations are also invariant. This means that the solvability or nonsolvability and the unique solvability of (J) as well as the number $n - r$ specified in the theorem are invariant.

HIGHER ALGEBRA

BY

HELMUT HASSE, Ph.D.

Professor of Mathematics, University of Hamburg

VOLUME II

Equations of Higher Degree

Translated from the third revised German edition

by

THEODORE J. BENAC, Ph.D.

Associate Professor of Mathematics, U.S. Naval Academy

FREDERICK UNGAR PUBLISHING CO.

NEW YORK

Printed in the United States of America

Library of Congress Catalog Card No. 54–7418

Introduction

Methodical Preliminary Observations and Survey

In Vol. 1, Section 5 we formulated the basic problem of algebra guiding our presentation and called attention to two especially important subproblems. The first of these, the problem of solving a system of linear equations, was completely solved in Vol. 1, Chapters III and IV. The present Vol. 2 will be concerned with the second of these subproblems:

Let K *be a field and*

$$f(x) \equiv a_0 + a_1 x + \cdots + a_n x^n \qquad (a_n \neq 0, n \geqq 1)$$

an element of K$[x]$ *not belonging to* K. *We seek to develop methods for obtaining all solutions of the* ***algebraic equation***

$$f(x) \doteq 0.$$

Since the conditions for solving the equation $f(x) \doteq 0$ are the same as those for solving $\frac{f(x)}{a_n} \doteq 0$, there will be no loss of generality if we restrict ourselves in the following to equations of the form

$$f(x) \equiv a_0 + a_1 x + \cdots + a_{n-1} x^{n-1} + x^n \doteq 0 \qquad (n \geqq 1).$$

We call such elements $f(x)$ of K$[x]$ *polynomials* (in x) ***in*** or ***of***[1] or ***over*** K and the uniquely determined index $n \geqq 1$ their degree [cf. Vol. 1, Section 5, (2) [56]]. Furthermore, the solutions of an algebraic equation $f(x) \doteq 0$ are called, in accordance with the usual terminology, the ***roots of the polynomial*** $f(x)$.

[1] Strictly speaking, this is not correct, since the $f(x)$ are elements of K$[x]$. Therefore, our terminology refers to the coefficients.

The methods to be used to handle our present problem are basically different from those employed in Vol. 1 to handle systems of linear equations. This is due to the following two closely connected facts:

1) There can exist (in contrast to Vol. 1, Chapter IV) no process formed from the four elementary operations (briefly, *rational operations*) defined in the ground field K for deciding the solvability of an algebraic equation and in the solvability case for calculating all solutions.

2) The solvability and the totality of solutions of an algebraic equation over K are (in contrast to Vol. 1, Theorem 84 [163]) dependent on the choice of the ground field, that is, on whether the solutions are to be considered as lying only in the field K or in some extension field of K. In general, algebraic equations over K can be solved only in suitable extension fields of K.

To illustrate the latter general insight given in 2) we may cite the simple example of the equation $x^2 - 2 = 0$. Thus, this equation does not have a solution in the field of rational numbers but has the two solutions $\pm\sqrt{2}$ in the field of real numbers. Furthermore, 2) implies 1), for if a process, as cited in 1), were to exist, then this would be; as in Vol. 1, Theorem 84 [163] , independent of the choice of the ground field, which contradicts 2).[2]

Due to 1) our problem is not to be understood as one wherein the solutions of an algebraic equation shall be *computed* in

[2] This should not be taken to mean that solution processes do not exist for special ground fields, for example, the field of rational numbers. However, such methods are no longer thought of as belonging to algebra, since besides the four elementary operations they must involve tools belonging to analysis. In this regard, cf. Section 11 [247] .

the above sense. 2) tells us what we are to strive for instead of this. In the first place, 2) implies that for abstract ground fields (that is, under exclusive assumption of the conditions given in Vol. 1, Section 1) the extension field is not at our disposal beforehand as was the case in the above example, where the real number field was assumed as known from elementary mathematics (foundations of analysis). In the second place, on the contrary, 2) implies that in the general case we have first of all no knowledge whatsoever regarding the existence of extension fields which make the solution of an algebraic equation possible. Hence our problem amounts to that of *constructing* such extension fields and thereby the roots of algebraic equations.

Accordingly, our presentation will run as follows: In Chapters I and II we have to explain some preliminary facts, on the one hand, about polynomials over K formed from *the left sides of algebraic equations* and, on the other hand, the (for the time being, hypothetical) *roots of algebraic equations* over K in extension fields; in Chapter III we will construct the *root fields of algebraic equations* and thereby their roots. We then can think of the above problem as solved from a practical standpoint (analogous to Vol. 1, Chapter IV: determination of solutions). From a theoretical standpoint the question, which is of very special interest to us here, is raised beyond this (analogous of Vol. 1, Chapter III: the structure of the totality of solutions) as to what can be said about the *structure of the root field of algebraic equations*, especially about its construction from components as simple as possible. This question, about which our considerations will be centered, will be handled in Chapter IV by the presentation of the so-called *Galois theory*, whereby the structure of these fields will be closely tied to the structure of certain finite groups, their *Galois groups*. Finally, in Chapter V this theory will be used to answer the question of the *solvability of algebraic equations by radicals*, that is, the famous question: *When can the roots of an algebraic equation be computed by including the operation of root extraction* (which, with a fixed ground field, is not defined without restriction and uniquely)?

I. The Left Sides of Algebraic Equations

In Sections 1, 2 of this chapter we will successively derive significant theorems about polynomials over K in connection with the developments of Vol. 1, Chapter I. At first, these theorems will have nothing to do with the fact that the polynomials constitute the left sides of algebraic equations; they will be linked to this fact only in the chapters to follow. The theorems themselves are exact analogues of the theorems in elementary number theory centered around the fundamental theorem of the unique factorization of integers into prime numbers; here they deal with the integral domain $K[x]$ of the integral rational functions of an indeterminate x over the ground field K, whereas in elementary number theory they deal with the integral domain Γ of integers — just as the construction of the field $K(x)$ of the rational functions of x over K from $K[x]$ is exactly analogous to the construction of the field P of rational numbers from Γ, for in both cases the fields are constructed as quotient fields. Here we will not assume elementary number theory as known, which is to be frequently used later on. Instead, we will deduce the cited theorems for the two cases $K[x]$ and Γ at the same time, that is, in terms of words and symbols bearing a twofold significance. Accordingly, in Sections 1, 2 $f, g, h, \ldots$ will designate elements in $K[x]$ or Γ. By means of the results of Sections 1, 2 relative to the case Γ we will then develop in Sections 3, 4 of this chapter some more concepts and facts about groups, integral domains and fields. These are important in the following and would already have been inserted at an earlier place (Vol. 1, Chapters I and II) if we could have assumed elementary number theory as known.

1. The Fundamental Theorem of the Unique Decomposability into Prime Elements in $\mathsf{K}[x]$ and Γ

A. Divisibility Theory in an Integral Domain

The fundamental theorem specified in the title presupposes for its exact formulation the concepts of the so-called *divisibility theory* in $\mathsf{K}[x]$ or Γ. Since this divisibility theory requires no properties of $\mathsf{K}[x]$ or Γ, other than that each is an integral domain, we will develop it for an arbitrary integral domain I. $f, g, h, \ldots$ shall then designate elements in I.

Definition 1. *g is said to be* ***divisible*** *by f or a* ***multiple*** *of f, and f a* ***divisor*** *of g or* ***contained in*** *g (notation $f \mid g$, contrariwise, $f \nmid g$), if an $\bar{f}$ exists so that $g = f\bar{f}$.*

It will naturally be required that $\bar{f}$ exist in I. The notation we have adopted permits us to omit this kind of additional statements, here and at similar places. However, it should be expressly emphasized that this is implicit in Def. 1. For, if the "existence" of such an element were also allowed to take place in the quotient field of I, then Def. 1 would be trivial except for the distinction between $f \neq 0$ and $f = 0$. Accordingly, the divisibility theory becomes meaningless if I coincides with its quotient field. This is not the case for $\mathsf{K}[x]$ or Γ.

From the basic properties of integral domains developed in Vol. 1, Section 1 we can immediately obtain the following theorems about divisibility. The proofs of these facts are so simple that we omit them[1].

[1] Furthermore, we will indicate the entirely elementary proofs of a series of further theorems of Section 1 by merely making a reference to the earlier theorems that are involved.

Theorem 1. *The divisibility relations*

$$e \mid f,\ f \mid f,\ f \mid 0 \text{ for every } f$$

$$0 \nmid f \text{ for } f \neq 0$$

are valid.

Theorem 2. $f \mid g$, $g \mid h$ *implies* $f \mid h$; $f_1 \mid g_1$, $f_2 \mid g_2$ *implies* $f_1 f_2 \mid g_1 g_2$; $hf \mid hg$, $h \neq 0$ *implies* $f \mid g$.

Theorem 3. $f \mid g_1$, $f \mid g_2$ *implies* $f \mid g_1\bar{g}_1 + g_2\bar{g}_2$ *for arbitrary* $\bar{g}_1$, $\bar{g}_2$.

Definition 2. f *is called a* ***unit*** *if* $f \mid e$.

In the following we designate units by a, b. For instance, e is a unit.

Theorem 4. *The units of* I *form a subgroup (normal divisor) of the multiplicative Abelian group of all elements* $\neq 0$ *of the quotient field of* I.

Proof: $a_1 \mid e$, $a_2 \mid e$ implies $a_1 a_2 \mid e$ (Theorem 2); also $e \mid e$ (Theorem 1); $a \mid e$ implies that $\frac{e}{a}$ belongs to I and $\frac{e}{a} \mid e$ (Def. 1). The theorem follows from this by Vol. 1, Theorem 19, 26 [63, 69] (cf. also Vol. 1, Section 6, Example 1 [61]).

Definition 3. *If* f_1, f_2 *are different from* 0 *and congruent relative to the normal divisor of units, that is, if* $\frac{f_1}{f_2} = a$, *then* f_1 *and* f_2 *are said to be* ***associates.*** *The residue classes relative to this normal divisor are called the* ***classes of associates.***

This means that the class of elements associated to an element $f \neq 0$ consists of all af, where a runs through all units. For $f = 0$ the totality af, that is, the single element 0, may likewise be regarded as the class of associated elements belonging to f. — In the sense of Vol. 1, Sections 7 to 9 the partition into residue classes relative to the normal divisor of the units extends not only to the integral domain I but also to its quotient field. Here, however, we consider it only in the integral domain I itself. We can do this all the more as the class corresponding to an f in I belongs entirely to I.

Definitions 1 to 3 immediately imply:

Theorem 5. *f_1 and f_2 are associates if and only if $f_1 | f_2$ and $f_2 | f_1$.*

By Theorems 2, 5 a divisibility relation $f | g$ is equivalent to any relation $f' | g'$, where f' is an associate of f, g' of g. Therefore, for the divisibility theory it is sufficient to consider only a representative from each class of associated elements; however, for general I it is not possible to distinguish one such representative by a universal principle (cf., however, Def. 7 [177]).

According to the preceding each g is divisible by all units and all elements associated to g. These divisors are called the *trivial divisors* of g. In order to exclude these conveniently, we formulate

Definition 4. *f is said to be a **proper divisor** of g if $f | g$ but f is neither a unit nor an associate of g.*

The fundamental theorem to be proved rests on the following definition:

Definition 5[2]. *p is called a **prime element** if it is neither zero nor a unit and has no proper divisors.*

Def. 5 does not say whether such prime elements exist. Furthermore, it cannot be decided without the addition of further assumptions regarding I. For instance, if I coincides with its quotient field, there are no prime elements.

B. Absolute Value in K[x] and Γ

In order to be able to prove the fundamental theorem (which is not universally valid in integral domains) of the unique decomposition into prime elements in K[x] and Γ, we must have

[2] Cf. also Def. 8 [178] to be added later.

recourse to special properties of these integral domains; namely, in Γ to the ordering of the integers by their *absolute value*, whose rules we here assume[3] as known, in K[x] to the ordering of the integral rational functions of x by their *degree*. The possibility of being able to continue handling both cases at the same time rests then on the fact that the ordering according to the degrees in K[x] can also be described by a more exact analogue to the absolute value in Γ than the degree itself. For this purpose we formulate:

Definition 6. *By the* ***absolute value*** $|f|$ *of an element* f *in* K[x] *we understand*

$$|f| = 0 \text{ if } f = 0,$$
$$|f| = k^n, \text{ if } f \text{ is of degree } n.$$

Here k *is an arbitrary integer* > 1 *fixed once it is chosen.*

k could also be taken as any real number > 1; here, however, we will avoid the real numbers for technical reasons.

The following rules for absolute values, valid in the case of Γ, are also valid in K[x]:

$$(1) \qquad |f| \geqq 1, \text{ if } f \neq 0,$$
$$(2) \qquad |f \pm g| \leqq |f| + |g|,$$
$$(3) \qquad |f \cdot g| = |f| \cdot |g|.$$

Proof: (1) is clear by Def. 6; similarly, (2) and (3) are also valid in the case $f = 0$ or $g = 0$. However, if $f \neq 0$, $g \neq 0$, namely,

$$f(x) \equiv a_0 + \cdots + a_n x^n \quad (a_n \neq 0), \quad |f| = k^n,$$
$$g(x) \equiv b_0 + \cdots + b_m x^m \quad (b_m \neq 0), \quad |g| = k^m,$$

[3] Namely, we assume as known: 1. the relation $<$ in Γ and its rules; 2. the connection existing between this relation and the arithmetical operations; 3. the definition of absolute value; 4. the connections based on 1. and 2. between the absolute value, on the one hand, and the ordering and arithmetical operations, on the other hand.

then $f \pm g$ contains no higher power of x than $x^{\text{Max}(n,m)}$. Therefore,

$$|f \pm g| \leqq k^{\text{Max}(n,m)} = \text{Max}\,(k^n, k^m) \leqq k^n + k^m = |f| + |g|.$$

Accordingly, even though the relation

$$(2\text{ a}) \qquad |f \pm g| \leqq \text{Max}\,(|f|, |g|)$$

is generally not correct in Γ, it is valid in $\mathsf{K}[x]$. Furthermore, we have

$$\begin{aligned} f(x)\,g(x) &\equiv \sum_{\nu=0}^{n} a_\nu x^\nu \cdot \sum_{\mu=0}^{m} b_\mu x^\mu \equiv \sum_{\nu=0}^{n} \sum_{\mu=0}^{m} a_\nu b_\mu x^{\nu+\mu} \\ &\equiv \sum_{i=0}^{n+m} \Big(\sum_{\nu+\mu=i} a_\nu b_\mu\Big) x^i \qquad \begin{pmatrix} \nu = 0, \ldots, n \\ \mu = 0, \ldots, m \end{pmatrix} \\ &\equiv a_0 b_0 + (a_0 b_1 + a_1 b_0)\,x + \cdots \\ &\quad + (a_{n-1} b_m + a_n b_{m-1})\,x^{n+m-1} + a_n b_m x^{n+m} \quad (a_n b_m \neq 0), \end{aligned}$$

therefore $\qquad |f \cdot g| = k^{n+m} = k^n \cdot k^m = |f| \cdot |g|.$

Besides (1) to (3) later on we will also have to apply repeatedly the following principle, whose validity is a consequence of the fact that by Def. 6 all absolute values are natural numbers or 0.

(4) *In any non-empty subset of* $\mathsf{K}[x]$ *or* Γ *there are elements of smallest possible absolute value.*

The absolute value in $\mathsf{K}[x]$ or Γ is now related to the concepts, explained under A, of the divisibility theory in these integral domains as follows:

Theorem 6. *If* $f \mid g$, $g \neq 0$, *then* $1 \leqq |f| \leqq |g|$.

Proof: If $g = f\bar{f}$, $g \neq 0$, then we also have $f \neq 0, \bar{f} \neq 0$; therefore, by (1) $|f| \geqq 1, |\bar{f}| \geqq 1$. Since by (3) we further have $|g| = |f| \cdot |\bar{f}|$ it follows that $1 \leqq |\bar{f}| = \dfrac{|g|}{|f|}$, that is, $|f| \leqq |g|$.

Theorem 7. *f is a unit if and only if* $|f| = 1$. *Hence in the case* $\mathsf{K}[x]$ *the elements* $a \neq 0$ of K *are the only units; in the case* Γ, *the integers* $a = \pm 1$.

Proof: a) By Theorem 6 $f \mid e$ implies $|f| = 1$ since $|e| = 1$.

b) That the f with $|f|=1$, that is, the a specified in the theorem, are units is clear by Def. 2 [173] (in the case $\mathsf{K}[x]$ because division is unrestricted in K).

By means of (3), Theorems 6, 7 yield

Theorem 8. *If f_1 and f_2 are associates, then $|f_1|=|f_2|$. If $|f_1|=|f_2|$ and $f_1 | f_2$, then f_1 and f_2 are associates.*

The extra assumption $f_1 | f_2$ for the converse is not necessary in the case Γ; however, in the case $\mathsf{K}[x]$ it is necessary.

From Theorems 6 to 8 we have

Theorem 9. *If $f | g$, $g \neq 0$, then f is a proper divisor of g if and only if $1 < |f| < |g|$.*

C. Formulation of the Fundamental Theorem

In the special integral domains $\mathsf{K}[x]$ and Γ we can pick out a special representative for a class of associates. It is characterized by the following convention:

Definition 7. *f is said to be **normalized** first, if $f \neq 0$ and secondly,*

a) *in the case $\mathsf{K}[x]$* if *the coefficient a_n of the highest power of x ocurring in $f(x) = a_0 + \cdots + a_n x^n$ $(a_n \neq 0)$ (briefly: the **leading coefficient** of $f(x)$) is equal to e.*

b) *in the case Γ* if $f > 0$.

It is appropriate to restrict the concept of *normality* by the condition $f \neq 0$ even though 0 is also a well defined (namely single) representative of a class of associated elements. Therefore, in the case $\mathsf{K}[x]$ *normalized* is the same as the designation *polynomial* cited in the introduction if we disregard the single normalized element of 0-th degree $f = e$ which we did not think appropriate to include in the concept *polynomial.* Incidentally, the terminology that we have adopted, whereby only the *normalized* elements in $\mathsf{K}[x]$ are called *polynomials,* is not generally used.

Theorem 7 immediately implies that Def. 7 actually accomplishes what we are after.

Theorem 10. *In every class of associates different from the zero class there exists one and only one normalized representative.*

Furthermore, for normalized elements we have

Theorem 11. *If f and g are normalized, so also is fg; further, if $g \mid f$, then $\frac{f}{g}$ is normalized.*

Proof: The theorem is obvious in the case Γ. In the case $K[x]$ the theorem follows by applying the multiplication formula previously applied in the proof of (3) [175] to fg and to $\frac{f}{g}g$.

For later use we formulate along with Def. 7:

Definition 8. *A normalized prime element is called in the case of $K[x]$ a **prime function** or **irreducible polynomial,** in the case Γ a **prime number.***

In Sections 1, 2 we will use, in addition, the common designation *normalized prime element* in order to be able to handle the cases $K[x]$ and Γ at the same time.

The **Fundamental Theorem** to be proved can now be stated as follows:

Theorem 12. *Every element $f \neq 0$ in $K[x]$ or Γ has a decomposition*

$$f = ap_1 \cdots p_r$$ [4]

into $r \geqq 0$ normalized prime elements $p_1, \cdots, p_r$ and a unit factor a. This decomposition is unique except for the order of the factors, that is, a and $p_1, \cdots, p_r$ are uniquely determined by f.

[4] We make the convention that a product $p_1 \ldots p_r$ with $r = 0$ shall mean the element e (cf. also the footnote to the Theorem of Toeplitz in Vol. 1, Section 12 [95].

This theorem does not state that $p_1, \ldots, p_r$ are different. The uniqueness statement, however, refers as well to the frequency of the occurrence of the different prime factors.

The proof, as the statement of the theorem, will be broken up into two parts. The first, the simpler of the two, will be given under D; the second, which is deeper-lying, under F. Before giving the latter, however, a number of theorems will be derived under E. These are not only necessary to prove the second part but are also very important for reasons over and above this purpose.

D. Possibility of the Decomposition into Normalized Prime Elements

First of all we prove the lemma

(D_1). *If f is not a unit, then f has at least one normalized prime divisor.*

Proof: In the case $f=0$ a normalized divisor of f different from units can be any normalized element $\neq e$; in the case $f \neq 0$, the normalized representative which is an associate of f. Consequently, by (4) [176] there is a normalized divisor p of f of lowest possible absolute value which is not a unit. This divisor p is a normalized prime divisor of f, for by construction it is normalized and not a unit. Furthermore, if p had a proper divisor, then its normalized representative would be a normalized divisor of f different from units (Theorem 2 [173]) of lower absolute value than p (Theorem 9 [177]), which contradicts the fact that p was chosen so as to have the minimal absolute value.

In particular (D_1) implies the *existence of prime elements.* For the special element $f = 0$ our proof in the case $K[x]$ shows that every polynomial of 1-st degree $a_0 + x$ is a normalized prime element; in the case Γ, that the number 2 is a prime number.

(D_1) now yields D, that is, the theorem:

(D_2) *Every* $f \neq 0$ *has a decomposition*

$$f = ap_1 \cdots p_r$$

into $r \geq 0$ *normalized prime elements* $p_1, \cdots, p_r$ *and a unit factor* a.

Proof: The statement is clear if f is a unit ($r = 0$). If f is not a unit, then by (D_1) we can set

$$f = p_1 f_1$$

with a normalized prime element p_1. If f_1 is a unit, then this is a decomposition as stated ($r = 1$). If f_1 is not a unit, then by (D_1) we can set

$$f_1 = p_2 f_2, \text{ therefore } f = p_1 p_2 f_2$$

with a normalized prime element p_2. After finitely many steps we must encounter a unit f_r by this process. For, since $f \neq 0$ by Theorem 9 [ ] it must be true, as long as f_i is not a unit, that

$$|f| > |f_1| > \cdots > |f_i| > 1,$$

which is incompatible with an infinite sequence of such f_i, since all of the $|f_i|$ are whole numbers. If f_r is the first unit, then

$$f = ap_1 \cdots p_r$$

is valid, where $p_1, \cdots, p_r$ are normalized prime elements and $a (= f_r)$ is a unit.

This proves (D_2) and therefore D.

E. Division with Remainder. Greatest Common Divisor

Theorem 13. *If* $f \neq 0$ *and* g *is arbitrary, then there exist uniquely determined elements* $\bar{f}$ *and* h *such that*

$$g = f\bar{f} + h \text{ and } \begin{cases} |h| < |f| & \text{in the case } \mathsf{K}[x], \\ |h| < |f| \text{ and } h \geq 0, & \text{that is,} \\ & 0 \leq h < |f| \text{ in the case } \Gamma \end{cases}$$

is valid.

Proof: a) By (4) [176] an $\bar{f}$ can be chosen so that $h = g - f\bar{f}$ has the smallest possible absolute value among all $g - ff^*$. Let us assume that $|h| \geqq |f|$. Then

1) in the case $K[x]$, if l, n are the degrees and c_l, a_n the leading coefficients of h, f we would have $l \geqq n$, therefore

$$f_1(x) = \frac{c_l}{a_n} x^{l-n}$$

would be an element in $K[x]$. Hence ff_1 would have the same degree l and leading coefficient c_l as h. This means that

$$h - ff_1 = g - f\bar{f} - ff_1 = g - f(\bar{f} + f_1)$$

would have a lower degree than h, therefore a smaller absolute value.

2) In the case Γ, from

$$h \mp f = g - f\bar{f} \mp f = g - f(\bar{f} \pm 1)$$

one of the two signs would give an element whose absolute value is smaller than h.

But the existence of one such $f^* = \bar{f} + f_1$ or $= \bar{f} \pm 1$ contradicts in both cases the fact that $h = g - f\bar{f}$ was chosen so as to have the minimal absolute value. Therefore $|h| < |f|$.

In the case Γ besides the condition $|h| < |f|$ which has just been established we also wish to show that $h \geqq 0$. For this purpose, if we let $h < 0$ so that $-|f| < h < 0$, then we only have to form

$$h_1 = h + |f| = h \pm f = g - f(\bar{f} \mp 1),$$

for which $0 < h_1 < |f|$ is valid.

b) From $g = f\bar{f} + h$, $g = f\bar{f}' + h'$, where h and h' satisfy the conditions of the theorem, it follows that

$$f(\bar{f} - \bar{f}') = h' - h, \text{ therefore, } f \mid h' - h.$$

Now, if $h' \neq h$ were true, then by Theorem 6 $|f| \leqq |h' - h|$

would follow. According to the conditions of the theorem for h, h' this inequality would yield

1) in the case $\mathsf{K}[x]$ by (2 a) [176]:

$$|f| \leqq \text{Max}\,(|h|, |h'|) < |f|,$$

2) in the case Γ:

$$|f| \leqq (h' - h \text{ or } h - h') < |f| - 0 = |f|,$$

a contradiction in both cases. Consequently, $h = h'$; therefore, since $f \neq 0$, $\bar{f} = \bar{f}'$. This completes the proof of Theorem 13.

Since 0 satisfies the conditions of Theorem 13 regarding h, the possibility and uniqueness of the relation appearing there yields in addition:

Corollary. *If $f \neq 0$ and g is arbitrary, then $f \mid g$ if and only if the h in Theorem* 13 *is equal to* 0.

The process based on Theorem 13 for determining $\bar{f}$ and h from $f \neq 0$ and g is called the *division of g by f with remainder*, $\bar{f}$ the quotient and h the remainder. In order to carry out the division with remainder from a practical standpoint we assume as known (1) in the case Γ the process based on the decimal numeration (or any other number system) of integers; (2) in the case $\mathsf{K}[x]$ the process based in a corresponding manner on the normal representation (Vol. 1, Def. 9 [45]) which follows by direct application of the indirect proof under a), 1). In particular, these processes make possible the practical determination by the Corollary whether a divisibility relation $f \mid g$ exists.

By the repeated application of a similar inference we deduce from Theorem 13:

Theorem 14. *If f_1 and f_2 are not both* 0, *then there exists a uniquely determined normalized d such that*

(1) $d \mid f_1, d \mid f_2$,

(2) *from $h \mid f_1, h \mid f_2$ follows $h \mid d$*

is valid. d can be represented in the form

$$d = f_1 \bar{f}_1 + f_2 \bar{f}_2.$$

In view of the properties (1), (2) d *is called the* ***greatest common divisor*** *of* f_1 *and* f_2 *(notation* $d = (f_1, f_2)$*).*

Proof: Let $\overline{f}_1, \overline{f}_2$ be so chosen that $d = f_1\overline{f}_1 + f_2\overline{f}_2$ is normalized and has the smallest possible absolute value among all normalized elements of the form $f_1\overline{f}_1^* + f_2\overline{f}_2^*$. This is possible by (4) [176] ; for, if we say that $f_1 \neq 0$, then the normalized representative $a_1 f_1$ to f_1 is a normalized element of the prescribed form ($\overline{f}_1^* = a_1$, $\overline{f}_2^* = 0$); therefore, the set of absolute values in question is not empty. It is clear that (2) is satisfied for the d thereby determined (Theorem 3) [173]. Furthermore, if (1) were not satisfied and, let us say, $d \nmid f_1$, then there would exist, since d as a normalized element is $\neq 0$, an $h = f_1 - d\overline{d}$ with $|h| < |d|$ (Theorem 13) for which $h \neq 0$ would be valid (Corollary). Hence, if h is normalized by the factor a, then

$$ah = af_1 - ad\overline{d} = f_1(a - a\,\overline{d}\,\overline{f}_1) + f_2(-a\,\overline{d}\,\overline{f}_2)$$

would be a normalized element of the form $f_1\overline{f}_1^* + f_2\overline{f}_2^*$ of smaller absolute value than d. This contradicts the fact that $d = f_1\overline{f}_1 + f_2\overline{f}_2$ was chosen so as to have a minimal absolute value. Therefore $d \mid f_1$ and similarly $d \mid f_2$.

b) If the normalized d' also satisfies the conditions (1) and (2), then it follows from (1) for d' and from (2) for d (with d' as h) that $d' \mid d$. Similarly, it follows conversely that $d \mid d'$. This implies $d = d'$ (Theorems 5, 10 [174, 178]).

The following process for the practical determination of the greatest common divisor is obtained by the repeated application of the process mentioned above for the division with remainder. It is known under the name of *Euclidean Algorithm.*

Let us suppose that $f_2 \neq 0$. Then the following divisions with remainder can be performed until a remainder $f_{r+1} = 0$ is met:

$$f_1 = f_2 g_1 + f_3, \qquad |f_3| < |f_2|$$
$$f_2 = f_3 g_2 + f_4, \qquad |f_4| < |f_3|$$
$$\cdots\cdots\cdots\cdots\cdots\cdots\cdots\cdots\cdots\cdots\cdots\cdots$$
$$f_{r-2} = f_{r-1} g_{r-2} + f_r, \qquad |f_r| < |f_{r-1}|$$
$$f_{r-1} = f_r g_{r-1} + f_{r+1}, \qquad 0 = |f_{r+1}| < |f_r|.$$

Since the absolute values $|f_i|$ continually decrease, we must obtain after finitely many steps $f_{r+1} = 0$. Then the normalized representative of f_r is the greatest common divisor of f_1, f_2. For, by reversing these steps starting from the last relation it follows by Theorem 3 [ ] that we successively have $f_r \mid f_{r-1}$, $f_r \mid f_{r-2}, \ldots,$ $f_r \mid f_2$, $f_r \mid f_1$, therefore (1) is valid; and by reversing these steps starting from the next to the last relation, that f_r can be represented by the pairs $f_{r-2}, f_{r-1}; \ldots; f_1, f_2$ in the form of the theorem, therefore (2) is valid.

In addition we note the validity of the special relations

$$(0, f) = f, \quad (f, f) = f \qquad \text{for normalized } f,$$
$$(a, f) = e \qquad \text{for any } f.$$

By elementary inferences we can now deduce the following facts from the basic Theorem 14. These will lead stepwise to the uniqueness proof that we are seeking.

Theorem 15. *If g is normalized, then $(f_1, f_2)g = (f_1 g, f_2 g)$.*

Proof: If $(f_1, f_2) = d$, $(f_1 g, f_2 g) = d'$, then, on the one hand, $dg \mid f_1 g$, $dg \mid f_2 g$ (Theorem 14, (1) for d; Theorem 2 [ ]), therefore $dg \mid d'$ (Theorem 14, (2) for d'); on the other hand, $\frac{d'}{g} \Big| f_1$, $\frac{d'}{g} \Big| f_2$ (Theorem 14, (1) for d'; Theorem 2), therefore $\frac{d'}{g} \Big| d$ (Theorem 14, (2) for d), that is, $d' \mid dg$ (Theorem 2). This implies $d' = dg$ (Theorems 5, 10 [174, 178]).

Definition 9. *f_1 and f_2 are said to be* ***relatively prime*** *or* ***prime to each other*** *if $(f_1, f_2) = e$.*

According to this, in particular, 0 is relatively prime to all and only the units; a unit is relatively prime to all f. Furthermore, if $(f_1, f_2) = d$ and we set $f_1 = dg_1$, $f_2 = dg_2$, then g_1 and g_2 are relatively prime (Theorem 15).

Theorem 16. *If f and g_1 are relatively prime and $f \mid g_1 g_2$, then $f \mid g_2$.*

Proof: The theorem is obvious if $g_2 = 0$. If $g_2 \neq 0$ and $\bar{g}_2$ is the normalized representative to g_2. then by Theorem 15 it follows from $(f, g_1) = e$ that $(f\bar{g}_2, g_1\bar{g}_2) = \bar{g}_2$; therefore by Theorem 14, (2) and the assumption we have $f \mid \bar{g}_2$, that is, $f \mid g_2$ is also valid.

Theorem 17. *If p is a prime element, then $(p, g) = e$ is equivalent to $p \nmid g$, that is, p is prime to g if and only if p is not a divisor of g.*

Proof: If $\bar{p}$ is the normalized representative to p, then (p, g) can only be e or $\bar{p}$ (Def 4, 5 [174]), since it is a normalized divisor of p. Now, on the one hand, if $p \nmid g$, then $(p, g) = \bar{p}$ cannot be valid, since otherwise by Theorem 14, (1) $\bar{p} \mid g$, and therefore $p \mid g$, would follow; consequently, $(p, g) = e$. On the other hand, if $(p, g) = e$, then $p \mid g$ cannot be valid, since otherwise by Theorem 14, (2) we would have $p \mid e$, contrary to Def. 5; therefore $p \nmid g$.

Theorem 18. *If p is a prime element and $p \mid g_1 g_2$, then $p \mid g_1$ or $p \mid g_2$.*

Proof: If $p \nmid g_1$, then p is prime to g_1 (Theorem 17), therefore, on account of the hypothesis, $p \mid g_2$ (Theorem 16).

Theorem 19. *If p is a prime element and $p \mid g_1 \cdots g_r$, then $p \mid g_1$ or ... or $p \mid g_r$.*

Proof: It follows by repeated application of Theorem 18.

The uniqueness proof, which is now to be given, rests on the last theorem.

F. Uniqueness of the Decomposition into Normalized Prime Elements

Let
$$f = ap_1 \cdots p_r = bq_1 \cdots q_s$$
be two decompositions of an $f \neq 0$ into $r \geqq 0$ and $s \geqq 0$ normalized prime elements $p_1, \cdots, p_r$ and $q_1, \cdots, q_s$, respectively, with a and b unit factors. On dividing by b it then follows by Theorem 11 [2] that $\frac{a}{b}$ is normalized, therefore $= e$, that is, $a = b$. Therefore
$$p_1 \cdots p_r = q_1 \cdots q_s.$$
If $r = 0$, so also is $s = 0$; for otherwise $q_1 \mid e$, contrary to Def. 5 [174]. In such a case both decompositions $f = a$, $f = b$ coincide.

If $r > 0$, so also is $s > 0$ by the same inference. In this case $p_1 \mid q_1 \cdots q_s$, therefore by Theorem 19 $p_1 \mid q_1$ or ... or $p_1 \mid q_s$. Now, the q_i have no proper divisors; consequently, as p_1 is not a unit it must be an associate of one of the q_i, therefore equal to it (Theorem 10 [178]). The ordering can be so taken that $p_1 = q_1$. It then follows that
$$p_2 \cdots p_r = q_2 \cdots q_s.$$
If $r = 1$, then, as above, so also is $s = 1$. In this case, therefore, both decompositions $f = ap_1$, $f = bq_1$ coincide.

If $r > 1$, so also is $s > 1$. By continuing the above line of reasoning and ordering the q_i in a suitable manner we successively obtain
$$p_2 = q_2, \ldots, p_r = q_s \text{ and } r = s.$$
The latter statement is valid since by the above line of reasoning the p_i must be exhausted by the same number of steps as the q_i. Hence both decompositions coincide except for the ordering of the factors.

By D and F the fundamental theorem is now proved.

G. Consequences of the Fundamental Theorem

By having recourse to the decomposition into prime elements the concept of divisibility introduced under A and F can be looked upon from a new viewpoint. Namely, the following facts are valid: [5]

Theorem 20. *If* $g \neq 0$, *then* $f \mid g$ *if and only if the normalized prime factors of* f *occur among those of* g [6] (*Def.* 1 [172], *Theorem* 12 [178]).

The inferences, immediately following from this, in regard to the concepts *unit* and *associate* need not be cited in detail.

Theorem 21. *If* f_1 *and* f_2 *are different from* 0, *their greatest common divisor is the product of the normalized prime factors that* f_1 *and* f_2 *have in common* (Theorems 12, 14, 20).

Theorem 22. f_1 *and* f_2, *different from* 0, *are relatively prime if and only if they have no common prime factor.* (*Def.* 9 [184], Theorem 21).

Theorem 22 immediately implies the following generalization of Theorem 18 [185] in the direction of Theorem 16 [185] :

Theorem 23. *If* f *is prime to* g_1 *and* g_2, *then it is also prime to* $g_1 g_2$.

H. Dependence on the Ground Field

It is important for us to establish how the concepts and facts developed in the preceding for the case $\mathsf{K}[x]$ are affected if our investigations are based on the integral domain $\overline{\mathsf{K}}[x]$ over an

---

[5] Cf. the footnote before Theorem 1 [172]. The previous theorems and definitions which substantiate our arguments are inserted in parenthesis.

[6] This statement and the following are aimed at the frequency of the occurrence of the different prime factors.

extension field $\overline{\mathsf{K}}$ of K instead of $\mathsf{K}[x]$. In this regard the following is valid:

Theorem 24. *If the elements belonging to* $\mathsf{K}[x]$ *are regarded as elements of the integral domain* $\overline{\mathsf{K}}[x]$ *over an extension field* $\overline{\mathsf{K}}$ *of* K, *then the relations* "$f \mid g$, $f \nmid g$, *h is the remainder on dividing g by f*, $(f_1 f_2) = d$" *are preserved; on the contrary, the relation "p is prime function" is not necessarily preserved.*

Proof: a) The determination of h from f and g, and the determination of d from f_1 and f_2 can be performed, according to the expositions after Theorem 13 [180] and Theorem 14 [182], by calculating processes which consist in the application of the four elementary operations on the coefficients of these elements, where the coefficients belong to K. The interpretation of these coefficients as elements of $\overline{\mathsf{K}}$ does not change any of these processes, therefore neither are the results h and d changed. Consequently, the alternative $h = 0$, $h \neq 0$, too, is preserved. By Theorem 13, Corollary [182] this yields the invariance of the alternative $f \mid g$, $f \nmid g$ in the case $f \neq 0$. For $f = 0$ this invariance is trivial by Theorem 1 [173].

b) The example specified in the introduction already shows that the prime function $x^2 - 2$ in $\mathsf{P}[x]$ [7] acquires the decomposition $(x - \sqrt{2})(x + \sqrt{2})$ into proper divisors on extending P to the field $\overline{\mathsf{P}}$ of real numbers.

b) implies, just as in the introduction under 1), that on principle no rational arithmetical processes can exist for deciding whether a specific element in $\mathsf{K}[x]$ is a prime function, nor is there such a process for obtaining the prime factor decomposition of a specific f

[7] That $x^2 - 2$ is a prime function in $\mathsf{P}[x]$ amounts to the *irrationality* of $\sqrt{2}$, which can be easily deduced from Theorem 12 [178] for the case Γ.

in $\mathsf{K}[x]$. Rather, we are dependent on a *trial and error process* for this purpose in each concrete case.

If we have to consider, as frequently in the following, extension fields $\overline{\mathsf{K}}$ of K besides the ground field K, we must state when using the designations *prime function, irreducible* (Def. 8 [178]) whether they are used relative to $\mathsf{K}[x]$ or $\overline{\mathsf{K}}[x]$. We do this through the addition of the phrase *in* K or *in* $\overline{\mathsf{K}}$, respectively (cf. the first footnote in the introduction [167]).

The fundamental theorem (applied in $\overline{\mathsf{K}}[x]$) immediately yields in addition the following theorem to be used many times in the sequel;

Theorem 25. *If* $\overline{\mathsf{K}}$ *is an extension field of* K, *then the prime factor decomposition in* $\overline{\mathsf{K}}[x]$ *of an* f *belonging to* $\mathsf{K}[x]$ *is generated from the prime factor decomposition in* $\mathsf{K}[x]$ *by decomposing the prime factors of* f *in* $\mathsf{K}[x]$ *into their prime factors in* $\overline{\mathsf{K}}[x]$.

2. Residue Class Rings in $\mathsf{K}[x]$ and Γ

In Vol. 1, Section 2 we introduced the general concept of congruence relation in a domain. The results of Section 1 enable us to survey all possible congruence relations in the integral domains $\mathsf{K}[x]$ and Γ in a sense corresponding exactly to what was done in Vol. 1, Theorem 34, 35 [75, 75] for the congruence relations in groups. We obtain this survey from the following theorem:

Theorem 26. *To a congruence relation* $\equiv$ *in* $\mathsf{K}[x]$ *or* Γ *there exists an element* f, *uniquely determined except for associates, such that*

(1) $h_1 \equiv h_2$ *if and only if* $f \mid h_1 - h_2$.

Conversely, for every f a congruence relation in $\mathsf{K}[x]$ or Γ is generated by (1).

Proof: a) According to (1) every congruence relation $\equiv$ arises from an f. Let M be the set of all elements $g \equiv 0$. By Vol. 1, Section 2, (α), (β), (γ), (1), (2) we have that $h_1 \equiv h_2$ is then equivalent to $h_1 - h_2 \equiv 0$, that is, equivalent to saying that $h_1 - h_2$ is contained in M. Now, either M consists only of the element 0. In this case $h_1 \equiv h_2$ is equivalent to $h_1 = h_2$ that is, our congruence relation is equivalent to equality, and the statement of the theorem is correct for $f = 0$ (Theorem 1 [173]). Or, instead, M contains elements different from 0. In this case among the elements of M different from zero there is by Section 1, (4) [176] an f of smallest possible absolute value. Now, if g is any element in M and by Theorem 13 [180] we set

$$g = f\bar{f} + h, \, |h| < |f|,$$

then $h = g - f\bar{f}$ also belongs to M, since by the definition of the congruence relation in Vol. 1, Section 2 we have that $f \equiv 0$ implies $f\bar{f} \equiv 0$ and consequently $g \equiv 0$ implies $h = g - f\bar{f} \equiv 0$. Therefore, since f was chosen so as to have the minimal absolute value, we must have $h = 0$, that is, $f \mid g$. Conversely, since $f \equiv 0$ implies for every multiple $g = f\bar{f}$ of f that $g \equiv 0$, M consists of all and only the multiples of f; namely, $g \equiv 0$ is equivalent to $f \mid g$ and therefore, by the statements already made, $h_1 \equiv h_2$ is equivalent to $f \mid h_1 - h_2$.

b) For any fixed f the relation (1) is a congruence relation. That the conditions Vol. 1, Section 2, (α), (β), (γ) [22] are satisfied can be seen as follows: first, $f \mid 0$ (Theorem 1 [173]); secondly, $f \mid h_1 - h_2$ implies $f \mid h_2 - h_1$ (Theorem 3 [173]); and thirdly, $f \mid h_1 - h_2$, $f \mid h_2 - h_3$ implies $f \mid h_1 - h_3$ (Theorem 3). The conditions Vol. 1. Section 2, (1), (2) [27] are satisfied;

for, from $f \mid h_1 - h_2$, $f \mid g_1 - g_2$ we first have $f \mid (h_1 + g_1) - (h_2 + g_2)$ (Theorem 3), and secondly $f \mid h_1 g_1 - h_2 g_1$, $f \mid h_2 g_1 - h_2 g_2$ (Theorem 3), so that as above $f \mid h_1 g_1 - h_2 g_2$.

c) f is determined uniquely by the congruence relation except for associated elements (naturally, anyone of these can be chosen without changing the congruence relation (1)). Namely, let the congruence relation $h_1 \equiv h_2$ be equivalent to $f \mid h_1 - h_2$ as well as to $\bar{f} \mid h_1 - h_2$. Then $f \mid f - 0, \bar{f} \mid \bar{f} - 0$ implies $f \equiv 0$, $\bar{f} \equiv 0$. As a consequence of the above assumption this also means that $f \mid \bar{f} - 0, \bar{f} \mid f - 0$, in other words, f and $\bar{f}$ are associates (Theorem 5 [174]).

On the basis of Theorem 26 we define:

Definition 10. *The element f belonging to a congruence relation $\equiv$ in $K[x]$ or Γ according to Theorem 26, and uniquely determined except for associates, is called the* ***modulus*** *of this congruence relation. We then write in full*

$$h_1 \equiv h_2 \bmod f^{8} \text{ for } h_1 \equiv h_2, \text{ that is, for } f \mid h_1 - h_2,$$

and the classes thereby determined are called the ***residue classes mod f;*** *the ring*[9] *formed by these classes, the* ***residue class ring mod f.***

If $f \neq 0$, we assume that f is *normalized* for the sake of uniqueness. — In the case $K[x]$ we designate the residue class ring mod f

[8] Incidentally, in the case $K[x]$ the addition of "mod $f(x)$" prevents the confusion with equality in $K[x]$ which may arise when the elements are written in terms of the argument x (Vol. 1, by Theorem 12 [47]).

[9] Here we speak of a *ring* in somewhat more general terms than in Vol. 1, Theorem 8 [28] , since we are also including the case excluded there. In other words, here all elements of a ring may be congruent to one another. In such a case f would be a unit, since $e \equiv 0 \bmod f$. Consequently, the set would contain only a single element, therefore it would no longer satisfy the postulate stated in Vol. 1, Section 1, (a) [13].

by $K[x, \bmod f(x)]$; in the case Γ, by Γ_f. Furthermore, we will write on occasion $\{h\}$ for the residue class determined by the element h relative to the modulus considered at the time.

Even though the calculations with residue classes (Vol. 1, Theorem 8 [28] generating the residue class ring are independent of the particular representatives that are used, it is still important for our later applications as well as for obtaining a comprehensive view of the residue classes to have a complete system of representatives (Vol. 1, Section 2, [23]) for the residue classes mod f which is as simple as possible. Such a system is specified in the following theorem:

Theorem 27. *If $f=0$, then every element of $K[x]$ or Γ forms by itself a residue class. If $f \neq 0$, a complete system of representatives of the residue classes mod f is formed by the elements h with the property*

$$|h| < |f| \text{ in the case } K[x],$$
$$0 \leqq h < f \text{ in the case } \Gamma.$$

Proof: a) For $f=0$, $h_1 \equiv h_2 \bmod 0$ is equivalent to $0 \mid h_1 - h_2$, that is, to $h_1 = h_2$.

b) For $f \neq 0$ the existence statement of Theorem 13 [180] implies that every element is congruent to one of the specified elements mod f; and the uniqueness statement, that it is congruent to only one such element. Hence the specified elements represent all residue classes mod f, each once.

The complete system of representatives mod f for $f \neq 0$ can be described in more explicit form as follows:

In the case $K[x]$: $c_0 + c_1 x + \cdots + c_{n-1} x^{n-1}$, if f is of degree $n > 0$, where $c_0, c_1, \ldots, c_{n-1}$ run through all systems of n elements in K; 0, if f is of degree 0 ($f = e$);

In the case Γ: $0, 1, \ldots, f-1$; here, therefore, the number of residue classes mod f is *finite*, namely f.

The facts of Theorem 27 motivate the designation *residue classes* in so far as these are formed by all elements which have one and the same *remainder* with respect to division by f.[10]

Especially important for us is the condition for what f the residue class ring mod f is an integral domain or even a field. The following theorem gives information in this regard:

Theorem 28. *The residue class ring mod f is an integral domain if and only if $f=0$ or f is a prime element. If f is a prime element, it is actually a field.*

Proof: a) If $f=0$, then by Theorem 27 the residue class ring coincides with the integral domain $K[x]$ or Γ. Next, let $f=p$ be a prime element. In this case if $g_1g_2 \equiv 0 \bmod p$, that is, $p \mid g_1g_2$, then by Theorem 18 [185] we have $p \mid g_1$ or $p \mid g_2$, that is, $g_1 \equiv 0 \bmod p$ or $g_2 \equiv 0 \bmod p$. Therefore, if the product of two residue classes $\{g_1\}\{g_2\}=0$, at least one of the factors $\{g_1\}$ or $\{g_2\}=0$, that is, the analogue to Vol. 1, Theorem 4 [18] is valid in the residue class ring mod p. It is clear that the analogue to Vol. 1, Theorem 3 [17] is also valid, since $\{e\}$ is the unity element of the residue class ring. Hence this is first of all an integral domain. Furthermore, it is actually a field. For, if $g \not\equiv 0 \bmod p$, that is, $p \nmid g$, so that p is prime to g (Theorem 17 [185]), then by Theorem 14 [182] we have $p\bar{h}^* + g\bar{g}^* = e$, therefore, in the case of the given h we also have $p\bar{h} + g\bar{g} = h$. The latter relation says, however, that $g\bar{g} \equiv h \bmod p$, namely, that $\{g\}\{\bar{g}\} = \{h\}$ or $\{\bar{g}\} = \frac{\{h\}}{\{g\}}$. This means that the division by residue classes mod p different from zero can be carried out

[10] Besides the special integral domains $K[x]$ and Γ, the residue classes relative to congruence relations in general integral domains can also be similarly related to division (cf. Vol. 1, footnote to Def. 6 [27]), whereby the general designation *residue classes* is justified.

without restriction [Vol. 1, Section 1, (7) [16]]. Hence the proposed residue class ring is a field.

b) Let $f \neq 0$ and not a prime element. Then, either f is a unit or there exists a decomposition $f = g_1 g_2$ into proper divisors g_1, g_2. In the first case there is only one residue class so that it cannot be an integral domain [Vol. 1, Section 1, (a) [13]]. In the second case the relation $g_1 g_2 \equiv 0 \bmod f$, that is, $\{g_1\}\{g_2\} = 0$ says that the product of two residue classes mod f different from 0 is equal to 0, so that the given residue class ring is again not an integral domain.

In the following we designate the residue class field relative to a prime function $p(x)$ by $\mathsf{K}(x, \bmod p(x))$; the residue class field relative to a prime number p, by P_p.[11]

By Theorem 27 the residue class field P_p is a *finite field* [12] of p elements. In regard to this field we prove the following additional theorem, which is to be applied later:

Theorem 29. *For every a in P_p we have $a^p = a$; for every $a \neq 0$, therefore, $a^{p-1} = e$.*

Proof: This is obvious for $a = 0$. Let $a \neq 0$ and $0, a_1, \ldots a_{p-1}$ be the p different elements of P_p. Due to the uniqueness of the division by a in P_p the p elements $a0 = 0, aa_1, \ldots, aa_{p-1}$ are then different from one another, therefore they must again be the totality of elements of P_p in some order, so that $aa_1, \ldots, aa_{p-1}$ are identical with $a_1, \ldots, a_{p-1}$ except for the ordering. This means on forming products that

$$a^{p-1} a_1 \ldots a_{p-1} = a_1 \ldots a_{p-1}.$$

However, since $a_1 \ldots a_{p-1} \neq 0$, we obtain $a^{p-1} = e$, $a^p = a$ as stated.

[11] The new designations are dispensable in view of the conventions in Def. 10 [191] . They are chosen so as to be more in harmony with the nomenclature adopted in Vol. 1, Def. 9 [45] , 10 [46] , Theorem 5 [19].

[12] For $p = 2$, P_2 is the field specified in Vol. 1, Section 1, Example 4 [20] and quoted as an example at various places in Vol. 1.

Theorem 28 says that division is unrestricted and unique in the *full* residue class ring mod f if and only if f is a prime element. However, in any residue class ring a *sub*set can always be found in which division is so characterized. The following theorem and the adjoined definition lead to this subset.

Theorem 30. *All elements of a residue class mod f have one and the same greatest common divisor with f; consequently, it is called the divisor of this residue class.*

Proof: If $g_1 \equiv g_2 \bmod f$, that is, $g_1 - g_2 = f\bar{f}$, then by Theorems 3 [173], 14 [182] we have $(g_1, f) \mid (g_2, f)$ and $(g_2, f) \mid (g_1, f)$, therefore $(g_1, f) = (g_2, f)$.

Definition 11. *The residue classes mod f of the divisor e are called the* ***prime residue classes mod f.***

Hence these represent the partition into residue classes mod f within the set of all elements prime to f (Def. 9 [184]).

The above statement is confirmed by the following theorem:

Theorem 31. *The prime residue classes mod f form an Abelian group $\mathfrak{P}_f$ with respect to multiplication.*[13]

Proof: Since $\mathfrak{P}_f$ is a subset of the residue class ring mod f, it is sufficient to show that $\mathfrak{P}_f$ is closed with respect to multiplication and that division in $\mathfrak{P}_f$ is unique and likewise without restriction. The former immediately follows from Theorem 23 [187] ; the latter, by inferences corresponding exactly to those in the proof of Theorem 28 under a) by using Theorem 16 [185] instead of Theorem 18 [185] .

Theorem 31 is significant above all in the case Γ. The group $\mathfrak{P}_f$ is then *finite*; its order is designated by $\varphi(f)$ (*Euler's function*). We have $\varphi(0) = 2$;[14] furthermore, by Theorems 17 [185] , 27 [192] we

[13] For $f = 0$, cf., by the way, Theorem 4 [173] .

[14] Cf. footnote 13 [195] as well as Theorem 7 [176] .

have $\varphi(p) = p - 1$ for prime numbers p. The general formula that can be proved without difficulty by means of the theorems of Section 1, E is

$$\varphi(f) = f \prod_{p|f} \left(1 - \frac{1}{p}\right), \quad (f > 0),$$

where p runs through the different prime numbers dividing f without a remainder. However, this formula will not be needed in the following. Likewise, we will not need the generalization of Theorem 29, which can be proved in an entirely corresponding manner,

$$a^{\varphi(f)} \equiv 1 \bmod f$$

for every a in Γ prime to f, the so-called *Fermat Theorem.*[15] We quote these facts here only in order to round out our developments relative to Γ, which form an important chapter of the *elementary theory of numbers.*

3. Cyclic Groups

In this section we will make an application to the theory of groups of the results of Sections 1, 2 relative to the case Γ. This application is important for later developments.

Definition 12. *A group $\mathfrak{Z}$ is said to be* **cyclic** *if it consists of the integral powers of one of its elements A. In this case $\mathfrak{Z}$ is also said to be* **generated by** *A and A a* **primitive element** *of $\mathfrak{Z}$.*

For the integral powers of A we have by definition (Vol. 1 [60] the calculating rules

(1) $$A^m A^n = A^{m+n}, \quad (A^m)^n = A^{mn}.$$

This implies first of all (Vol. 1, Def. 13 [58]):

Theorem 32. *Every cyclic group is Abelian.*

From (1) we further infer the following basic theorem about cyclic groups.

---

[15] *Fermat* himself stated it (Theorem 29) only for $f = p$; it was first given in this general form by *Euler.*

Theorem 33. *Let $\mathfrak{Z}$ be a cyclic group generated by A. Then there exists a uniquely determined integer $f \geqq 0$ such that the correspondence*

(2) $$A^m \longleftrightarrow \{m\}$$

maps $\mathfrak{Z}$ isomorphically onto the additive group $\mathfrak{R}_f$ of the residue classes mod f.[16]

Proof: a) The convention

(3) $m_1 \equiv m_2$ if and only if $A^{m_1} = A^{m_2}$, defines a congruence relation in Γ.

For, Vol. 1, Section 2 (α), (β), (γ) [22] are satisfied, since equality in $\mathfrak{Z}$ satisfies these laws. Furthermore, Vol. 1, Section 2, (1), (2) [27] are also valid; namely, if $m_1 \equiv m_2$, $n_1 \equiv n_2$, therefore $A^{m_1} = A^{m_2}$, $A^{n_1} = A^{n_2}$, then by (1) it follows that

$$A^{m_1+n_1} = A^{m_1} A^{n_1} = A^{m_2} A^{n_2} = A^{m_2+n_2}$$
$$A^{m_1 n_1} = (A^{m_1})^{n_1} = (A^{m_2})^{n_1} = (A^{n_1})^{m_2} = (A^{n_2})^{m_2} = A^{m_2 n_2},$$

therefore $m_1 + n_1 \equiv m_2 + n_2$, $m_1 n_1 \equiv m_2 n_2$.

If f is the modulus of the congruence relation (3), then

(4) $A^{m_1} = A^{m_2}$ if and only if $m_1 \equiv m_2 \bmod f$

is also valid. By (4) the correspondence (2) between $\mathfrak{Z}$ and $\mathfrak{R}_f$ is biunique. Furthermore, it is also an isomorphism, since by (1) the multiplication of the powers A^m corresponds to the addition of the exponents m, therefore also to that of their residue classes $\{m\}$. Consequently, $\mathfrak{Z} \cong \mathfrak{R}_f$ in virtue of (2).

b) The $\mathfrak{R}_f$ belonging to different $f \geqq 0$ are characterized by the number of their elements (Theorem 27 [192]), therefore are not isomorphic. Consequently, f is uniquely determined by $\mathfrak{Z}$.

By Theorem 33 the possible types of cyclic groups correspond biuniquely to the non-negative integers $f = 0, 1, 2, \ldots,$ and all these types actually exist, since they are represented, as we have seen, by the $\mathfrak{R}_f$. If $\mathfrak{Z}$ is a cyclic group generated by A of the type

[16] Cf. Vol. 1, Section 6, Example 1 [61]

$\mathfrak{R}_f$, then by Theorem 27 [192] the different elements of $\mathfrak{Z}$ are given

a) if $f = 0$, by the totality of integral powers

$$\ldots, A^{-2}, A^{-1}, A^0 = E, A^1, A^2, \ldots;$$

in this case the order of $\mathfrak{Z}$ is infinite;

b) if $f > 0$, let us say, by the f powers $A^0 = E, A^1, \ldots, A^{f-1}$; for if this system of f elements is continued in both directions it successively repeats itself in the same order.[17] This means that in this case $\mathfrak{Z}$ is finite of order f.

In order to determine all subgroups of a cyclic group we first observe the following fact, which is immediately clear from Vol. 1, Theorems 19, 25 [63, 68].

Theorem 34. *If A is an element of a group $\mathfrak{G}$, then the integral powers of A form a cyclic subgroup $\mathfrak{A}$ of $\mathfrak{G}$,* ***the period of A,*** *whose order is also called the* ***order of A.*** *If $\mathfrak{G}$ is finite of order n, then A is also of finite order m and $m \mid n$.*

In case A has finite order m then by Theorem 33 m can also be characterized as equivalent to

$$A^k = E \text{ with } k \equiv 0 \bmod m, \text{ that is, with } m \mid k;$$

or also as the *smallest of the positive exponents k for which $A^k = E$.* For later use we prove in addition:

Theorem 35. If A_1, A_2 *are commutative elements in $\mathfrak{G}$ of finite orders m_1, m_2* and $(m_1, m_2) = 1$, *then A_1A_2 has the order m_1m_2.*

Proof: If $(A_1A_2)^k = E$, then on raising this to the m_2-th and m_1-th powers, respectively, it follows in view of the assumption $A_2A_1 = A_1A_2$ that

$$A_1^{m_2k} = E, \quad A_2^{m_1k} = E,$$

therefore $m_1 \mid m_2k, m_2 \mid m_1k$. Since $(m_1, m_2) = 1$, we must also have $m_1 \mid k, m_2 \mid k$ (Theorem 16 [185]). This implies $m_1m_2 \mid k$ (Theorems 22, 20 [187]). Conversely, since

$$(A_1A_2)^{m_1m_2} = (A_1^{m_1})^{m_2} (A_2^{m_2})^{m_1} = E,$$

then $(A_1A_2)^k = E$ if and only if $m_1m_2 \mid k$, that is, m_1m_2 is the order of A_1A_2.

---

[17] This is the reason for the designation *cyclic.* A circle degenerating to a straight line can be thought of as an image of case a).

By applying Theorem 34 to a cyclic group $\mathfrak{G} = \mathfrak{Z}$ we easily obtain all subgroups of $\mathfrak{Z}$.

Theorem 36. *If $\mathfrak{Z}$ is a cyclic group of finite order n (of infinite order[18]) generated by A, then to every positive divisor j of n (every positive j) there corresponds a normal divisor $\mathfrak{A}_j$ of order $m = \frac{n}{j}$ (of infinite order), namely, the period of A^j. Its factor group $\mathfrak{Z}/\mathfrak{A}_j$ is again cyclic of order j. All subgroups (different from the identity subgroup) of $\mathfrak{Z}$ are generated in this way. Each and every one of these, as well as their factor groups, is therefore again cyclic.*

Proof: a) By Theorem 34 the periods $\mathfrak{A}_j$ of the specified A^j are subgroups with the orders designated, and by Vol. 1, Theorem 26 [69] they are naturally normal divisors of $\mathfrak{Z}$.

b) According to the explanation of the congruence relative to $\mathfrak{A}_j$ (Vol. 1, Def. 16 [65] and by Def. 10 [191]

$$A^{m_1} \equiv A^{m_2} \ (\mathfrak{A}_j) \text{ if and only if } m_1 \equiv m_2 \bmod j.$$

The residue classes relative to $\mathfrak{A}_j$ can therefore be represented by $A^0 = E, A^1, \ldots, A^{j-1}$. Accordingly, $\mathfrak{Z}/\mathfrak{A}_j$ is cyclic of order j, namely, is generated by the residue class of A.

c) If $\mathfrak{Z}'$ is any subgroup (therefore normal divisor) of $\mathfrak{Z}$, then the convention, analogous to (3) [197],

$$m_1 \equiv m_2 \text{ if and only if } A^{m_1} \equiv A^{m_2} \ (\mathfrak{Z}')$$

yields a congruence relation in Γ. If j is its modulus, then A^m is in $\mathfrak{Z}'$ if and only if $m \equiv 0 \bmod j$ (Vol. 1, Theorem 35 [75]), that is, if $j \mid m$; therefore $\mathfrak{Z}'$ consists of all and only the integral powers of A^j, that is, it is the period $\mathfrak{A}_j$ of A^j. If $\mathfrak{Z}$ is finite of order n, then $j \mid n$, since $A^n = E$ belongs to $\mathfrak{Z}'$. If $\mathfrak{Z}$ is infinite, then $j = 0$ corresponds to the identity subgroup, while positive

18 The facts relative to this case — not necessary for the following — are enclosed in parentheses.

j correspond to subgroups different from the identity subgroup.

Theorem 34 also makes it possible to determine all primitive elements of a cyclic group.

Theorem 37. *If $\mathfrak{Z}$ is a cyclic group of type $\mathfrak{R}_f$ generated by A, then the primitive elements of $\mathfrak{Z}$ with respect to the correspondence* (2) *correspond to the prime residue classes mod f, that is, A^m is primitive if and only if m is prime to f.*

Proof: A^m is primitive if and only if its period is exactly $\mathfrak{Z}$; this is the case if and only if it contains A, that is, if an $\bar{m}$ exists so that $A^{m\bar{m}} = A$, namely, $m\bar{m} \equiv 1 \bmod f$. However, by Theorems 3, 14 [173, 182] this is a necessary condition and by Theorem 31 [195] a sufficient condition that m be prime to f.

According to this, if $f = 0$ (namely, if $\mathfrak{Z}$ is infinite) A^1, A^{-1} are the only primitive elements; if $f > 0$ (namely, if $\mathfrak{Z}$ is finite of order f) there are $\varphi(f)$ primitive elements [196] among the f elements. In particular, if $f = p$ is a prime number, all $\varphi(p) = p - 1$ elements $\neq E$ are primitive.

4. Prime Integral Domains. Prime Fields. Characteristic

In this section we derive a basic distinction between integral domains and fields based on the results of Sections 1, 2 for the case Γ. For this purpose I shall designate throughout an arbitrary integral domain, K its quotient field. Since every field K can be regarded as the quotient field of an integral domain (namely, K itself), this will in no way impose a restriction on the fields K drawn into consideration.

We consider the integral multiples me of the unity element e of I. As explained (Vol. 1, at the end of Section 1 [19]) these satisfy the calculating rules.

(1) $m_1 e + m_2 e = (m_1 + m_2)e, \quad (m_1 e)(m_2 e) = (m_1 m_2)e.$

The me are the integral "powers" of e, that is, the *period of e* in the additive Abelian group formed by the elements of I, and in this sense the formulae (1) are merely the formulae (1) of Section 3 [196], though the second formula is slightly different. As an analogue to Theorem 34 [198] (but with due consideration of the second rule of combination, namely, multiplication, which exists in I besides the addition which we are using as the rule of combination of the group) we have from (1) by Vol. 1, Theorem 6 [25]:

Theorem 38. *The integral multiples of the unity element of* I *form an integral subdomain* I_0 *of* I. *Its quotient field is a subfield* K_0 *of* K.

Since e and consequently also all me are contained in every integral subdomain of I, and since the quotients of the me are contained in every subfield of K, we have

Theorem 39. I_0 *is the smallest (intersection of all) integral subdomain(s) of* I. K_0 *ist the smallest (intersection of all) subfield(s) of* K.

The characterization of I_0 and K_0 given in Theorem 39 justifies

Definition 13. I_0 *is called the* ***prime integral domain*** *of* I, K_0 *the* ***prime field*** *of* K.

The distinction, mentioned above, between the integral domains I and the fields K will now be expressed in terms of the type of their prime integral domains I_0 and prime fields K_0. Even though the *calculating operations* with the me in I_0 in accordance to (1) are *isomorphic* to the corrésponding calculating operations with the m in Γ, this does not mean that I_0 has the type Γ. For, as the example of P_p shows, the correspondence $me \longleftrightarrow m$ is not necessarily *one-to-one*, that is, *equality* and *distinctness* in I_0 need not be preserved under this correspondence in passing over to Γ. On the contrary, for the possible types of I_0 the situation corresponds exactly to that established in Section 3 (Theorem 33 [197]) for the types of cyclic groups.

Theorem 40. *To* I *there exists a uniquely determined integer* $f \geqq 0$ *such that* I_0 *is isomorphic to the residue class ring* Γ_f under the correspondence

(2) $$me \longleftrightarrow \{m\}.$$

Proof: From the interpretation of I_0 as the period of e in I it follows by Section 3, (3) [197] that the relation

(3) $$m_1 \equiv m_2 \text{ if and only if } m_1 e = m_2 e$$

is a congruence relation in Γ. If f is its modulus, namely,

(4) $$m_1 e = m_2 e \text{ if and only if } m_1 \equiv m_2 \bmod f,$$

then by (4) the correspondence (2) between I_0 and Γ_f is one-to-one. As in the proof to Theorem 33 [197] it is by (1) also an isomorphism; this is valid not only for addition (which corresponds to the group operation appearing there) but also for the multiplication defined in I_0 and Γ_f.

On the basis of Theorem 40 we define:

Definition 14. *The integer* $f \geqq 0$ *of Theorem* 40, *that is, the modulus of the congruence relation* (3), *is called the* ***characteristic*** *of* I *and* K.

Now, since I_0 is an integral domain isomorphic to Γ_f, we have by Theorem 28 [193] :

Theorem 41. *The characteristic of* I *and* K *is either* 0 *or a prime number p. If it is* 0, *then* $I_0 \cong \Gamma$, $K_0 \cong P$; *if it is p, then* $I_0 = K_0 \cong P_p$.

By Theorem 41 the designation *characteristic of* I and K is motivated by the fact that this number *characterizes* the type of the prime integral domain I_0 and prime field K_0, respectively. That all characteristics possible by Theorem 41 actually occur, is shown by the domains Γ, P, P_p, which are their proper prime domains.[19] By the methods of Vol. 1, Section 3, d) [36] any domain I or K can be mapped isomorphically on a domain which contains Γ or P or a P_p (that is, the integers or rational numbers, or the residue classes. relative to a prime number p, respectively) as a prime domain. Hence in the following we speak simply of *the* prime domains Γ, P, P_p.

Furthermore, the following facts are evident (cf. Theorem 39):

Theorem 42. *All extension domains and subdomains of a domain have the same characteristic.*

From rule (4) for the integral multiples of e it easily follows in virtue of the transformation

$$m_1 a - m_2 a = (m_1 - m_2)\, a = (m_1 - m_2)\, e \cdot a = (m_1 e - m_2 e) \cdot a$$

that a corresponding rule is valid for the integral multiples of an $a \neq 0$:

Theorem 43. *If a is an element of a domain of characteristic f, then*

$$m_1 a = m_2 a \textit{ if and, in case } a \neq 0, \textit{ also only if}$$

$$\left\{\begin{array}{l} m_1 = m_2 \ (\textit{for } f = 0) \\ m_1 \equiv m_2 \bmod p \ (\textit{for } f = p) \end{array}\right\}.$$

In particular, therefore, we have

$$ma = 0 \textit{ if and, in case } a \neq 0, \textit{ also only if}$$

$$\left\{\begin{array}{l} m = 0 \ (\textit{for } f = 0) \\ m \equiv 0 \bmod p \ (\textit{for } f = p) \end{array}\right\}.$$

This theorem shows that domains with characteristic p behave differently from those with characteristic 0 (for instance, all number domains). As a consequence all the familiar inferences from the "algebra of numbers" cannot be used in our abstract "algebra of domains," as we have stressed many times in Vol. 1 [Proofs to Theorem 12, d); Theorem 13, d); Theorem 70 [49, 52, 141]].

---

[19] Here and in the following expositions the term *domain* stands for *integral domain* or *field.*

The following fact, to be applied later, also shows that domains with a characteristic p behave differently from the algebra of numbers:

Theorem 44. *In domains of characteristic p a sum can be raised to a power p by raising each summand to the p-th power:*

$$\left(\sum_{k=1}^{n} a_k\right)^p = \sum_{k=1}^{n} a_k^p .$$

Proof: It is sufficient to prove the theorem for $n = 2$, since it then follows in general by induction. According to the binomial theorem (assumed as known from the elements of arithmetic) we have in this case

$$(a_1 + a_2)^p = a_1^p + \sum_{\nu=1}^{p-1} \binom{p}{\nu} a_1^{\nu} a_2^{p-\nu} + a_2^p ,$$

where $\binom{p}{\nu}$ designates the number of combinations of p elements taken ν at a time. Now, we have already established (cf. Vol. 1, proof of Theorem 66 [133] the formula

$$\binom{p}{\nu} = \frac{p!}{\nu!(p-\nu)!} = \frac{p \cdot (p-1) \cdots (p-(\nu-1))}{1 \cdot 2 \cdots \nu} .$$

But, for $1 \leqq \nu \leqq p-1$ the product $1 . 2 \ldots \nu$ is prime to p (Theorem 23 [187]) and, as the number $\binom{p}{\nu}$ is an integer, must divide the product $p . [(p-1) \ldots (p-(\nu-1))]$ without a remainder; therefore, by Theorem 16 [185] it must divide the second factor $[\ldots]$ of this product without a remainder. This means that $\binom{p}{\nu} \equiv 0 \bmod p$. Hence from Theorem 43 it follows that

$$(a_1 + a_2)^p = a_1^p + a_2^p .$$

Moreover, it should be noted that a corresponding rule is also valid in the case of subtraction; for, since subtraction can be performed without restriction, $(a_1 + a_2)^p - a_1^p = a_2^p$ implies in general $b_1^p - b_2^p = (b_1 - b_2)^p$.

II. The Roots of Algebraic Equations

In this chapter we will derive a number of theorems about the roots α of polynomials $f(x)$ over K under the assumption that these roots belong to an extension field Λ of K. Here, however, we will not be concerned with the question whether the Λ and α exist for a given K and $f(x)$; this point will be discussed for the first time in Chapter III. Consequently, these theorems are merely regarded as consequences of the assumption that a polynomial over K has one or more roots in an extension field Λ of K.

To simplify our terminology we make the following

Notational conventions for Chapters II *to* IV.

Capital Greek letters, except those already disposed of, i. e., M (set), B (domain), I (integral domain), Γ (integral domain of integers), always stand for *fields* even though this may not be explicitly stated. In this respect K shall be the *ground field*; Λ any extension field (briefly, *extension*) of K. Other capital Greek letters that may be used will stand for extensions of K with special properties. Though these latter letters will always be used in the same sense, as in the case of P (field of rational numbers), we will always explicitly specify the attached properties for the sake of clarity. In the case of fields (later, also for groups) the property of *being contained in* or *containing* will be denoted by the symbols $\leqq, \geqq, <, >$. If $K \leqq \overline{K} \leqq \Lambda$, then we say that $\overline{K}$ is a *field between* K *and* Λ.

We will designate elements in the ground field K by a, b, $c, \ldots$, those in extensions Λ of K by $\alpha, \beta, \gamma, \ldots$. (cf. Vol. 1, footnote 1 to Section 1, [15]); similarly, elements in K[x] by $f(x)$, $g(x)$, $h(x), \ldots$, those in $\Lambda[x]$ by $\varphi(x), \psi(x), \chi(x), \ldots$[1] These conventions

1 Whenever *fractional* rational functions occur, designated as such in Vol. 1, they will be represented as quotients of integral rational functions.

frequently permit us to omit explanatory additional statements regarding the field to which the elements under consideration shall belong.

Likewise, we can also occasionally omit the additional statement "in K" when using the expressions "irreducible" and "decomposition into prime factors." Furthermore, in the course of our development we will introduce concepts which are defined in terms of a definite ground field. The specific reference to this ground field can also be omitted provided that in a given investigation no other ground field appears besides a *fixed* K. Definitions which shall use these conventions will be marked with an *.

5. Roots and Linear Factors

1) The fundamental theorem proved in Section 1 for $K[x]$ makes it possible, first of all, to show that the roots of a polynomial over K in an extension Λ of K are related to its prime factors in K. Namely, by Vol. 1, Theorem 4 [18] and the principle of substitution we have:

Theorem 45. *If*

$$f(x) \equiv p_1(x) \cdots p_r(x) \text{ [2]}$$

is a polynomial over K decomposed into its prime factors, then every root of $f(x)$ in Λ is also a root of at least one of the $p_i(x)$; and, conversely, every root of one of the $p_i(x)$ in Λ is also a root of $f(x)$.

Consequently, the roots of $f(x)$ are under control if those of the $p_i(x)$ are under control; therefore, we could restrict ourselves to the investigation of the roots of irreducible polynomials. However, we will not impose this restriction, since it turns out to be superfluous for the theory to be developed in Chapters III, IV. This also seems desirable in view of the non-existence of a rational calculating process for bringing about the decomposition into prime factors.

---

[2] According to the definition of *polynomial* given in the introduction, as well as by Def. 8 [178] and Theorem 11 [178], the unit factor appearing in Theorem 12 [178] is $a = e$.

2) We will further prove some theorems connecting the roots of a polynomial over K with its prime factors of 1-st degree (so-called ***linear factors***) in an extension Λ of K.

Theorem 46. *If* α *is a root of* $f(x)$ *in* Λ, *then* $f(x)$ *is divisible by the linear factor* $x-\alpha$, *that is, there exists in* Λ *a decomposition*

$$f(x) \equiv (x-\alpha)\,\varphi(x).$$

Conversely, such a decomposition implies that α *is a root of* $f(x)$.

Proof: a) By Theorem 13 [180] we can set

$$f(x) \equiv (x-\alpha)\,\varphi(x) + \psi(x) \text{ with } |\psi(x)| < |x-\alpha|.$$

Since $|x-\alpha| = k^1$, then $|\psi(x)| = k^0 = 1$, so that $\psi(x) \equiv \beta$ is an element of Λ. Hence, on setting $x=\alpha$ it also follows that $\beta = 0$ since $f(\alpha)=0$. This means that there exists a decomposition of the type indicated.

b) The converse is clear.

Theorem 47. *If* $\alpha_1, \ldots, \alpha_\nu$ *are different roots of* $f(x)$ *in* Λ, *then there exists in* Λ *a decomposition*

$$f(x) \equiv (x-\alpha_1) \cdots (x-\alpha_\nu)\,\varphi(x).$$

Conversely, such a decomposition implies that $\alpha_1, \ldots, \alpha_\nu$ *are roots of* $f(x)$.

Proof: a) By assumption the prime functions $x-\alpha_1, \ldots, x-\alpha_\nu$ are different, and by Theorem 46 each appears in the prime factor decomposition of $f(x)$ in the field Λ. Hence, due to the uniqueness of the decomposition, its product must also be contained in $f(x)$, that is, there exists a decomposition of the type stated.

b) The converse is clear.

On comparing the degrees on both sides, Theorem 47 immediately yields the important fact:

Theorem 48. *There is no extension* Λ *of* K *in which a polynomial of n-th degree over* K *has more than n different roots.*

The following theorem, to be used later, is a consequence of Theorem 48:

Theorem 49. *If* K *consists of infinitely many elements and* $g_1(x_1, \ldots, x_n), \ldots, g_r(x_1, \ldots, x_n)$ *are elements of* $K[x_1, \ldots, x_n]$, *different from one another, then in every infinite subset* M *of* K *there are systems of elements* $a_1, \ldots, a_n$ *such that the elements* $g_1(a_1, \ldots, a_n), \ldots, g_r(a_1, \ldots, a_n)$ *of* K *are likewise different from one another.*

Proof: By considering the product of differences $g = \prod_{\substack{i,k=1 \\ i<k}}^{r} (g_i - g_k)$ the statement immediately reduces to one of the following two equivalent propositions:

(a) If $g(x_1, \ldots, x_n) \not\equiv 0$, then there are elements $a_1, \ldots, a_n$ in M for which $g(a_1, \ldots, a_n) \neq 0$.

(b) If $g(a_1, \ldots, a_n) = 0$ for all $a_1, \ldots, a_n$ in M, then $g(x_1, \ldots, x_n) \equiv 0$.[3]

We will prove this by mathematical induction. For $n = 1$, (a) is a consequence of Theorem 48. Namely, if $g(x) \not\equiv 0$, then either $g(x) \equiv b \neq 0$ (unit) and therefore $g(a) = b \neq 0$ for all a in M, or $g(x)$ is a polynomial except for a factor in K different from zero. In the latter case, $g(a) = 0$ for only finitely many a in K, so that according to the assumption on K and M there exist elements a of M for which $g(a) \neq 0$. Now, let us suppose that (a), and consequently (b), is already proved for $n = \nu - 1$. Then we consider the polynomials

$$\bar{g}(x_\nu) \equiv g(x_1, \ldots, x_\nu) \text{ over } K[x_1, \ldots, x_{\nu-1}],$$
$$\bar{g}^*(x_\nu) \equiv g(a_1, \ldots, a_{\nu-1}, x_\nu) \text{ over } K,$$

where the latter is generated from the former by replacing $x_1, \ldots, x_{\nu-1}$ by the systems $a_1, \ldots, a_{\nu-1}$ in M. Now, if $g(a_1, \ldots, a_\nu) = 0$ for

[3] This confirms the statement made in Vol. 1, Proof to Theorem 12, d) [49] [cf. for this Vol. 1, Proof to Theorem 13, d) [52]]. For this purpose we regard K as the quotient field of the integral domain I appearing there and M as the I appearing there.

all $a_1, \ldots, a_\nu$ in M, then by (b) ($n = 1$) we have, first of all, that every $\bar{g}^*(x_\nu) \equiv 0$. Consequently, by (b) ($n = \nu - 1$) the coefficients of $\bar{g}(x_\nu)$, that is $\bar{g}(x_\nu)$ itself, are $\equiv 0$, which means that $g(x_1, \ldots, x_\nu) \equiv 0$. Hence (b) is also valid for $n = \nu$, and therefore valid in general.

The following theorem is more precise than Theorems 47, 48 in that the roots are no longer assumed to be different.

Theorem 50. *If $f(x)$ is completely decomposed in* Λ *into linear factors*

$$f(x) \equiv (x - \alpha_1) \cdots (x - \alpha_n),$$

then $\alpha_1, \ldots, \alpha_n$ are roots of $f(x)$. In such a case $f(x)$ can have other roots neither in Λ *nor in any extension* $\bar{\Lambda}$ *of* Λ.

Proof: a) The first part of the theorem is obvious (Theorem 47 [207]).

b) If α is a root of $f(x)$ (in Λ or in an $\bar{\Lambda}$)), then $f(\alpha) = 0$ implies that $(\alpha - \alpha_1) \cdots (\alpha - \alpha_n) = 0$, so that α must be equal to one of the roots α_i (Vol. 1, Theorem 4 [18]).

Let $f(x)$ satisfy the hypothesis of Theorem 50. By *the* roots of $f(x)$ in Λ we will understand, from now on, the *entire* sequence $\alpha_1, \ldots, \alpha_n$ corresponding to the linear factors of $f(x)$, whether it contains any terms that are alike or not.

Theorems 46, 47, 50 tell us how to proceed in order to construct the roots of a polynomial $f(x)$ over K. This construction will be carried out in Chapter III. For this purpose we will have to extend K stepwise so that at least one linear factor will be split off of $f(x)$ at each step. If an extension Λ is found in this way in which $f(x)$ is completely decomposed into linear factors, then we can put a stop to the extension process, since by Theorem 50 no more new roots can be obtained by continuing the extension in such a case.

3) Finally, we prove some facts about the roots of irreducible polynomials.

First of all, it immediately follows from Theorem 46 [207] and the concept of irreducibility:

Theorem 51. *An irreducible polynomial over* K *has a root in* K *if and only if it is of the first degree.*

This makes the fact 2) stressed in the introduction, that in general the ground field must be extended in order to obtain the roots of a polynomial, more evident. We must add, of course, the fact, which is not to be fully discussed here, that in general there are irreducible polynomials over the ground field of degree higher than the 1-st. (For special theorems in this direction, see Section 23.)

Theorem 52. *There is no extension of* K *in which two relatively prime polynomials have a common root. In particular, this is valid for two different irreducible polynomials over* K.

Proof: If α is a common root of $f_1(x)$ and $f_2(x)$ in Λ, then by Theorem 46 [207] $x-\alpha$ is a common divisor of $f_1(x)$ and $f_2(x)$ in Λ. By Theorem 24 [188] this means that $(f_1(x), f_2(x)) \neq e$.

From Theorem 52 we obtain the following, so-called ***Fundamental Theorem about irreducible polynomials:***

Theorem 53. *Let* $f(x)$ *be irreducible in* K. *If* $f(x)$ *has a root in common with any* $h(x)$ *over* K *in an extension of* K, *then* $f(x) \mid h(x)$.

Proof: By Theorem 17 [185] $f(x)$ would otherwise be prime to $h(x)$, which by Theorem 52 contradicts the assumption.

In this theorem $h(x)$ does not have to be a polynomial, namely, it has to be neither different from 0 and units nor normalized. In particular, the theorem is trivial for $h(x) \equiv 0$; for $h(x) \equiv a$, it is meaningless.

Our construction of the roots of $f(x)$, to be carried out in Chapter III, depends above all on Theorem 53.

6. Multiple Roots. Derivative

Definition 15. *A root* α *of* $f(x)$ *in* Λ *is called* ν-***fold*** *if a decomposition*

$$f(x) \equiv (x-\alpha)^{\nu}\,\varphi(x) \quad \textit{with} \quad \varphi(\alpha) \neq 0$$

exists in Λ *(and consequently in every extension of* Λ*);* ***multiple*** *if* $\nu > 1$.

The designation ν-*fold* is justified by

Theorem 54. *If* α *is a* ν*-fold root of* $f(x)$ *in* Λ*, then there are exactly* ν *roots of* $f(x)$ *in* Λ *(and in every extension of* Λ*) equal to* α.

Proof: By Def. 15 $f(x)$ then contains the prime factor $x-\alpha$ at least ν times; moreover, since $\varphi(\alpha) \neq 0$, it does not occur more often by Theorem 46 [207] .

The multiplicity of a root of $f(x)$ is related to the derivative $f'(x)$ of $f(x)$, a concept taken from analysis. Naturally, here we cannot define the derivative for our abstract ground field as is usually done in analysis, namely, by means of a limit process. Therefore, we give the following formal definition.

Definition 16. *By the* ***derivative*** *of*

$$f(x) \equiv a_0 + a_1 x + \cdots + a_n x^n \equiv \sum_{k=0}^{\infty} a_k x^k \;[4]$$

we understand

$$f'(x) \equiv a_1 + 2a_2 x + \cdots + n a_n x^{n-1} \equiv \sum_{k=1}^{\infty} k a_k x^{k-1}$$
$$\equiv \sum_{k=0}^{\infty} (k+1) a_{k+1} x^k.$$

This formal process for forming derivatives coincides with the corresponding differentiation rules of analysis. As in analysis, it satisfies the formulae

(1) $$(f(x) \pm g(x))' \equiv f'(x) \pm g'(x),$$

(2) $$(f(x)g(x))' \equiv f'(x)g(x) + f(x)g'(x);$$

[4] Cf. Vol. 1, footnote 10 to Theorem 11 [39] .

in particular, therefore,

$$(af(x))' \equiv af'(x),$$
$$(f(x)^n)' \equiv nf(x)^{n-1}f'(x).$$

Proof: If

$$f(x) \equiv \sum_{k=0}^{\infty} a_k x^k, \quad g(x) \equiv \sum_{k=0}^{\infty} b_k x^k,$$

therefore

$$f'(x) \equiv \sum_{k=1}^{\infty} ka_k x^{k-1} \equiv \sum_{k=0}^{\infty} (k+1)\, a_{k+1} x^k,$$
$$g'(x) \equiv \sum_{k=1}^{\infty} kb_k x^{k-1} \equiv \sum_{k=0}^{\infty} (k+1)\, b_{k+1} x^k,$$

then by Vol. 1. Section 4, (2), (3) [40] (cf. also Vol. 1, end of Section 1 [19]) we have

$$(f(x)+g(x))' \equiv \Big(\sum_{k=0}^{\infty} (a_k+b_k)\, x^k\Big)' \equiv \sum_{k=1}^{\infty} k(a_k+b_k)\, x^{k-1}$$
$$\equiv \sum_{k=1}^{\infty} ka_k x^{k-1} + \sum_{k=1}^{\infty} kb_k x^{k-1} \equiv f'(x)+g'(x),$$
$$(f(x)\,g(x))' \equiv \Big(\sum_{k=0}^{\infty}\Big(\sum_{\nu+\mu=k} a_\nu b_\mu\Big)\, x^k\Big)' \equiv \sum_{k=1}^{\infty}\Big(k \sum_{\nu+\mu=k} a_\nu b_\mu\Big)\, x^{k-1}$$
$$\equiv \sum_{k=1}^{\infty}\Big(\sum_{\nu+\mu=k} (\nu+\mu)\, a_\nu b_\mu\Big)\, x^{k-1}$$
$$\equiv \sum_{k=1}^{\infty}\Big(\sum_{\nu+\mu=k} \nu a_\nu b_\mu\Big)\, x^{k-1} + \sum_{k=1}^{\infty}\Big(\sum_{\nu+\mu=k} \mu a_\nu b_\mu\Big)\, x^{k-1}$$
$$\equiv \sum_{k=0}^{\infty}\Big(\sum_{\nu+\mu=k} (\nu+1)\, a_{\nu+1} b_\mu\Big)\, x^k + \sum_{k=0}^{\infty}\Big(\sum_{\nu+\mu=k} (\mu+1)\, a_\nu b_{\mu+1}\Big)\, x^k$$
$$\equiv f'(x)\, g(x) + f(x)\, g'(x).$$

Furthermore, as if to compensate for the omitted limit relation, we have:

Theorem 55. *If we set for an* α

$$\varphi(x) \equiv \frac{f(x)-f(\alpha)}{x-\alpha},$$

then

$$\varphi(\alpha) = f'(\alpha).$$

Proof: Since α is a root of $f(x) - f(\alpha)$, then by Theorem 46 [207] $\varphi(x)$ is actually an integral rational function. Hence from

$$f(x) \equiv f(\alpha) + (x - \alpha)\,\varphi(x)$$

it follows by (1), (2) that

$$f'(x) \equiv \varphi(x) + (x - \alpha)\,\varphi'(x),$$

therefore

$$f'(\alpha) = \varphi(\alpha).$$

As a consequence of Theorem 55 the multiplicity of a root α of $f(x)$ is related to the value of the derivative $f'(\alpha)$ as follows:

Theorem 56. *A root α of $f(x)$ is a multiple root if and only if $f'(\alpha) = 0$.*

Proof: If α is a root of $f(x)$, then by Theorem 46 [207] there exists a decomposition

$$f(x) \equiv (x - \alpha)\,\varphi(x),$$

where $\varphi(x)$ has the same meaning as in Theorem 55. Now, by Def. 15 [211] the multiplicity of α is equivalent to $\varphi(\alpha) = 0$; therefore, by Theorem 55, to $f'(\alpha) = 0$.

The relationship just determined has an important consequence regarding the multiplicity of the roots of an irreducible polynomial. This result rests on the analogue to the theorem of analysis which says that $f'(x) \equiv 0$ implies $f(x) \equiv a_0$. Since the coefficients of $f'(x)$ are the integral multiples ka_k of a_k, the situation here deviates from that in analysis:

Theorem 57. *If K has characteristic 0, then all and only the units $f(x) \equiv a_0$ in $\mathsf{K}[x]$ have the derivative $f'(x) \equiv 0$. If K has the characteristic p, then all and only the elements of the form*

(3) $$f(x) \equiv \sum_{l=0}^{\infty} a_{lp}\, x^{lp}, \textit{ therefore } f(x) \equiv f_0(x^p)$$

in $\mathsf{K}[x]$ have the derivative $f'(x) \equiv 0$.

Proof: a) That $f'(x) \equiv 0$ for all of the specified $f(x)$, is clear by Theorem 43 [203] and Def. 16 [211].

b) Let $f(x) \equiv \sum_{k=0}^{\infty} a_k x^k$ and $f'(x) \equiv \sum_{k=1}^{\infty} k a_k x^{k-1} \equiv 0$, therefore

$ka_k = 0$ $(k = 1, 2, \ldots)$. Then by Theorem 43 if the characteristic is 0,

$$a_k = 0 \quad (k = 1, 2, \ldots),$$

that is, $f(x) \equiv a_0$; whereas, if the characteristic is p, then only

$$a_k = 0 \text{ for } k \not\equiv 0 \bmod p,$$

so that $f(x)$ has the form (3).

In Theorem 57 we noted that irreducible polynomials of the form (3) behave quite differently from those which do not have this form. This difference will force us to restrict the result to be announced regarding the multiplicity of the roots of an irreducible polynomial in the case of characteristic p to the irreducible polynomials which do not have the form (3). *Steinitz* [5] called these irreducible polynomials *of the first kind*; those of the form (3), *of the second kind.*

Following the precedence of *van der Waerden,* we will use the nomenclature given in the following definition:

Definition 17. *An* ***irreducible polynomial*** $f(x)$ *over* K *is said to be* ***separable*** *if its derivative* $f'(x) \not\equiv 0$. *Hence, if* K *has characteristic* 0, *all irreducible polynomials are separable; if* K *has characteristic p, all the irreducible polynomials which do not have the form* (3) *in Theorem* 57 *are separable and only these.*

In other cases $f(x)$ *is said to be* ***inseparable.***

The designation *separable* refers to the following fact, the consequence of Theorem 56 already announced:

---

[5] When we refer to the name of *Steinitz,* here and in the following, we always mean the text *E. Steinitz: Algebraische Theorie der Körper* (*Algebraic Theory of Fields*), new edition, Berlin 1930. Chapters I and II of this text except for the part relating to extensions of the second kind are incorporated into our Vol. 1, Chapter I and Vol. 2, Chapters I to IV; in fact, they constitute their content. Every algebraist should at some time look into this basic original work on field theory.

Theorem 58. *If an irreducible polynomial $f(x)$ is separable, then $f(x)$ has only simple roots.*

Proof: If α were a multiple root of $f(x)$, then $f'(\alpha)=0$ (Theorem 56) would be valid and therefore $f(x) \mid f'(x)$ (Theorem 53 [210]). Due to the assumed separability of $f(x)$, we now have $f'(x) \not\equiv 0$ (Def. 17). Hence $f'(x)$ has a degree, and this is smaller than that of $f(x)$ (Def. 16 [211]). But this contradicts the result $f(x) \mid f'(x)$ (Theorem 6 [176]) of the assumption that $f(x)$ has a multiple root.

Moreover, Theorem 58 has the following converse:

Theorem 59. *If an irreducible polynomial $f(x)$ has one root α which is only simple, then $f(x)$ is separable.*

Proof: In this case $f'(\alpha) \neq 0$ (Theorem 56), therefore we certainly have $f'(x) \not\equiv 0$, and consequently $f(x)$ is separable (Def. 17).

We further define in conjunction with Def. 17:

***Addendum to Definition 17.**[6] *An **arbitrary polynomial** over* K *is said to be **separable** in* K, *if its prime factors in* K *are separable; otherwise, **inseparable** in* K.

This means that in the case of characteristic 0 *every* polynomial is separable. In the case of characteristic p it is easy to see that the separability of arbitrary polynomials cannot be made to depend simply on the derivative as is done in Def. 17 for irreducible polynomials. It can very well be that $f'(x) \equiv 0$ is also valid for separable $f(x)$ (for instance, if $f(x) \equiv f_0(x)^p$, where $f_0(x)$ is separable and irreducible); furthermore, we may have $f'(x) \not\equiv 0$ for inseparable $f(x)$ (for instance, if $f(x) \equiv x f_0(x)$, where $f_0(x)$ is inseparable and irreducible). Nor does the relationship, given in Theorems 58, 59, between separability and the multiplicity of roots, which justified the designation *separable*, carry over to arbitrary

[6] For the significance of * cf. the introduction to Chapter II [206].

polynomials. Nevertheless, the extension of this nomenclature to arbitrary polynomials given in the Addendum to Def. 17 is useful for later purposes.

Due to lack of space we refer to *Steinitz* for a method that can be used to decide the separability of arbitrary polynomials, which does not at the same time depend on the decomposition into prime factors (in view of the remarks made in connection with Theorem 24 [188], this must be desirable). Here we will only note the following fact sufficient for our purposes, which immediately follows from Theorem 59 according to Def. 17, Addendum.

Corollary to Theorem 59. *If an arbitrary polynomial $f(x)$ over K decomposes in an extension of K into different linear factors, that is, the roots $\alpha_1, \ldots, \alpha_n$ of*

$$f(x) \equiv (x - \alpha_1) \cdots (x - \alpha_n)$$

are different from one another, then $f(x)$ is separable (in K and every extension of K).

Those fields in which *every* polynomial is separable are significant. They are called *perfect fields*. We will make some rather brief statements about perfect fields by using, in part, results which will not be deduced until later.

First, the above considerations immediately yield that every field of characteristic 0 is perfect. — Furthermore, if a field K of characteristic a prime number p is to be perfect, then, in particular, every polynomial $x^p - a$ over K must be separable. In this case the equation $x^p \doteq a$ can be solved in K. For, the unsolvability in K implies by Theorem 123, b) [312], to be given later, the irreducibility of the polynomial $x^p - a$ in K and therefore by Def. 17 its inseparability. Moreover, the solution of $x^p \doteq a$ in K is unique. From $a_1^p = a$, $a_2^p = a$ we have that $0 = a_1^p - a_2^p = (a_1 - a_2)^p$ (Theorem 44 [204]), therefore $a_1 - a_2 = 0$, $a_1 = a_2$. We designate this unique solution of $x^p \doteq a$ by $\sqrt[p]{a}$.

Conversely, if K is a field whose characteristic is the prime number p, let us assume that the equation $x^p \doteq a$ can be solved for every a in K. In this case, if the irreducible polynomial $f(x)$ over K were inseparable, then by Def. 17 $f(x)$ would have the form

$$f(x) = \sum_{\nu=0}^{n} a_\nu x^{\nu p} = \sum_{\nu=0}^{n} \left(\sqrt[p]{a_\nu}\right)^p x^{\nu p},$$

and Theorem 44 [204] would yield

$$f(x) = \left(\sum_{\nu=0}^{n} \sqrt[p]{a_\nu} x\right)^p$$

contradicting the irreducibility of $f(x)$. — This means that we have found that:

A field K whose characteristic is a prime number p is perfect if and only if $\sqrt[p]{a}$ is contained in K whenever a is.

According to this and by Theorem 29 [194] the prime fields P_p are perfect fields. — That not every field is perfect, that is, that there are so-called *imperfect fields*, is shown by the example $P_p(x)$; for, this field has the characteristic p, and the element x has no p-th root in this field. Namely, if $\left(\frac{f(x)}{g(x)}\right)^p \equiv x$ were true, that is, $(f(x))^p = x(g(x))^p$ (where we must naturally have that $f(x)$, $g(x) \not\equiv 0$) and if n, m were the degrees of $f(x), g(x)$, then by Section 1, B, (3) [175] $pn = 1 + pm$, that is, $0 \equiv 1 \bmod p$, which is not valid.

III. The Fields of the Roots of Algebraic Equations

In this chapter we will construct the roots of a polynomial $f(x)$ over K according to the scheme given in Theorem 50 [209]. For this purpose we will first set up an extension Σ (*stem field*) in which a linear factor splits off of $f(x)$ (Section 8); from this extension we will ascend stepwise to an extension W (*root field*) in which $f(x)$ resolves completely into linear factors (Section 10). Besides this we will develop a *general theory of the extensions* of a field in order to prepare the way for our investigations in Chapter IV regarding the structure of these root fields. In this theory no role will be played by the fact that these extensions arise from definite polynomials (Sections 7, 9). In conclusion (Section 11) we will add a section on the so-called *Fundamental Theorem of Algebra*, which will be an interesting digression only from a technical and historical point of view.

7. General Theory of Extensions

(1) Basic Concepts and Facts

In Vol. 1, Section 4 we constructed and investigated the special extension domains $\mathsf{I}[x_1, \ldots, x_n]$ and $\mathsf{K}(x_1, \ldots, x_n)$ of ground domains I and K, respectively. These developments will now be pushed to a greater depth and expanded. For brevity, in the following we restrict ourselves to the case wherein the ground *field* K is the only ground domain to be used.

A. Adjunction. Simple and Finite Extensions

Definition 18. *Let* Λ *be an extension field of* K *and* M *a subset of* Λ. *The integral domain of all integral rational functions over* K, *each of which consists of finitely many elements of* M, *is called the* ***integral subdomain of*** Λ ***generated by the adjunction of*** M ***to*** K (*notation* K[M]). *The field of all rational functions over* K, *each of which consists of finitely many elements of* M, *is called the* ***subfield of*** Λ ***generated by the adjunction of*** M ***to*** K (*notation* K(M)).

That K[M] is actually an integral subdomain, K(M) a subfield of Λ, follows from Vol. 1, Theorem 6 [25] and the properties of the integral rational and the rational functions, respectively, over K. Furthermore, since the elements of K, in particular, can be regarded as integral rational functions over K, K[M] and K(M) are extension domains of K. Consequently, we have

$$K \leqq K[M] \leqq K(M) \leqq \Lambda.$$

By using the concept of intersection, introduced in Vol. 1, Theorem 7 [26], K[M] and K(M) (as shown by *Steinitz*) can also be defined as the *intersection of all integral domains and fields, respectively, between* K *and* Λ *which contain the subset* M *of* Λ.

It is true that the field Λ in Def. 18 only plays the role of an *auxiliary field* which can be replaced by any other extension $\bar{\Lambda}$ of K containing M without affecting K[M] and K(M) in any way, namely, without changing the *result* of the adjunction. However, its existence is absolutely necessary for the *process* of adjunction. In this regard the word *adjunction* is easily misunderstood. We wish to emphasize that the adjunction of a set M to K in the two ways explained in Def. 18 has a sense only if it takes place within an extension Λ of K, that is, if it is, so to speak, initiated *from above*. In other words, it must be known that the elements of M can be combined with one another and with the elements of K by means of the four elementary operations according to the field laws. An adjunction *from below,* that is, without the knowledge of an extension Λ of K containing M, is never allowable. For, if K satisfies only the field axioms given in Vol. 1, Section 1, we have no right whatever to take for granted the existence of a set M of elements outside K which can be submitted along with the elements of K to the four elementary operations. Therefore, for instance, just because the indispensable field Λ occurring in Def. 18 can be identified with $K(x_1, \ldots, x_n)$ (or some still more extensive field), we have no right to conclude that the *definition* of adjunction enables us to circumvent the existence *proofs* of the domains $K[x_1, \ldots, x_n]$ and $K(x_1, \ldots, x_n)$ over K given in Vol. 1, Section 4, each of which is (trivially) generated by the adjunction of $x_1, \ldots, x_n$ to K in the two ways of Def. 18. A similar remark is also valid for the existence proof of the quotient field K carried out in Vol. 1, Section 3 as well as for the existence proof of stem fields and root fields to be given in the following Sections 8, 10. We note that the quotient field is generated by the adjunction of all quotients of elements of the integral domain I and that in its existence proof K plays the role of Λ.[1]

Regarding the dependence of the adjunction on the ground field K the following facts can be immediately established. For brevity they will be stated only in terms of the field adjunction K(M) as this is the only case to be used later.

Theorem 60. $K(M) = K$ *if and only if* M *is a subset of* K.

Theorem 61. *If* $\Lambda \geqq \overline{K} \geqq K$ *and* $\Lambda = K(M)$, *then* $\Lambda = \overline{K}(M)$ *is also valid.*

Theorem 62. *If* $\Lambda \geqq \overline{K} \geqq K$ *and* $\Lambda = \overline{K}(\overline{M})$, $\overline{K} = K(M)$, *then* $\Lambda = K(M, \overline{M})$, *where* $(M, \overline{M})$ *is the union of* M *and* $\overline{M}$.

By Theorem 62 the *successive adjunction* first of M and then of $\overline{M}$ is equivalent to the *simultaneous adjunction* of M, $\overline{M}$. By

---

[1] Cf. the "preliminary remarks to the existence proof" in Vol. 1, Sections 3, 4 [34, 41].

applying the concept of *composite*, introduced in Vol. 1, Def. 5 [27] , $K(M, \bar{M})$ can also be described as the *composite of* $K(M)$ *and* $K(\bar{M})$, namely, as the smallest subfield of Λ containing $K(M)$ and $K(\bar{M})$.

We now make a special definition, again only for the case of field adjunction.

Definition 19.** *An extension Λ of K is said to be* ***simple *or* ***finite*** *over K, if it is derived by the adjunction of one or finitely many, respectively, of its elements to K, therefore, if it consists of the rational functions over K of an element α or of finitely many, respectively, elements $\alpha_1, \ldots, \alpha_n$.*[2] *Any such element α or system of elements $\alpha_1, \ldots, \alpha_n$ of Λ for which $\Lambda = K(\alpha)$ or $\Lambda = K(\alpha_1, \ldots, \alpha_n)$, respectively, is said to be a* ***primitive element*** *or* ***primitive system of elements*** *of Λ relative to K.*

In particular, therefore, the field $K(x)$ of rational functions over K of an indeterminate x is simple over K, and the field $K(x_1, \ldots, x_n)$ of rational functions over K of n indeterminates $x_1, \ldots, x_n$ is finite over K. Naturally, Def. 19 does not say that every simple or finite extension is of this kind, for α or $\alpha_1, \ldots, \alpha_n$ do not have to be indeterminates. Since in the following we will be concerned almost exclusively with this latter case, we will later investigate under B more exactly the situation in which the elements are not *indeterminates.*

In addition we note that the concept of adjunction introduced in Def. 18, as well as that of simplicity and finiteness introduced in Def. 19, are related to the concept of relative isomorphism already introduced in Vol. 1, Def. 7, Addendum [30] :

If the extensions $\Lambda = K(M)$ and $\Lambda' = K(M')$ generated by adjunction are isomorphic relative to K, and if the sets M and

[2] This formulation is not essentially different from that given in Def. 18, since the rational functions over K of every subsystem of $\alpha_1, \ldots, \alpha_n$ occur among those of $\alpha_1, \ldots, \alpha_n$.

M′ correspond to one another with respect to an isomorphism relative to K between the two extensions, then by specifying the correspondences

$$(1) \qquad \alpha \longleftrightarrow \alpha', \ \beta \longleftrightarrow \beta', \dots \left(\begin{matrix}\alpha, \beta, \dots \text{in } \mathsf{M} \\ \alpha', \beta', \dots \text{in } \mathsf{M}'\end{matrix}\right)$$

the correspondences for all remaining elements of Λ and Λ′ are necessarily determined. Namely, according to the conditions for an isomorphism relative to K (cf. Vol. 1, Theorem 9 and Corollary, Def. 7 and Addendum [29, 30] , as well as the enclosed remarks) we must have

$$(2) \qquad \frac{g(\alpha, \beta, \dots, \gamma)}{h(\alpha, \beta, \dots, \gamma)} \longleftrightarrow \frac{g(\alpha', \beta', \dots, \gamma')}{h(\alpha', \beta', \dots, \gamma')}.$$

Hence to describe the isomorphism (2) it is sufficient to specify completely the correspondences (1). In the following we will frequently use this fact. To simplify our terminology we set up:

Definition 20. *Let* $\Lambda = \mathsf{K}(\mathsf{M})$ *and* $\Lambda' = \mathsf{K}(\mathsf{M}')$ *be isomorphic relative to* K. *Let there be an isomorphism relative to* K *between these extensions such that the sets* M *and* M′ *correspond to one another according to* (1). *Then the complete isomorphism* (2) *is said to be* ***generated by the correspondences*** (1), *and* Λ *and* Λ′ *are said to be isomorphic relative to* K ***on the basis of the correspondences*** (1).

In particular, let Λ and Λ′ be simple or finite extensions of K which are isomorphic relative to K. Then an isomorphism relative to K between these extensions can be generated by a single or by a finite number, respectively, of correspondences $\alpha_1 \longleftrightarrow \alpha'$ or $\alpha_1 \longleftrightarrow \alpha_1', \dots, \alpha_r \longleftrightarrow \alpha_r'$, respectively, of two primitive elements α; α' or two primitive systems of elements $\alpha_1, \dots, \alpha_r$; $\alpha_1', \dots, \alpha_r'$, respectively, of Λ and Λ′. Naturally, it is not true that $\alpha_i \longleftrightarrow \alpha_i'$ generates an isomorphism relative to K between Λ and Λ′ if α_i and α_i' are *arbitrary* primitive elements. For this purpose the α_i' must be chosen so as to be *adapted* to α_i.

B. (Separable) Algebraic Elements. (Separable) Algebraic Extensions [3]

***Definition 21.** *An **element** α of an extension $\mathsf{\Lambda}$ of K is said to be **(separably) algebraic** over K if it is a root of a (separable) polynomial over K; if it is not algebraic over K, then it is said to be **transcendental** over K.*

By Vol. 1, Section 4 (cf., in particular, the explanation of Def. 9 [45] appearing there) *transcendental over* K says the same as *indeterminate over* K, so that *algebraic over* K is the opposite of *indeterminate over* K. — Algebraic elements (at the time, of course, they were hypothetical) have already been used in Chapter II.

Theorem 63. *If α is (separably) algebraic over K, then one and only one irreducible polynomial $f(x)$ exists in K which has the root α (and it is separable).*

Proof: a) By Def. 21 α is a root of a (separable) polynomial $\bar{f}(x)$ over K; therefore, by Theorem 45 [206] at least one of the (separable — Def. 17, Addendum [215]) irreducible factors of $\bar{f}(x)$ is in K.

b) By Theorem 52 [210] α cannot be a root of two different irreducible polynomials over K.

Definition 22. *The polynomial $f(x)$ in Theorem 63 is said to be the **irreducible polynomial** over K **belonging to** α; its degree n, also the **degree of** α over K (notation: $n = [\alpha : \mathsf{K}]$).*

Theorem 51 [210] immediately yields:

Theorem 64. $[\alpha : \mathsf{K}] = 1$ *if and only if α is an element of K.*

Furthermore we have:

Theorem 65. *If $\mathsf{\Lambda} \geqq \bar{\mathsf{K}} \geqq \mathsf{K}$ and the element α of $\mathsf{\Lambda}$ is (separably) algebraic over K, then α is also (separably) algebraic*

[3] In the following, whenever *separable* is enclosed in parentheses, the text can be read throughout without this addendum as well as with it.

over $\overline{K}$, and the irreducible polynomial over $\overline{K}$ belonging to it is a divisor of the irreducible polynomial over K belonging to this element; therefore, in particular,

$$[\alpha:\overline{K}] \leqq [\alpha:K].$$

Proof: The statements without "separable" immediately follow from Theorem 53 [210]. If in addition α is separable over K, then by Theorem 63, 58 [215] it must be a simple root of the irreducible polynomial over K belonging to it, therefore all the more of the irreducible polynomial over $\overline{K}$. Consequently, by Theorem 59 [215], Def. 21 it is also separable over $\overline{K}$.

***Definition 23.** *An **extension** Λ of K is said to be **(separably) algebraic** over K if each of its elements is (separably) algebraic over K; if it is not algebraic over K, it is said to be **transcendental** over K.*

The simple extension $K(x)$ is transcendental over K, since by the above the indeterminate x is transcendental over K. A corresponding statement is also true for the finite extension $K(x_1, \ldots, x_n)$. In the following we will study algebraic extensions in detail.

Analogously to Theorems 61 [220], 65, we immediately obtain from Theorem 65 the following theorem, which shows the dependence of Def. 23 on the fields K and Λ.

Theorem 66. *If $\Lambda \geqq \overline{K} \geqq K$ and Λ is (separably) algebraic over K, then Λ is also (separably) algebraic over $\overline{K}$ and naturally $\overline{K}$ over K.*

We will be able to prove the converse (analogous to Theorem 62 [220] only later (Theorem 86 [242], Theorem 92 [255]), that is, after proving it for the special class of algebraic extensions defined under C, which follows, (Theorem 71 [228]) and acquiring more precise knowledge regarding these (Theorem 84 [241], Theorem 91 [254]).

C. Extensions of Finite Degree

Analogous to the concepts introduced in Vol. 1, Def. 23, 24, [80] we first formulate

***Definition 24.** 1) *n elements $\alpha_1, \ldots, \alpha_n$ of an extension $\mathsf{\Lambda}$ of K are called **linearly dependent** relative to K if a linear homogeneous relation*

$$\sum_{k=1}^{n} a_k \alpha_k = 0$$

*exists with coefficients a_k in K which are not all 0; otherwise, **linearly independent** relative to K.*

2) *An element α of $\mathsf{\Lambda}$ is called **linearly dependent on** $\alpha_1, \ldots, \alpha_n$ relative to K, if there is a linear homogeneous representation*

$$\alpha = \sum_{k=1}^{n} a_k \alpha_k$$

*with coefficients a_k in K; otherwise, **linearly independent of** $\alpha_1, \ldots, \alpha_n$ relative to K.*

Referring to the proofs of Theorems 38, 39, 41, 42 [201—203] given in Vol. 1, Section 10 we deduce that these theorems can be meaningfully carried over to the concepts explained in Def. 24 if we replace the linear forms (vectors) in K, appearing there, by elements of an extension $\mathsf{\Lambda}$ of K.

We now define the special class of algebraic extensions in which we are interested:

***Definition 25.** *An extension $\mathsf{\Lambda}$ of K is said to be **of finite degree** over K, if there is a finite maximal system of elements of $\mathsf{\Lambda}$ linearly independent relative to K. Any such maximal system $\alpha_1, \ldots, \alpha_n$ is called a **basis of** $\mathsf{\Lambda}$ relative to K; the uniquely determined number n, the **degree** of $\mathsf{\Lambda}$ over K (notation: $n = [\mathsf{\Lambda} : \mathsf{K}]$).*

The designation *basis* shall mean that *every* element α of $\mathsf{\Lambda}$ is linearly dependent on $\alpha_1, \ldots, \alpha_n$, therefore, has a *basis representation*

$$\alpha = a_1 \alpha_1 + \dots + a_n \alpha_n$$

with coefficients $a_1, \dots, a_n$ in K. By Vol. 1, Theorem 41 [81] this basis representation is *unique*. Conversely, by this theorem the uniqueness of the basis representation in terms of $\alpha_1, \dots, \alpha_n$ implies their linear independence, and the fact that every α can be expressed in terms of these implies their maximality. Therefore, we have

Addendum to Definition 25. *The condition of Def.* 25 *can also be expressed as follows: All elements of* Λ *shall possess a unique basis representation in terms of finitely many elements.*

The following theorem shows something that is not readily seen from Def. 25, namely, that the extensions of finite degree form a special class of algebraic extensions, and, in addition, somewhat more.

Theorem 67. *If* Λ *has finite degree over* K, *then* Λ *is algebraic over* K. *More exactly*:

If $[\Lambda : K] = n$, *then every element* α *of* Λ *is algebraic over* K *and its degree is* $[\alpha : K] \leqq n$.

Proof: The $n+1$ elements $\alpha^0 = e$, $\alpha^1 = \alpha, \alpha^2, \dots, \alpha^n$ are then linearly dependent (Def. 25). Hence there exists a relation

$$a_0 + a_1\alpha + \cdots + a_n\alpha^n = 0$$

with coefficients a_k in K which are not all 0 (Def. 24). This says that α is a root of a polynomial $\bar{f}(x)$ over K of at most n-th degree. But the irreducible polynomial $f(x)$ over K belonging to α also has the degree n at most, since it is a divisor of $\bar{f}(x)$. Therefore, α is algebraic over K of degree $\leqq n$ (Def. 21, 22 [223, 223]).

The condition that an algebraic extension Λ of K must have finite degree over K imposes the restriction that Λ can contain no elements of arbitrarily high degree over K. This restriction, however, is not sufficient in general to ensure the finiteness of the degree of Λ[4] (cf., however, Theorem 91, Corollary [254] to be given later).

[4] Counterexamples are given in *Steinitz: Algebraische Theorie der Körper* (Cf. footnote [5] to Vol. 2, Chapter 2 [214].

That there actually exist algebraic extensions which are *not* of finite degree is shown by the field of all algebraic numbers over P, since this field contains elements of arbitrarily high degree (cf. Theorem 123 [312] to be given later).

Furthermore we prove:

Theorem 68. *If* $\mathsf{\Lambda}$ *has finite degree over* K, *then* $\mathsf{\Lambda}$ *is finite over* K.

Proof: If $\alpha_1, \ldots, \alpha_n$ is a basis of $\mathsf{\Lambda}$, then the basis representation implies that every element of $\mathsf{\Lambda}$ belongs to the integral domain $K[\alpha_1, \ldots, \alpha_n]$. On the other hand, since

$$K \leqq K[\alpha_1, \ldots, \alpha_n] \leqq K(\alpha_1, \ldots, \alpha_n) \leqq \mathsf{\Lambda}$$

is now valid, we have $\mathsf{\Lambda} = K[\alpha_1, \ldots, \alpha_n] = K(\alpha_1, \ldots, \alpha_n)$, therefore $\mathsf{\Lambda}$ is finite over K.

In the remaining theorems we will establish how the concepts explained in Def. 25 depend on the fields K and $\mathsf{\Lambda}$.

Theorem 69. $[\mathsf{\Lambda} : K] = 1$ *if and only if* $\mathsf{\Lambda} = K$.

Proof: a) If $\mathsf{\Lambda} = K$, then the system consisting of e alone is a basis of $\mathsf{\Lambda}$ relative to K, since in this case every a in $\mathsf{\Lambda}$ actually has the unique basis representation $a = a \cdot e$. Therefore, in this case we have $[\mathsf{\Lambda} : K] = 1$.

b) If $[\mathsf{\Lambda} : K] = 1$, then by Theorem 67 $[\alpha : K] \leqq 1$, therefore $= 1$ for every α in $\mathsf{\Lambda}$. By Theorem 64 [223] this means that every α in $\mathsf{\Lambda}$ is an element of K, that is, $\mathsf{\Lambda} = K$.

Theorem 70. *If* $\mathsf{\Lambda} \geqq \overline{K} \geqq K$ *and* $\mathsf{\Lambda}$ *has finite degree over* K, *then* $\mathsf{\Lambda}$ *has finite degree over* $\overline{K}$, *also* $\overline{K}$ *has finite degree over* K, *and* $[\mathsf{\Lambda} : \overline{K}] \leqq [\mathsf{\Lambda} : K], [\overline{K} : K] \leqq [\mathsf{\Lambda} : K]$.

Proof: Let $[\mathsf{\Lambda} : K] = n$. Then more than n elements of $\mathsf{\Lambda}$ are linearly dependent relative to K, therefore a fortiori relative to $\overline{K}$; and more than n elements of $\overline{K}$, as they are also elements of $\mathsf{\Lambda}$, are linearly dependent relative to K. Therefore, in both cases there exists a finite maximal system of at most n linearly independent elements.

The following converse of Theorem 70 is particularly important for the sequel. At the same time the above relations between the degrees will be put in a more precise form.

Theorem 71. *If $\mathsf{\Lambda} \geqq \overline{\mathsf{K}} \geqq \mathsf{K}$ and the degree of $\mathsf{\Lambda}$ over $\overline{\mathsf{K}}$ as well as of $\overline{\mathsf{K}}$ over K is finite, then the degree of $\mathsf{\Lambda}$ over K is also finite and* $[\mathsf{\Lambda} : \mathsf{K}] = [\mathsf{\Lambda} : \overline{\mathsf{K}}] \cdot [\overline{\mathsf{K}} : \mathsf{K}]$.

Proof: Let $[\mathsf{\Lambda} : \overline{\mathsf{K}}] = m$ and $\alpha_1, \ldots, \alpha_m$ be a basis of $\mathsf{\Lambda}$ relative to $\overline{\mathsf{K}}$. Furthermore, let $[\overline{\mathsf{K}} : \mathsf{K}] = j$ and $\overline{\alpha}_1, \ldots, \overline{\alpha}_j$ be a basis of $\overline{\mathsf{K}}$ relative to K. Then we will show that the mj elements $\alpha_i \overline{\alpha}_k$ $(i = 1, \ldots, m;\ k = 1, \ldots, j)$ form a basis of $\mathsf{\Lambda}$ relative to K.

a) Since every α in $\mathsf{\Lambda}$ has a representation

$$\alpha = \sum_{i=1}^{m} \overline{a}_i \alpha_i$$

with $\overline{a}_i$ in $\overline{\mathsf{K}}$, and these $\overline{a}_i$ in $\overline{\mathsf{K}}$ have in turn representations

$$\overline{a}_i = \sum_{k=1}^{j} a_{ik} \overline{\alpha}_k \qquad (i = 1, \ldots, m)$$

with a_{ik} in K, every α in $\mathsf{\Lambda}$ has a representation

$$\alpha = \sum_{i=1}^{m} \sum_{k=1}^{j} a_{ik} \alpha_i \overline{\alpha}_k .$$

Consequently, every α in $\mathsf{\Lambda}$ is linearly dependent on the $\alpha_i \overline{\alpha}_k$ relative to K.

b) Let us set

$$\sum_{i=1}^{m} \sum_{k=1}^{j} a_{ik} \alpha_i \overline{\alpha}_k = 0$$

Then the linear independence of the α_i relative to $\overline{\mathsf{K}}$ first implies that

$$\sum_{k=1}^{j} a_{ik} \overline{\alpha}_k = 0 \qquad (i = 1, \ldots, m).$$

This in turn due to the linear independence of the $\overline{\alpha}_k$ relative to K implies that

$$a_{ik} = 0 \; (i = 1, \ldots, m; \; k = 1, \ldots, j).$$

Consequently, the $\alpha_i\overline{\alpha}_k$ are linearly independent relative to K.

a) and b) imply that the mj elements $\alpha_i\overline{\alpha}_k$ form a maximal system relative to K of linearly independent elements of Λ. This completes the proof of the theorem.

In particular, if we take Theorem 69 into account, Theorem 71 yields:

Theorem 72. *If* Λ *and* $\overline{\Lambda}$ *have finite degrees over* K *and* $\Lambda \leqq \overline{\Lambda}$, *then* $\Lambda = \overline{\Lambda}$ *if and only if* $[\Lambda : K] = [\overline{\Lambda} : K]$.

D. Conjugate Extensions. Conjugate Elements

In Vol. 1, with respect to Def. 7, Addendum [30] , we saw that though extensions Λ_1 and Λ_2 of K isomorphic relative to K were not to be distinguished, still a distinction between two such extensions must be made if they are contained in the same extension Λ. Regarding this point we define the following equivalence relation:

Definition 26.** *Two fields* Λ_1 *and* Λ_2 *isomorphic relative to* K *between* K *and* Λ *are also called* ***conjugate *relative to* K. *Elements* α_1 *and* α_2 *corresponding under an isomorphism relative to* K *are likewise called* ***conjugate*** *relative to* K.

Just as in Def. 18 [219], here too Λ plays only the role of an *auxiliary field* which makes it actually possible to have the relation: "Λ_1 and Λ_2 *are conjugate,*" but, without affecting this relation, can be replaced by any extension $\overline{\Lambda}$ of K containing Λ_1 and Λ_2. If, in speaking of fields Λ_1, Λ_2 conjugate relative to K, we make no reference to such an auxiliary field Λ it simply means that there actually exists an extension Λ which contains Λ_1 as well as Λ_2. As an example of conjugate extensions of K which are actually different we can cite the n fields $K(x_1), \ldots, K(x_n)$ contained in $K(x_1, \ldots, x_n)$. In these $x_1, \ldots, x_n$, in general $\frac{g(x_1)}{h(x_1)}, \ldots, \frac{g(x_n)}{h(x_n)}$, are examples of conjugate elements.

According to the expositions to Vol. 1, Def. 7, Addendum [30], the following fact is obviously valid for conjugate elements which are algebraic over K:

Theorem 73. *If α is an algebraic element over K of an extension Λ of K and $f(x)$ the irreducible polynomial over K belonging to this element, then all elements of Λ conjugate to α are also roots of $f(x)$.*

8. Stem Fields

In this section we will carry out the first step towards the construction of the roots of a polynomial $f(x)$ over K by proving the existence of a special extension of K in which a linear factor of $f(x)$ splits off. This will be done by actually constructing this extension. In addition to this we will obtain a general view of all such extensions. Technically, our investigations will be entirely analogous to the existence- and uniqueness proofs in Vol. 1, Section 4,[5] except that here the main task has already been performed in advance by the construction in Section 2 of the residue class field $K(x, \bmod f(x))$ of an irreducible polynomial $f(x)$. Our present existence proof is based on this field.

By Theorem 45 [206] we can assume without loss of generality that $f(x)$ is irreducible. Our basic theorem is then the following:

[5] The existence- and uniqueness proofs for $K(x)$ in Vol. 1, Section 4 are in fact merely the proofs of this section carried out for $f(x) \equiv 0$.

Theorem 74. *Let $f(x)$ be an irreducible polynomial of degree n over K. Then there exists an extension Σ of K with the properties:*

(I) *$f(x)$ has a root α in Σ, therefore a decomposition $f(x) \equiv (x-\alpha)\ \varphi(x)$.*

(II) *Σ is simple over K and α is a primitive element of Σ, that is, $\Sigma = \mathsf{K}(\alpha)$.*

(III) *Σ is algebraic of finite degree over K; namely, Σ has a basis $\alpha^0, \alpha^1, \ldots, \alpha^{n-1}$, therefore $[\Sigma : \mathsf{K}] = n$. This also means that $\Sigma = \mathsf{K}[\alpha]$.*

If Σ^* is any extension of K satisfying (I), (II), *and α^* is the root of $f(x)$ given in* (I), (II), *then Σ^* is isomorphic to Σ relative to K under the correspondence $\alpha^* \longleftrightarrow \alpha$ (and therefore also has property* (III)). *The extension type of K is therefore uniquely determined by* (I), (II).

a) *Existence Proof*

The residue class field K (x, mod $f(x)$) contains a subdomain K' which is made up of the special residue classes $\{a\}$ determined by elements a of K. On the basis of the correspondence

(1) $$\{a\} \longleftrightarrow a$$

this subdomain is a field isomorphic to K.

Namely, since the polynomial $f(x)$ is not a unit, $a \equiv b$ mod $f(x)$ is equivalent to $a = b$. Hence (1) is a biunique correspondence between K' and K; that it also satisfies the conditions of an isomorphism follows from the rules of combination defined for residue classes.

Therefore, just as in Vol. 1, Proof to Theorem 10, d) [36] and Theorem 11, d) [43] we can form a field Σ isomorphic to $\mathsf{K}(x$, mod $f(x))$ by replacing the elements of the subfield K' by the elements of K corresponding to them according to (1) while preserving all relations of combination. This field contains K itself as a subfield. It will next be shown that this field Σ has the properties (I) to (III).

(I) If we think of the normal representation

$$f(x) \equiv x^n + a_1 x^{n-1} + \cdots + a_n$$

as a relation between the elements $f(x), x, a_1, \ldots, a_n$ *of* $\mathsf{K}[x]$, then this implies by Vol. 1, Theorem 8 [28] the existence of the analogous relation

$$\{f(x)\} = \{x\}^n + \{a_1\}\{x\}^{n-1} + \cdots + \{a_n\}$$

between the corresponding residue classes mod $f(x)$, therefore between elements of $\mathsf{K}(x, \text{mod } f(x))$. Now, since $f(x) \equiv 0$ mod $f(x)$, which means that $\{f(x)\}$ is the zero of $\mathsf{K}(x, \text{mod } f(x))$, then in $\mathsf{K}(x, \text{mod } f(x))$ we have

$$\{x\}^n + \{a_1\}\{x\}^{n-1} + \cdots + \{a_n\} = 0.$$

Let us now see what happens to this relation in passing from $\mathsf{K}(x, \text{mod } f(x))$ to Σ by (1). For this purpose let α designate the element $\{x\}$ not belonging to K', and therefore to be preserved. Then in Σ the relation

$$\alpha^n + a_1\alpha^{n-1} + \cdots + a_n = 0, \text{ that is, } f(\alpha) = 0$$

is valid. The element $\alpha = \{x\}$ of Σ is therefore a root of $f(x)$.

The root α which did *not exist* beforehand is *created* by this proof with as much conceptual preciseness as possible. To be briefer but less precise, our train of thought can be expressed as follows: Since the residue class x mod $f(x)$ satisfies the relation $f(x) \equiv 0$ mod $f(x)$, it is a root of $f(x)$ in $\mathsf{K}(x, \text{mod } f(x))$.[6]

(II) Let β be an element of Σ not belonging to K. Then, according to the construction of Σ this element is a residue class mod $f(x)$. Let $h(x)$ be any element of this residue class, so

[6] To say that the above proof is "trivial" and that it yields "nothing new" is not a valid objection, for it would also have to be raised in the case of the construction of the integers from the natural numbers and of the rational numbers from the integers.

that $\beta = \{h(x)\}$. Then, by returning to the normal representation

$$h(x) \equiv \sum_{k=0}^{\infty} c_k x^k$$

in $\mathsf{K}[x]$ and the relation following from this

$$\{h(x)\} = \sum_{k=0}^{\infty} \{c_k\} \{x_k\}^k$$

in $\mathsf{K}(x, \bmod f(x))$, we obtain the existence of the relation

$$\beta = \{h(x)\} = \sum_{k=0}^{\infty} c_k \{x\}^k = \sum_{k=0}^{\infty} c_k \alpha^k = h(\alpha)$$

in Σ. In case β belongs to K, the corresponding statement is naturally valid (with an $h(x)$ of degree 0). This means that the integral subdomain $\mathsf{K}[\alpha]$ contained in Σ exhausts the totality of elements β of Σ; therefore, the subfield $\mathsf{K}(\alpha)$ likewise contained in Σ must all the more exhaust this set (Def. 19, [221]). Hence $\Sigma = \mathsf{K}[\alpha] = \mathsf{K}(\alpha)$.

(III) By using the reduced residue system of Theorem 27 [192] it follows from the proof for (II) that in the representations $\beta = h(\alpha)$ we can assume $h(x)$ as having a unique representation in the form

$$c_0 + c_1 x + \cdots + c_{n-1} x^{n-1}.$$

This means that all β in Σ can be uniquely represented as linear homogeneous expressions in terms of $\alpha^0, \alpha^1, \ldots, \alpha^{n-1}$ with coefficients in K. Consequently, $\alpha^0, \alpha^1, \ldots, \alpha^{n-1}$ is a basis of Σ (Def. 25, Addendum [226]) and therefore $[\Sigma : \mathsf{K}] = n$.

b) *Uniqueness Proof*

Let Σ^* be an extension of K satisfying (I), (II) and α^* the root of $f(x)$ given in (I), (II). We will first show that the integral subdomain $\mathsf{K}[\alpha^*]$ contained in Σ^* is isomorphic to $\mathsf{K}(x, \bmod f(x))$ by means of the correspondence

(2) $$\beta^* \longleftrightarrow \{h(x)\} \text{ if } \beta^* = h(\alpha^*).$$

Namely, the validity of Vol. 1, Section 2, (δ), (δ') follows from Def. 19 [221]. The validity of Vol. 1, Section 2, (ε), (ε') can be shown as follows: First $\beta_1^* = \beta_2^*$ says that $h_1(\alpha^*) = h_2(\alpha^*)$. By Theorem 53 [210] this yields that $f(x) \mid h_1(x) - h_2(x)$ since $f(\alpha^*) = 0$; that is, $h_1(x) \equiv h_2(x) \mod f(x)$, therefore $\{h_1(x)\} = \{h_2(x)\}$. Secondly, we note that this line of reasoning can also be carried out in the opposite direction. Finally, the validity of Vol. 1, Section 2, (3), (4) [29] follows from the rules of combination defined for the residue classes.

Consequently, since $\mathsf{K}(x, \bmod f(x))$ is a field, the integral domain $\mathsf{K}[\alpha^*]$ is also a field and therefore identical with its quotient field $\mathsf{K}(\alpha^*) = \Sigma^*$. Hence (2) stands for an isomorphism between Σ^* and $\mathsf{K}(x, \bmod f(x))$. Now, since by a) (or by applying to Σ what has been demonstrated for Σ^*) the correspondence

(3) $$\beta \longleftrightarrow \{h(x)\} \text{ if } \beta = h(\alpha)$$

is an isomorphism between Σ and $\mathsf{K}(x, \bmod f(x))$, Σ^* is isomorphic to Σ relative to K on the basis of the correspondence

$$\beta^* \longleftrightarrow \beta \text{ if } \beta^* = h(\alpha^*),\ \beta = h(\alpha)$$

generated by combining (2) and (3). This correspondence actually maps the elements of K onto themselves, and it is generated by the correspondence $\alpha^* \longleftrightarrow \alpha$ specified in the theorem.

This completes the proof of Theorem 74. As we will see later, an extension of K can contain different fields Σ with the properties (I), (II) of Theorem 74. Therefore, here, we set up the following definition in contrast to the formulation of Def. 8 to 10 in Vol. 1 [37, 45, 46] wherein the *definite* article was used:

Definition 27.** *Every extension* Σ *of* K *with the properties* (I), (II), *and therefore also* (III), *of Theorem* 74 *is called a* ***stem field *of* $f(x)$ *over* K.

Theorem 74 then yields:

Theorem 75. *If the irreducible polynomial* $f(x)$ *over* K *has a root* α *in an extension* Λ *of* K, *then* Λ *contains a stem field of* $f(x)$, *namely,* $K(\alpha)$.

Proof: $K(\alpha)$ has the properties (I), (II) of Theorem 74.

As far as the extension type is concerned, this theorem completely describes the structure of any extension of K in which an irreducible $f(x)$ over K has a root. Namely, apart from isomorphisms relative to K all and only the extensions of a stem field of $f(x)$ are such extensions of K. Hence the stem fields themselves represent the *smallest* such extension type.

9. General Theory of Extensions (2). Simple and Finite Algebraic Extensions

In this section we will derive some important relations between the general concepts introduced in Section 7. For this purpose we will use the results of Section 8.

A. Simple Algebraic Extensions

In the first part of Theorem 74 [231] it was established that the stem fields over K are simple and algebraic of finite degree. Conversely, from the second part of this theorem we immediately obtain:

Theorem 76. *If* Λ *is simple over* K *and a primitive element* α *of* Λ *is algebraic of degree* n *over* K, *then* $\Lambda = K(\alpha)$ *is a stem field for the irreducible polynomial of* n*-th degree* $f(x)$ *over* K *belonging to* α. *This means that* A *is algebraic of finite degree, namely, of degree* n *over* K.

In particular, this implies the following relation between the two degrees defined independently of one another in Def. 22 [223] and Def. 25 [225] :

Theorem 77. *The degree of an algebraic element* α *over* K *is equal to the degree of the corresponding stem field* $\mathsf{K}(\alpha)$ *over* K:

$$[\alpha : \mathsf{K}] = [\mathsf{K}(\alpha) : \mathsf{K}].$$

The statement of Theorem 76 can be sharpened by also bringing in the separability. For this purpose we first derive the following *criterion for separability*:

Theorem 78. *If* K *has characteristic* p, *then an element* α *algebraic over* K *is separable over* K *if and only if* $\mathsf{K}(\alpha^p) = \mathsf{K}(\alpha)$.

Proof: Let α be separable. If

$$f(x) \equiv x^n + a_1 x^{n-1} + \cdots + a_n$$

is the irreducible polynomial, separable by Theorem 63 [223] , belonging to α, then

$$f_1(x) \equiv x^n + a_1^p x^{n-1} + \cdots + a_n^p$$

is the irreducible polynomial belonging to α^p.

For, in the first place, $f_1(\alpha^p) = f(\alpha)^p = 0$ by Theorem 44 [204] . Secondly, $f_1(x)$ is irreducible. For the proof note that $h(x) \mid f_1(x)$ implies $h(x^p) \mid f_1(x^p) \equiv f(x)^p$ (Theorem 44). Therefore, the irreducibility of $f(x)$ yields $h(x^p) \equiv f(x)^r$ with $0 \leqq r \leqq p$. Now, on taking derivatives of both sides we obtain $0 \equiv r f'(x)$ (Theorem 57 [213] ; this yields $r = 0$ or p — since $f'(x) \not\equiv 0$ (Def. 17 [214]) —, therefore $h(x^p) \equiv f(x)^0 \equiv e$ or $h(x^p) \equiv f(x)^p \equiv f_1(x^p)$, and consequently $h(x) \equiv e$ or $h(x) \equiv f_1(x)$.

Accordingly,

$$[\alpha : \mathsf{K}] = n = [\alpha^p : \mathsf{K}],$$

therefore by Theorem 77

$$[K(\alpha):K] = [K(\alpha^p):K]$$

and by Theorem 72 [229],

$$K(\alpha) = K(\alpha^p).$$

b) Let α be inseparable. Then the irreducible polynomial belonging to α is inseparable (Theorem 63 [223]); therefore, it has the form $f(x) \equiv f_0(x^p)$ (Def. 17 [214]). This means that $f_0(x)$ is the irreducible polynomial belonging to α^p.

For, in the first place, $f_0(\alpha^p) = f(\alpha) = 0$. In the second place, $f_0(x)$ is irreducible, since $h(x) \mid f_0(x)$ implies $h(x^p) \mid f_0(x^p) \equiv f(x)$ and $f(x)$ is irreducible by assumption.

Accordingly,

$$[\alpha:K] = p[\alpha^p:K] > [\alpha^p:K],$$

therefore by Theorem 77

$$[K(\alpha):K] > [K(\alpha^p):K],$$

and consequently by Theorem 72 [229]

$$K(\alpha) > K(\alpha^p).$$

If $K(\alpha) = K(\alpha^p)$, then α must be separable.

We now prove the sharpened form of Theorem 76 announced above:

Theorem 79. *If* K *has characteristic* p, *and* α *in Theorem 76 is assumed to be separable over* K, *then* $\Lambda = K(\alpha)$ *is also separable over* K.

Proof: According to Def. 23 [224] we have to show that every element β of $K(\alpha)$ is separable. By the criterion of Theorem 78 this will follow by showing that the relation $K(\alpha^p) = K(\alpha)$, which is valid by assumption, yields the corresponding relation $K(\beta^p) = K(\beta)$.

For this purpose let us set

$$[K(\alpha):K(\beta)] = m, \qquad [K(\beta):K] = j,$$
$$[K(\alpha):K(\beta^p)] = [K(\alpha^p):K(\beta^p)] = m', \qquad [K(\beta^p):K] = j'.$$

Then by Theorem 71 [228] we have

$$mj = m'j',$$

and by Theorem 70 [227]

$$m \leq m', \quad j' \leq j.$$

Now, let

$$\varphi(x) \equiv x^m + \alpha_1 x^{m-1} + \cdots + \alpha_m$$

be the irreducible polynomial in $\mathsf{K}(\beta)$ belonging to α (cf. Theorem 77). According to Theorem 74, (III) [231] and Theorem 76 its coefficients can be represented in the form

$$\alpha_k = \sum_{i=0}^{j-1} a_{ik}\,\beta^i \qquad (k = 0, \ldots, m-1).$$

Then, on raising the relation $\varphi(\alpha) = 0$ to the p-th power according to Theorem 44 [204], we obtain that α^p is a root of the polynomial

$$\varphi_1(x) \equiv x^m + \alpha_1' x^{m-1} + \cdots + \alpha_m'$$

of degree m with the coefficients

$$\alpha_k' = \sum_{i=0}^{j-1} a_{ik}^p\,\beta^{pi} \qquad (k = 0, \ldots, m-1)$$

in $\mathsf{K}(\beta^p)$. By Theorem 53 [210] the irreducible polynomial in $\mathsf{K}(\beta^p)$ belonging to α^p is then a divisor of $\varphi_1(x)$. This implies that its degree satisfies the relation (cf. Theorem 77)

$$m' \leq m.$$

Consequently, due to the previous relation we have

$$m' = m, \text{ therefore } j' = j,$$

that is, by Theorem 72 [229] we actually have $\mathsf{K}(\beta^p) = \mathsf{K}(\beta)$.

Theorem 76 shows that there are only two possible cases for a simple extension Λ of K: Either the relations of Theorem 76 are valid or every primitive element α of Λ, therefore also Λ itself, is transcendental over K. In the latter case each such α behaves as an indeterminate over K (see Def. 21 [223]), and $\Lambda = \mathsf{K}(\alpha)$ has the extension type of the field $\mathsf{K}(x)$ of rational functions of an indeterminate x over K.[7] Accordingly, by Theorem 76 we have (see also Theorem 79):

Theorem 80. *The concept* ***stem field of a (separable) irreducible polynomial*** *is the same as that of* ***simple (separable) algebraic extension*** *(just as the concept* ***field of rational functions of an indeterminate*** *and* ***simple transcendental extension****).*

With regard to the separability we can be more precise: Every irreducible polynomial is separable which has a simple separable algebraic extension as a stem field.

Hence these concepts are only technically different, inasmuch as we think of *stem fields* as generated from a definite irreducible polynomial $f(x)$, while the term *simple algebraic extension* is free from such a reference to a definite $f(x)$, that is, to a definite primitive element α. The latter, more general, interpretation is useful because it appears naturally suited for investigating, not only the special $f(x)$ and its root α, by which a stem field is generated, but also its other elements which are primitive. This will be done in the following.

If Λ is a simple algebraic extension of K and n its degree, then every element β of Λ is algebraic over K, and so by Theorem 67 [226] has a degree $\leqq n$. Now, by Theorem 77 $[\beta : \mathsf{K}] = [\mathsf{K}(\beta) : \mathsf{K}]$. Hence the application of Theorem 71 [228] and Theorem 72 [229] yields the more precise

---

[7] The simple extensions are exact analogues of cyclic groups (different from the identity) (see Def. 12 [196] and Def. 19 [221]). Here a distinction is made between simple extensions according to whether they are algebraic, that is, are $\cong \mathsf{K}(x, \bmod f(x))$ with $f(x) \not\equiv 0$, *e* and of finite degree (degree of $f(x)$), or transcendental, that is, are $\cong \mathsf{K}(x, \bmod f(x))$ with $f(x) \equiv 0$ and of infinite degree. This distinction corresponds to that made in connection with Theorem 33 [197] between cyclic groups (different from the identity); namely, into those which are $\cong \mathfrak{R}_f$ with $f \neq 0, 1$ and so of finite order (absolute value of f), and those which are $\cong \mathfrak{R}_f$ with $f = 0$ and so of infinite order.

Theorem 81. *If* Λ *is a simple algebraic extension of degree* n *over* K *and* β *an element of* Λ *of degree* j *over* K, *then* $j \mid n$ *and* $m = \frac{n}{j}$ *is the degree of* Λ *over* K(β).

In particular, β *is a primitive element of* Λ, *if and only if it has degree* n *over* K.

We stress in addition the following important consequence of Theorem 74, (II) and (III) [231]:

Theorem 82. *If* α *is an algebraic element over* K, *then* $K[\alpha] = K(\alpha)$.

This property, which is not valid for transcendental elements, is naturally very useful for operating with an algebraic element. It arises from the last conclusion in Theorem 28 [193] in virtue of the reduction, carried out in Section 8, of K(α) to the residue class field K(x, mod $f(x)$) for the $f(x)$ belonging to α. The proof of Theorem 28, combined with the reduction of Section 8, also tells us how to handle this property in a practical way when operating with an algebraic element (removal of all denominators which may occur not belonging to K).

B. Finite Algebraic Extensions

First of all we prove an analogue to Theorem 76 [235]:

Theorem 83. *If* Λ *is finite over* K *and a primitive system of elements* $\alpha_1, \ldots, \alpha_r$ *of* Λ *is algebraic over* K, *then* $\Lambda = K(\alpha_1, \ldots, \alpha_r)$ *is algebraic of finite degree over* K.

Proof: The simultaneous adjunction of $\alpha_1, \ldots, \alpha_r$ leading from K to Λ can be replaced by the successive adjunctions

$$K = \Lambda_0,\ \Lambda_0(\alpha_1) = \Lambda_1,\ \Lambda_1(\alpha_2) = \Lambda_2,\ \ldots,\ \Lambda_{r-1}(\alpha_r) = \Lambda_r = \Lambda$$

(Theorem 62 [220]). Here α_i is algebraic over Λ_{i-1} for $i = 1, \ldots, r$ (Theorem 65 [223]), so that Λ_i has finite degree over Λ_{i-1} (Theorem 76 [235]); therefore, Λ has finite degree over K (Theorem 71 [228]), and consequently is also algebraic over K (Theorem 67 [226]).

A sharpened form of Theorem 83 analogous to Theorem 79 [237] will be proved later (Theorem 90 [251]) by including the separability.

There are various types of finite extensions $\mathsf{\Lambda} = \mathsf{K}(\alpha_1, \ldots, \alpha_r)$. On the one hand, we may have the two extremes: $\alpha_1, \ldots, \alpha_r$ algebraic over K and $\alpha_1, \ldots, \alpha_r$ transcendental over K; these two cases are the only possibilities if the extensions are *simple.* On the other hand, we may have the still further possibilities that some of the α_i are algebraic while some are transcendental over K. Here we are only interested in the case first specified, given in Theorem 83, since it is only in this case that $\mathsf{\Lambda}$ can be algebraic over K, as it is by Theorem 83. From now on we apply ourselves to this case.

In Theorem 83 we have established when a finite extension is algebraic. Conversely, we next investigate when an algebraic extension is finite. In Theorem 80 [239] the requirement of *simplicity* forced us to stress the *special* class of algebraic extensions of finite degree which have a basis of the special form $\alpha^0, \alpha^1, \ldots, \alpha^{n-1}$ (namely, consisting of the first n powers of a single element α). Now the requirement of finiteness will make us stress, however, the class of *all* extensions of finite degree among the algebraic extensions. Namely, from the results of Theorems 67, 68 [226, 227] on the one hand, and from Theorem 83, on the other hand, we immediately obtain:

Theorem 84. *The concept* ***finite algebraic extension*** *is the same as that of* ***extension of finite degree.***

By the successive application of Theorem 82 to the chain of simple algebraic extensions appearing in the proof of Theorem 83 we further obtain the following generalization of the theorem first mentioned:

Theorem 85. *For finitely many elements $\alpha_1, \ldots, \alpha_r$ of an extension of K algebraic over K we have* $\mathsf{K}[\alpha_1, \ldots, \alpha_r] = \mathsf{K}(\alpha_1, \ldots, \alpha_r)$.

Moreover, along with Theorem 71 [228], Theorem 83 enables us to prove in addition the converse of this theorem, which was previously announced after Theorem 66 [224]:[8]

Theorem 86. *If* $\mathsf{\Lambda} \geqq \overline{\mathsf{K}} \geqq \mathsf{K}$ *and* $\mathsf{\Lambda}$ *is algebraic over* $\overline{\mathsf{K}}$, $\overline{\mathsf{K}}$ *is algebraic over* K, *then* $\mathsf{\Lambda}$ *is also algebraic over* K.

Proof: Let α be an element of $\mathsf{\Lambda}$ and $\varphi(x) \equiv x^r + \alpha_1 x^{r-1} + \cdots + \alpha_r$ the irreducible polynomial over $\overline{\mathsf{K}}$ belonging to it. Then, on the one hand, α is algebraic over $\mathsf{K}(\alpha_1, \ldots, \alpha_r)$, therefore $\mathsf{K}(\alpha_1, \ldots, \alpha_r, \alpha)$ has finite degree over $\mathsf{K}(\alpha_1, \ldots, \alpha_r)$ (Theorem 76 [235]); on the other hand, $\alpha_1, \ldots, \alpha_r$ are algebraic over K, therefore $\mathsf{K}(\alpha_1, \ldots, \alpha_r)$ has finite degree over K (Theorem 83). Consequently, $\mathsf{K}(\alpha_1 \ldots, \alpha_r, \alpha)$ also has finite degree over K (Theorem 71 [228]); therefore, α is algebraic over K (Theorem 67 [226]). Hence $\mathsf{\Lambda}$ is also algebraic over K (Def. 23 [224]).

10. Root Fields

In this section we will construct the roots of a polynomial $f(x)$ over K by proving the existence of a special extension of K through the repeated application of the stem field construction of Section 8. In this extension $f(x)$ resolves completely into linear factors. In addition we will obtain a general view of all extensions of this kind.

Our basic theorem, analogous to Theorem 74 [231], is the following:

Theorem 87. *Let* $f(x)$ *be a polynomial over* K. *Then there exists an extension* W *of* K *with the properties:*

[8] Without including the separability. — This can be taken into account only later (Theorem 92 [255]).

(I) *$f(x)$ resolves in* W *into linear factors*

$$f(x) \equiv (x - \alpha_1) \cdots (x - \alpha_r).$$

(II) W *is finite over* K *and* $\alpha_1, \ldots, \alpha_r$ *is a primitive system of elements, that is,* $\mathsf{W} = \mathsf{K}(\alpha_1, \ldots, \alpha_r)$.

(III) W *is therefore algebraic of finite degree over* K *and also* $\mathsf{W} = \mathsf{K}[\alpha_1, \ldots, \alpha_r]$.

If W^* *is any extension of* K *satisfying* (I), (II) *(and therefore also* (III)*) and* $\alpha_1^*, \ldots, \alpha_r^*$ *are the roots of* $f(x)$ *in* W^*, *then* W^* *is isomorphic to* W *relative to* K *with respect to a suitable ordering of* $\alpha_1^*, \ldots, \alpha_r^*$ *on the basis of the correspondences*

$$\alpha_1^* \longleftrightarrow \alpha_1, \ldots, \alpha_r^* \longleftrightarrow \alpha_r.$$

The extension type of W *is therefore uniquely determined by* (I), (II).

a) *Existence Proof*

The proof can be obtained by means of the following r steps which we will only indicate schematically:

1) $f(x) = p_1(x)\,\bar{f}(x)$, $p_1(x)$ prime factor in K, Σ_1 stem field of $p_1(x)$ over K, α_1 root of $p_1(x)$ in Σ_1, therefore

$$f(x) \equiv (x - \alpha_1)\,\varphi_1(x) \text{ in } \Sigma_1,\ \Sigma_1 = \mathsf{K}(\alpha_1).$$

2) $\varphi_1(x) = \pi_2(x)\,\bar{\varphi}_1(x)$, $\pi_2(x)$ prime factor in Σ_1, Σ_2 stem field of $\pi_2(x)$ over Σ_1, α_2 root of $\pi_2(x)$ in Σ_2, therefore

$$\varphi_1(x) \equiv (x - \alpha_2)\,\varphi_2(x) \text{ in } \Sigma_2,\ \Sigma_2 = \Sigma_1(\alpha_2),$$
$$f(x) \equiv (x - \alpha_1)(x - \alpha_2)\,\varphi_2(x) \text{ in } \Sigma_2,\ \Sigma_2 = \mathsf{K}(\alpha_1, \alpha_2).$$

....

r) ... $f(x) \equiv (x - \alpha_1) \ldots (x - \alpha_r)$ in Σ_r, $\Sigma_r = \mathsf{K}(\alpha_1, \ldots, \alpha_r)$.

The extension $\Sigma_r = \mathsf{W}$ arrived at through these r steps has the stated properties.

b) *Uniqueness Proof*

Let W^* be an extension of K satisfying (I), (II) and let $\alpha_1^*, \ldots, \alpha_r^*$ be the roots of $f(x)$ in W^*. We will show in the following r steps that a chain of fields exists between K and W*:

$$K \leq \Sigma_1^* \leq \Sigma_2^* \leq \cdots \leq \Sigma_r^* \leq W^*,$$

such that each field is isomorphic relative to K to the corresponding field of the chain in a) with respect to a suitable ordering of $\alpha_1^*, \ldots, \alpha_r^*$ on the basis of the correspondences of the theorem.

1) By Theorem 25 [189] the prime factor $p_1(x)$ of $f(x)$ in K is a product of certain of the prime factors $x - \alpha_1^*, \ldots, x - \alpha_r^*$ of $f(x)$ in W*. Therefore, $p_1(x)$ has one of the $\alpha_1^*, \ldots, \alpha_r^*$ as a root. Assume the ordering as chosen so that α_1^* is a root of $p_1(x)$. By Theorems 74, 75 [231, 235] W* then contains the stem field $\Sigma_1^* = K(\alpha_1^*)$ of $p_1(x)$ over K, and on the basis of the correspondence $\alpha_1^* \longleftrightarrow \alpha_1$ this is isomorphic to Σ_1 relative to K.

2) In Σ_1^* there is a decomposition $f(x) \equiv (x - \alpha_1^*)\,\varphi_1^*(x)$. Since the coefficients of $\varphi_1^*(x) \equiv \dfrac{f(x)}{x - \alpha_1^*}$ in α_1^* and those of $f(x)$ are computed in the same rational way (cf. the remark after Theorem 13 [180]) as in the case of $\varphi_1(x) \equiv \dfrac{f(x)}{x - \alpha_1}$ in α_1 and those of $f(x)$, the coefficients of $\varphi_1^*(x)$ and $\varphi_1(x)$ correspond to one another by the isomorphism $\alpha_1^* \longleftrightarrow \alpha_1$ between Σ_1^* and Σ_1. By the remarks to Vol. 1. Def. 7, Addendum [30] the polynomial $\pi_2^*(x)$ corresponding by this isomorphism to the prime factor $\pi_2(x)$ of $\varphi_1(x)$ is a prime factor of $\varphi_1^*(x)$ in Σ_1^*. Hence it is a product of certain of the prime factors $x - \alpha_2^*, \ldots, x - \alpha_r^*$ of $\varphi_1^*(x)$ in W*. Therefore, $\pi_2^*(x)$ has one of the $\alpha_2^*, \ldots, \alpha_r^*$ as a root, and we can assume the ordering as chosen so that α_2^* is a root of $\pi_2^*(x)$. In this case W* contains the stem field $\Sigma_2^* = \Sigma_1^*(\alpha_2^*) = K(\alpha_1^*, \alpha_2^*)$ of $\pi_2^*(x)$ over Σ_1^* and by the remarks to Vol. 1. Def. 7, Addendum this is isomorphic relative to

K to the stem field Σ_2 of $\pi_2(x)$ over Σ_1 on the basis of the correspondence $\alpha_2^* \longleftrightarrow \alpha_2$ together with the isomorphism $\alpha_1^* \longleftrightarrow \alpha_1$ between the subfields Σ_1^* and Σ_1.

. . . .

r) ... W^* contains the field $\Sigma_r^* = \mathsf{K}(\alpha_1^*, \ldots, \alpha_r^*)$, and this is isomorphic to $\Sigma_r = \mathsf{K}(\alpha_1, \ldots, \alpha_r)$ relative to K on the basis of the correspondences $\alpha_1^* \longleftrightarrow \alpha_1, \ldots, \alpha_r^* \longleftrightarrow \alpha_r$.

Since by (II) $\Sigma_r^* = \mathsf{W}^*$, $\Sigma_r = \mathsf{W}$, the statement follows from the r-th step.

This completes the proof of Theorem 87. Analogously to Def. 27 [235], here too we define with the *indefinite* article:

Definition 28.** *Every extension* W *of* K *with the properties* (I), (II), *and therefore also* (III), *of Theorem* 87 *is called a* ***root field *of* $f(x)$ *over* K.

Analogously to Theorem 75 [235], Theorem 87 then yields:

Theorem 88. *If the polynomial* $f(x)$ *over* K *resolves into linear factors in an extension* Λ *of* K: $f(x) \equiv (x-\alpha_1)\cdots(x-\alpha_r)$, *then* Λ *contains a root field of* $f(x)$, *namely* $\mathsf{K}(\alpha_1, \ldots, \alpha_r)$.

Proof: $\mathsf{K}(\alpha_1, \ldots, \alpha_r)$ has the properties (I), (II) of Theorem 87.

This enables us to survey the totality of all extensions of K in which a polynomial $f(x)$ over K resolves into linear factors, at least as long as only the extension type is taken into consideration. Namely, apart from isomorphisms relative to K, this totality consists of all and only the extensions of a root field of $f(x)$. Therefore, the root fields themselves represent the *smallest* extension types of this kind.

In Def. 27 [235] we were not permitted to define the stem field of an irreducible $f(x)$ by using the *definite* article, because by Theorem 75 [235] a root field $\mathsf{W} = \mathsf{K}(\alpha_1, \ldots, \alpha_n)$ of $f(x)$ contains the n stem fields $\Sigma_1 = \mathsf{K}(\alpha_1), \ldots, \Sigma_n = \mathsf{K}(\alpha_n)$ which can very well be different, as our later exposition will show. In the case of root fields, however, we have by Theorem 50 [209]:

Theorem 89. *Under the assumption of Theorem 88* $\mathsf{\Lambda}$ *contains no other root field of* $f(x)$ *besides the root field* $\mathsf{K}(\alpha_1, \ldots, \alpha_r)$.

This means that two different root fields of $f(x)$ cannot occur in one and the same extension of K. Consequently, (as in the case of quotient fields — cf. Vol. 1, Theorem 10, Corollary [37]) we can speak of *the* root field of $f(x)$ plain and simple, hence, also of *the* roots of $f(x)$ without expressly naming an extension containing them. If we start with a root α of $f(x)$, namely, with a stem field $\Sigma = \mathsf{K}(\alpha)$ of one of the prime factors $p(x)$ of $f(x)$, then, as immediately follows from the proof to Theorem 87, a) 1), the root field $\mathsf{W} = \mathsf{K}(\alpha_1, \ldots, \alpha_r)$ of $f(x)$ can be taken so that it contains α and therefore also $\Sigma = \mathsf{K}(\alpha)$. This will frequently be done in the following.

In our exposition we have, in principle, disregarded the *nature* of the roots. In the next section we will, for once, consider this nature, for historical reasons, in the special case of a ground field consisting of numbers. Except for this digression we will be concerned only with the *structure* (the extension type) of the root field under consideration. The following sections will be devoted to the investigation of this structure.

The constructions in Sections 8, 10 give us a complete solution of the problem of solving algebraic equations, as formulated and explained in the introduction. Accordingly, from now on the roots of a polynomial are no longer to be regarded as *unknowns*, that is, as *elements to be determined*, but as *completely determined elements*, *given* by the constructions in Sections 8, 10.

11. The So-called Fundamental Theorem of Algebra

As already stressed in connection with Def. 18 [219] we cannot get around the existence proofs of Sections 8, 10 by adjoining a root α or the roots $\alpha_1, \ldots, \alpha_r$ of $f(x)$ to the ground field K "from below." Only if we have somehow obtained beforehand an extension of K in which $f(x)$ has a linear factor or resolves into linear factors, can this simpler course be followed. Now, in the mathematical literature of the past this was generally arrived at on the basis of the *so-called Fundamental Theorem of Algebra.* This theorem states that every polynomial over a number field resolves into linear factors in the field of complex numbers; in particular, so also does every polynomial over the smallest possible number field P. This means that the existence of the roots of *all* algebraic equations with numerical coefficients is proved by constructing, *once and for all,* the field of complex numbers and proving that these facts are valid in this field.

Now, however, we no longer think of this theorem, first proved by *Gauss,* as belonging to algebra in the modern sense —, even if, as we did at the end of Vol. 1, Introduction, we take algebra to include not only the complex of theorems dealing with the solution of equations but also anything that can be deduced from the field axioms (that is, the *general rules of operations* of the rational numbers) or a part of them (ring, integral domain, group). — This theorem, it must be understood, cannot be proved without the tools of analysis (limit, continuity), even though, as in many of the extremely numerous proofs, these may be used to a very small extent.[9]. Also, the importance of the so-called Fundamental Theorem of Algebra does not extend beyond the special number fields. This fact likewise deprives it of its *fundamental role* for algebra from

[9] A simple proof of this theorem is given in *K. Knopp, Funktionentheorie* (Theory of Functions) I, 6, edition 1944, Section 28, Theorem 3, p. 112 (Sammlung Göschen 668), by making full use of analytic (complex-function-theoretic point of view) methods. In doing so it is presented in a natural way as a theorem in the theory of complex functions.

the standpoint formulated in Vol. 1, Introduction (cf. the second and third paragraphs of Vol. 1, Introduction).[10] Hence we were justified in deleting the so-called Gaussian Fundamental Theorem of Algebra from our presentation and adopting instead the existence proofs of Sections 8, 10 for the roots of algebraic equations. These proofs were devised by *Kronecker* and constructed by *Steinitz*; they rest on a foundation which is entirely abstract and consequently capable of giving much more far-reaching support than the so-called Fundamental Theorem of Algebra.

In addition *Steinitz* proved a complex of theorems analogous to those existing between number fields and the complex number field, which is probably his main contribution in the sphere of algebra. Namely, he showed that there exist extensions Λ to every ground field K in which *all* polynomials over K simultaneously resolve into linear factors and that the smallest possible field of this kind, A, just as our stem fields and root fields, is uniquely determined by K, except for isomorphisms relative to K, namely, as the *field of all algebraic elements over* K. Moreover, this field A has the property that there are no proper algebraic extensions of A; therefore every polynomial over A also resolves into linear factors in A. Hence *Steinitz* called it *algebraically closed*. In the special case of the ground field P, A is the field of all algebraic numbers. Since the Steinitz existence proof for A must depend on the special existence proofs of Sections 8, 10 we cannot get around these proofs by starting from the existence of A.

In order to prevent misunderstandings in regarding the use of the *definite* article, as introduced in Theorem 89, we wish to point

---

[10] However, *E. Artin* and *O. Schreier* [*Algebraische Konstruktion reeller Körper* (Algebraic Construction of Real Fields), Abhandlungen aus dem Mathematischen Seminar der Universität Hamburg (Papers of the Mathematical Seminar of Hamburg University) 5 (1926)] have extended the sphere of algebra so that the *general ordering rules* of rational numbers also appear in the circle of algebraic (axiomatic) considerations. The so-called Fundamental Theorem of Algebra as a special theorem of the complex number field is then subordinated to a corresponding theorem regarding a general class of fields and receives in this new extended form a new franchise in modern algebra.

out that in the special case wherein K is a number field our existence proofs in Sections 8 to 10 do not yield the existence of the roots of a polynomial over K. Furthermore, the roots and their rational functions over K do not turn up as *complex numbers* but merely as *abstract calculating elements.* The extent to which these elements can be called *numbers* then depends on the extension of the concept *number,* which is not universally settled. However to subsume it under the concept of *complex number* it would first have to be shown, over and above our existence proof, that these elements can be represented in the form $a + bi$, where i is a root of the polynomial $x^2 + 1$ and a, b are elements of a field which is isomorphic to a subfield of the real number field. Such a proof would generally amount to the proof of the so-called Fundamental Theorem of Algebra (or its generalization mentioned in footnote 10). Only for the special case of the polynomial $x^2 + 1$ itself, in a field K of real numbers, is it immediately obvious: If this polynomial is irreducible in K and i one of its roots in a stem field Σ over K (which, incidentally, is then, at the same time, a root field in which the decomposition $x^2 + 1 \equiv (x - i)(x + i)$ is valid), then by Theorem 74 [231] every element of Σ has a unique representation $a + bi$ with numbers a, b in K, and the operations with these elements behave isomorphically to the known operations with the complex numbers because of the equation $i^2 = -1$. *Cauchy,* the founder of the *concrete* theory of complex functions, was the first to take this *abstract* path in order to introduce the "imaginary" i starting from the real number field K.[11] In doing so, he laid down the cornerstone to the conceptual structure of *abstract algebra* which was placed on a broader foundation by *Kronecker* and *Steinitz* and has been continuously growing to the present day.

[11] *Cauchy* introduced the complex numbers according to the scheme of the existence proof in Section 8, therefore as residue classes mod $x^2 + 1$; in particular, i stood for the residue class x mod $x^2 + 1$. (Exerc. d'anal. et de phys. math. 4 (1847), p. 87).

IV. The Structure of the Root Fields of Algebraic Equations

In this chapter we will first derive (Sections 12, 13) some properties of root fields accessible by the foregoing methods. Then (Sections 14 to 16) we will introduce as new tools certain finite groups determined by extensions of finite degree, namely, their *Galois groups.* Finally (Sections 17, 18) we will develop the *Galois Theory* on this foundation. This theory will enable us to obtain a complete grasp of the structure of the root field in the sense in which the main objective of this volume was stated in the introduction.

In doing so we have to restrict ourselves throughout to *separable* polynomials and extensions. As shown by *Steinitz*, the theory to be developed in the following must undergo essential modifications in order to be applicable to *inseparable* polynomials and extensions. Due to the lack of space, here we cannot go into the points of deviation.

12. Simplicity and Separability of the Root Fields of Separable Polynomials, more Generally, of Finite Algebraic Extensions with Separable Primitive System of Elements

The property of the root fields of separable polynomials specified in the title of this section is basic for the sequel. It is generally valid for finite algebraic extensions with separable primitive system of elements, to which the root fields of separable polynomials actually belong (Theorem 87 [242]).

In the proof we must restrict ourselves for methodical reasons to ground fields K with *infinitely many elements.*

However, by using other methods of attack it can be shown that this restriction is actually superfluous (cf. end of Section 20 [309 ff]). Hence we are permitted to formulate the following theorems, as well as all others depending on them, without this restriction.

The theorem to be proved is called the **Abelian Theorem** after its discoverer. It is the following:

Theorem 90. *Every finite algebraic extension* $\mathsf{\Lambda}$ *of* K *with separable primitive system of elements, especially therefore the root field of any separable polynomial* $f(x)$ *over* K, *is simple, algebraic and separable over* K, *therefore a stem field of a separable irreducible polynomial* $g(x)$ *over* K.

Proof: [1] *Let* $\mathsf{\Lambda} = \mathsf{K}(\alpha_1, \ldots, \alpha_r)$, where $\alpha_1, \ldots, \alpha_r$ are separable and algebraic over K, For $r = 1$ there is nothing more to be proved (Theorems 76, 79 [235, 237]).

a) $r = 2$.

Let $f_1(x)$, $f_2(x)$ be the irreducible polynomials over K separable by the assumption and Theorem 63 [223] , belonging to α_1, α_2. Furthermore, let W be the root field of the polynomial $f_1(x)f_2(x)$ over K, and

$$f_1(x) \equiv \prod_{\nu_1=1}^{n_1} (x - \alpha_{1\nu_1}), \quad f_2(x) \equiv \prod_{\nu_2=1}^{n_2} (x - \alpha_{2\nu_2})$$

the decompositions of $f_1(x)$ and $f_2(x)$ in W into linear factors. Then α_1 is one of the $\alpha_{1\nu_1}$, α_2 one of the $\alpha_{2\nu_2}$. Furthermore, the $\alpha_{1\nu_1}$ and the $\alpha_{2\nu_2}$ are each different from one another (Theorem 58 [215]).

Hence the $n_1 n_2$ linear functions

---

[1] Hitherto this proof has nearly always been given using the *Theorem on Symmetric Functions* (cf. Theorem 131 [329] , given later). However, the basic idea of the proof given in this text, which does not use this theorem, was used already by *Galois* for the same purpose.

$$\vartheta_{\nu_1\nu_2}(\bar{x}) = \alpha_{1\nu_1} + \bar{x}\alpha_{2\nu_2}$$

in $W[\bar{x}]$ are all different from one another, since any two of them differ either in the coefficients of the indeterminate $\bar{x}$ or in the coefficients of the terms not containing $\bar{x}$. Therefore, if, as we assume here, K has *infinitely many elements*, then by Theorem 49 [208] (applied to W for K, K for M) an element $a \neq 0$ exists in K so that the $n_1 n_2$ elements

$$\vartheta_{\nu_1\nu_2} = \vartheta_{\nu_1\nu_2}(a) = \alpha_{1\nu_1} + a\alpha_{2\nu_2}$$

are all different from one another.

Now, let
$$\vartheta = \alpha_1 + a\alpha_2$$
be the element among the $\vartheta_{\nu_1\nu_2}$ corresponding to the system $(\alpha_{1\nu_1}, \alpha_{2\nu_2}) = (\alpha_1, \alpha_2)$. Then we form the polynomial $\varphi(x)$ according to [2]

$$(-a)^{n_1}\,\varphi(x) = \prod_{\nu_1=1}^{n_1}(\vartheta - (\alpha_{1\nu_1} + ax)) = \prod_{\nu_1=1}^{n_1}((\alpha_1 + a\alpha_2) - (\alpha_{1\nu_1} + ax))$$
$$= \prod_{\nu_1=1}^{n_1}((\vartheta - ax) - \alpha_{1\nu_1}) = f(\vartheta - ax).$$

The *first* representation enables us to recognize that $\varphi(x)$ actually has the root α_2, corresponding to the linear factor $\vartheta - (\alpha_1 + ax)$. However, none of the roots $\alpha_{2\nu_2}$ of $f(x)$ different from α_2 can be roots of this polynomial; for, otherwise the equality of $\vartheta = \alpha_1 + a\alpha_2$ with a $\vartheta_{\nu_1\nu_2} = \alpha_{1\nu_1} + a\alpha_{2\nu_2}$, where $(\alpha_{1\nu_1}, \alpha_{2\nu_2}) \neq (\alpha_1, \alpha_2)$ would follow contrary to our construction of the $\vartheta_{\nu_1\nu_2}$. [3] The *latter* representation tells us that $\varphi(x)$ is a polynomial in $K(\vartheta)$.

---

[2] The prefactor $(-a)^{n_1}$ has the effect of making $\varphi(x)$ into a *polynomial*, that is, of making its leading coefficient e.

[3] It is easy to see that the separability of α_1 is not necessary for this conclusion and consequently for the entire proof. An analogue to Theorem 90 is therefore also valid if we only assume that all are separable except for one of the primitive elements. Here, however, we won't have to make any use of this fact (essential for the theory of inseparable extensions).

Due to these two properties of $\varphi(x)$ the greatest common divisor $(\varphi(x), f_2(x))$ is, on the one hand, equal to the single common linear factor $x - \alpha_2$ (Theorem 21 [187]), on the other hand, a polynomial in $\mathsf{K}(\vartheta)$ (Theorems 24, 14 [188, 182]). Hence α_2 belongs to $\mathsf{K}(\vartheta)$; consequently, so also does $\alpha_1 = \vartheta - a\alpha_2$, that is, $\Lambda = \mathsf{K}(\alpha_1, \alpha_2) \leqq \mathsf{K}(\vartheta)$. Conversely, since $\vartheta = \alpha_1 + a\alpha_2$ belongs to $\Lambda = \mathsf{K}(\alpha_1, \alpha_2)$ it follows that $\Lambda = \mathsf{K}(\alpha_1, \alpha_2) = \mathsf{K}(\vartheta)$ is simple algebraic over K.

We will next show that $\Lambda = \mathsf{K}(\vartheta)$ is also separable over K. For this purpose by Theorems 78, 79 [236, 237] it is sufficient to show in the case of characteristic p that the relations

$$\alpha_1 \text{ in } \mathsf{K}(\alpha_1^p), \quad \alpha_2 \text{ in } \mathsf{K}(\alpha_2^p),$$

which are valid by assumption, yield the corresponding relation

$$\vartheta \text{ in } \mathsf{K}(\vartheta^p).$$

Now, on forming the p-powers of the representations of α_1 and α_2 as elements of $\mathsf{K}[\vartheta]$ we obtain by Theorem 44 [204]

$$\alpha_1^p \text{ in } \mathsf{K}(\vartheta^p) \qquad \alpha_2^p \text{ in } \mathsf{K}(\vartheta^p).$$

In view of the two relations given above this further yields

$$\alpha_1 \text{ in } \mathsf{K}(\vartheta^p), \qquad \alpha_2 \text{ in } \mathsf{K}(\vartheta^p),$$

and consequently, as a matter of fact, also

$$\vartheta \ (= \alpha_1 + a\alpha_2) \text{ in } \mathsf{K}(\vartheta^p).$$

This means that the statements of the theorem are proved for $r = 2$.

b) $r > 2$.

In this case the statements follow by mathematical induction. Let us assume that the statements are already proved up to $r - 1$. Then $\mathsf{K}(\alpha_1, \ldots, \alpha_{r-1}) = \mathsf{K}(\overline{\alpha}_{r-1})$ for a suitable separable algebraic $\overline{\alpha}_{r-1}$ over K. By Theorem 62 [220] we have $\Lambda = \mathsf{K}(\alpha_1, \ldots, \alpha_{r-1}, \alpha_r) = \mathsf{K}(\overline{\alpha}_{r-1}, \alpha_r)$, and consequently by the proof a) Λ is simple algebraic and separable over K, that is, the statement is also valid for r.

This proof easily yields the further result that a primitive element ϑ of $\Lambda = K(\alpha_1, \ldots, \alpha_r)$ can be found, in particular, among the linear combinations $a_1\alpha_1 + \cdots + a_r\alpha_r$ of a primitive system of elements $\alpha_1, \ldots, \alpha_r$. This fact is useful for the construction of such a ϑ in concrete cases.

By Def. 19 [221] a simple algebraic extension is a fortiori finite, algebraic. Hence Theorem 90 says in connection with Theorem 80 [239] and 84 [241] :

Theorem 91. *The following concepts are identical:* ***Separable extension of finite degree, finite separable algebraic extension, simple separable algebraic extension, stem field of a separable irreducible polynomial.***

In regard to the latter concept the following more precise statement is valid: ***Every*** *irreducible polynomial is separable for which such an extension is a stem field.*

In view of the remark after Theorem 67 [226] we add to the above theorem:

Corollary. *The concept of* ***separable algebraic extension with bounded degrees for its elements*** *is identical with the concepts of Theorem 91; in particular, the existing "maximal degree" of an element of Λ over K for such an extension Λ of K is equal to the degree of Λ over K.*

Proof: Let ϑ be an element of Λ of maximal degree. If ϑ were not a primitive element of Λ, there would be an element of Λ which could not be represented rationally by ϑ. If β were such an element, then

$$K \leqq K(\vartheta) < K(\vartheta, \beta) \leqq \Lambda$$

(Theorem 60 [220]); and since we can set $K(\vartheta, \beta) = K(\vartheta')$ (Theorem 90), $[\vartheta : K] < [\vartheta' : K]$ (Theorems 72, 77 [229, 236]) contrary to the maximal determination of the degree of ϑ. Hence ϑ is a primitive element of Λ; therefore $\Lambda = K(\vartheta)$ is simple algebraic over K and $[\Lambda : K] = [\vartheta : K]$.

Next, by the inclusion of separability a refinement of Theorem 86 [242] is obtained which is also valid for the case of characteristic p:

Theorem 92. *If* $\Lambda \geqq \overline{K} \geqq K$ *and* Λ *is separable algebraic over* $\overline{K}$, $\overline{K}$ *separable algebraic over* K, *then* Λ *is also separable algebraic over* K.

Proof: Let α be an element of Λ and $f(x)$ the irreducible polynomial over K (existing according to Theorem 86 [242]) belonging to this element. Let s be the greatest exponent for which $f(x) \equiv f_0(x^{p^s})$ with a polynomial $f_0(x)$ over K. Then, $f_0(x)$ is irreducible due to the irreducibility of $f(x)$ and separable due to the maximal property of s.

By assumption $\alpha, \alpha^p, \ldots, \alpha^{p^{s-1}}$ are separable over $\overline{K}$. Hence by Theorem 78 [236] we have

$$\overline{K}(\alpha) = \overline{K}(\alpha^p) = \cdots = \overline{K}(\alpha^{p^s}).$$

According to this (cf. also Theorem 82 [240]) α has a representation

$$\alpha = \varphi(\alpha^{p^s}) = h(\alpha^{p^s}, \alpha_1, \ldots, \alpha_r),$$

where $\varphi(x)$ is a polynomial in x over $\overline{K}$, which can also be regarded as an integral rational function $h(x, \alpha_1, \ldots, \alpha_r)$ over K of x and the coefficients α_i of φ belonging to $\overline{K}$. However, since the α_i are separable by assumption and the α^{p^s} are separable as roots of $f_0(x)$ over K, Theorem 90 yields that α is also separable over K. Hence Λ is separable over K (Def. 23 [224]).

13. Normality of the Root Fields and their Primitive Elements. Galois Resolvents

1) A further important property of root fields (of arbitrary polynomials) is that specified in

Definition 29.** *An extension* N *of* K *is called* ***normal *(or* ***Galois****) over* K *if every extension* N^* *conjugate to* N *relative to* K *is identical with* N, *that is (cf. Def. 26 [229]) if* $\Lambda \geqq N \geqq K$, $\Lambda \geqq N^* \geqq K$ *and* N^* *isomorphic to* N *relative to* K *always imply* $N^* = N$.

As a partial analogy to Theorems 66. 70 [224, 227] we have here:

Theorem 93. *If* $\mathsf{N} \geqq \overline{\mathsf{K}} \geqq \mathsf{K}$ *and* N *is normal over* K, *then* N *is also normal over* $\overline{\mathsf{K}}$.

Proof: According to Def. 26 [229] every extension N^* of $\overline{\mathsf{K}}$ conjugate to N relative to $\overline{\mathsf{K}}$ is also an extension of K conjugate to N relative to K.

However, we require neither, as in Theorems 66, 70 [224, 227], that $\overline{\mathsf{K}}$ be also normal over K, nor conversely, as in Theorems 71, 86 [228, 242], that N be normal over K if N is normal over $\overline{\mathsf{K}}$ and $\overline{\mathsf{K}}$ is normal over K. Examples of this can be found by means of the Fundamental Theorem to be proved in Section 17, which at the same time gives us the deeper reason for these statements.

We now prove:

Theorem 94. *The root field* W *of a polynomial* $f(x)$ *is normal over* K.

Proof: Let $f(x) \equiv (x - \alpha_1) \cdots (x - \alpha_r)$ and $\mathsf{W} = \mathsf{K}(\alpha_1, \ldots, \alpha_r)$. By Def. 26 [229] and the remarks to Vol. 1, Def. 7, Addendum [30] these two relations for $\alpha_1, \ldots, \alpha_r$ remain valid for the elements $\alpha_1^*, \ldots, \alpha_r^*$ conjugate to them in passing over to a field W^* conjugate to W relative to K. Therefore, W^* is likewise a root field of $f(x)$ and consequently by Theorem 89 [246] is identical with W, that is, W is normal over K.

2) In order to become better acquainted with the significance of normality for a simple algebraic extension Λ we must first of all acquire a general view of the totality of conjugates to Λ both for the case in which Λ is normal and that in which it is not normal. This is obtained by representing Λ as a stem field of an irreducible polynomial $f(x)$ (Theorem 76 [235]) and then studying it as a subfield of the root field W of $f(x)$ (cf. the statements in connection with Theorem 89 [246]). In this respect we immediately have according to Theorems 74, 75 [231, 235] and Def. 26 [229] (cf. also the statements already made before Theorem 89 [246] :

Theorem 95. *Let $f(x)$ be an irreducible polynomial in* K, *α a root of $f(x)$, $\Lambda = \mathsf{K}(\alpha)$ the stem field belonging to it and $\beta = h(\alpha)$ any element of Λ. Then, if $\alpha_1, \ldots, \alpha_r$ are the roots of $f(x)$, the root field $\mathsf{W} = \mathsf{K}(\alpha_1, \ldots, \alpha_r)$ of $f(x)$ (containing α, therefore $\Lambda = \mathsf{K}(\alpha)$) contains the r stem fields*

$$\Lambda_1 = \mathsf{K}(\alpha_1), \ldots, \Lambda_r = \mathsf{K}(\alpha_r).$$

These are conjugate to $\Lambda = \mathsf{K}(\alpha)$, and in these

$$\beta_1 = h(\alpha_1), \ldots, \beta_r = h(\alpha_r)$$

each represents a system of elements conjugate to $\beta = h(\alpha)$.

In these theorems α designates *any one* of the roots α_i, Λ the field Λ_i determined by it and β the element β_i corresponding to it. However, here and in similar considerations in the following (as has already been done in the proof to Theorem 90 [251]) we make no fixed agreement as to *which* of the a_i shall be equal to a. Such an understanding would create an entirely unjustified lack of symmetry, since the α_i, Λ_i, β_i of K cannot be distinguished (Vol. 1, in connection with Def. 7, Addendum [30]).[4]

Theorem 95 says, in particular, that the α_i are all conjugate to α. Conversely, Theorem 73 [230] implies

Theorem 96. *Let the data of Theorem 95 be given. Then the roots $\alpha_1, \ldots, \alpha_r$ are the only conjugates to α within* W *or any extension of* W.

The conjugates to an algebraic element are therefore identical with the roots of the irreducible polynomial belonging to the element.

Hence, for brevity, in the following we will also use the terminology, the *conjugates to* α instead of "the roots of the irreducible polynomial belonging to α."

The corresponding theorem is valid in regard to Λ_i. For, by an inference analogous to that used in the proof of Theorem 94 we can show that a field (within an arbitrary extension of W)

---

4 In the literature we frequently find the convention $\alpha = \alpha_1$.

conjugate to $\mathsf{\Lambda}$ is likewise a stem field of $f(x)$. Therefore it, too, is generated by the adjunction of a root of $f(x)$, that is, of an α_i (Theorem 50 [209]).

Theorem 97. *Let the data of Theorem 95 be given. Then the fields* $\mathsf{\Lambda}_1, \ldots, \mathsf{\Lambda}_r$ *are the only conjugates to* $\mathsf{\Lambda}$ *within* W *or any extension of* W.

The corresponding theorem cannot yet be stated for β_i. As far as our present considerations are concerned there may actually exist besides $\mathsf{\Lambda}_i$ still other extensions of K within W or in extensions of W, and such extensions would lead to the existence of elements distinct from the β_i but conjugate to β (cf. Def. 26 [229]). We will return to this later on (Theorem 103 [262]).

3) The facts established in 2) can be used to determine the significance of normality for simple algebraic extensions; in doing so, we can also trace, in particular, the significance of the concurrence of simplicity and normality for the root fields of separable polynomials. It is appropriate to extend Def. 29 by the following definition based on it:

***Definition 30.** *An element ϑ is called **normal** (or **Galois**) over K if the field $\mathsf{K}(\vartheta)$ is normal over K.*

If an element is normal over K, it is automatically algebraic over K, since by the remark after Def. 26 [229] an element x which is transcendental over K has conjugates different from $\mathsf{K}(x)$.

By combining Def. 19 [221] and Def. 30 we immediately obtain

Theorem 98. Let N be a simple algebraic extension of K. *If N is normal over K, then every primitive element of N is normal over K. Conversely, if a primitive element of N is normal over K, then N is normal over K.*

From the previous standpoint this theorem is naturally tautological with Def. 29, 30, therefore for the time being says nothing new. However, by retaining its wording we can give this theorem a new, more significant, meaning by characterizing the concept of *normal element* in another way. On the basis of the facts established in 2) this is done in

Theorem 99. *Let ϑ be an algebraic element over* K, *$q(x)$ the irreducible polynomial over* K *belonging to ϑ and $\vartheta_1, \ldots, \vartheta_n$ its roots — the conjugates to ϑ. If ϑ is normal over* K, *then we have:*

(I) $K(\vartheta) = K(\vartheta_1, \ldots, \vartheta_n)$, *that is, the root field of $q(x)$ coincides with a stem field of $q(x)$.*

(II) $K(\vartheta_1) = \cdots = K(\vartheta_n)$, *that is, the conjugate stem fields of $q(x)$ corresponding to the conjugates to ϑ coincide.*

(III) $\vartheta_1 = g_1(\vartheta), \ldots, \vartheta_n = g_n(\vartheta)$, *that is, the conjugates to ϑ belong to* $K(\vartheta)$.

Conversely, (I) *or* (II) *or* (III) *implies that ϑ is normal over* K.

Proof: a) If ϑ is normal over K, then by Def. 29, 30 and Theorem 95 we first have that (II) is valid; this in turn yields (I) according to Theorem 60 [220] as well as (III) by Def. 18 [219] and Theorem 82 [240].

b) First of all, (III) or (I) implies that $K(\vartheta_i) \leqq K(\vartheta)$; by Theorem 72 [229] this yields that (II) is valid. Therefore, it is sufficient to show that the normality of ϑ follows from (II). This, however, is the case by Theorem 97 and Def. 29, 30.

Theorem 99 states, in particular, that if ϑ is normal, or not normal, over K so also are all of its conjugates ϑ_i. Hence it has a meaning to stipulate:

Addendum to Definition 30. *A* ***polynomial*** *$q(x)$ over* K *is called* ***normal*** *(or* ***Galois****) over* K, *first, if it is irreducible, and secondly, if one of its roots ϑ is normal over* K.

Due to the meaning already attached to the statements in Theorem 98, Theorem 99 allows us to recognize what restriction the requirement of normality imposes on a simple algebraic extension N of K. Namely, every primitive element ϑ of N must satisfy conditions (I) to (III); conversely, for the normality of N it is actually enough that one of these conditions be valid for only one primitive element ϑ.

Form (I) of this restriction shows that in the converse to Theorems 90, 94 [251, 256] every simple (separable) normal extension of K is also a root field of a (separable) polynomial over K. In the case of separability we can be more precise: *Every* polynomial is separable for which such an extension is a root field. This follows from the fact that Theorem 63 [223] and Def. 17, Addendum [215] imply that a separable element can only be a root of separable polynomials.

Form (II) exhibits a remarkable analogy to the like-named concepts of group theory (Vol. 1, Section 9, especially Theorem 31 [73]). The fundamental theorem to be proved in Section 17 will enable us to see that this *formal analogy* springs from a factual connection.

Form (III) is the most understandable and is appropriate to establish normality in concrete cases.

According to the statements regarding (I) the following analogy to Theorem 91 [254] is valid:

Theorem 100. *The following concepts are identical:* ***root field of a separable polynomial*** $f(x)$, ***separable normal extension of finite degree, finite separable normal extension, simple separable normal extension, stem field of a separable normal polynomial*** $q(x)$.

More exactly, ***every*** *polynomial* $f(x)$ *is separable for which such an extension is a root field, and* ***every*** *normal polynomial* $q(x)$ *is separable for which it is a stem field.*

Therefore, these concepts differ only technically from one another. (Cf. the statement in this regard under Theorem 80 [239] .)

In the *Galois theory* to be discussed in the following sections we will be occupied with the more detailed structure of the extensions characterized in Theorem 100. Our aim will be to formulate this theory so as not to attach singular importance either to a definite polynomial or to a definite primitive element or primitive system of elements. We will attain this objective by developing the Galois theory as the *theory of separable normal extensions of finite degree.* Only incidentally shall we mention the way the relations to be demonstrated turn out if we take into consideration the fact that such an extension arises from a root field of a definite polynomial or from a stem field of a definite normal polynomial.

4) As a preparation for the latter investigations we will summarize in the following theorem the results about the structure of the root field of a separable polynomial which were obtained in this and the preceding sections (Theorems 90, 94, 98, 99). After this we will make a definition basic in this regard.

Theorem 101. *Let $f(x)$ be a separable polynomial over* K *and* $\alpha_1, \ldots, \alpha_r$ *its roots. Then in its root field* $\mathsf{W} = \mathsf{K}(\alpha_1, \ldots, \alpha_r)$ *there exists a primitive element*

$$\vartheta = h(\alpha_1, \ldots, \alpha_r)$$

so that $\mathsf{W} = \mathsf{K}(\vartheta)$ *and accordingly representations*

$$\alpha_1 = k_1(\vartheta), \ldots, \alpha_r = k_r(\vartheta)$$

are valid. Any such ϑ *is normal over* K. *This means that if* $q(x)$ *is the irreducible polynomial over* K *belonging to it and* $\vartheta_1, \ldots, \vartheta_n$ *are its roots — the conjugates to* ϑ *—, then the representations*

$$\vartheta_1 = g_1(\vartheta), \ldots, \vartheta_n = g_n(\vartheta)$$

exist.

Definition 31.** *Any normal polynomial* $q(x)$ *(occasionally also a* ϑ *belonging to it) determined for* $f(x)$ *according to Theorem* 101 *is called a* ***Galois resolvent *of* $f(x)$ *relative to* K.

The designation *resolvent* descends from the older literature. It signifies that the equation $f(x) \doteq 0$ is to be regarded as *solved* if the resolvent $q(x) \doteq 0$ is solved. For, by Theorem 101 the roots of

$f(x)$ are actually obtained by operating rationally on a root of $q(x)$. Underlying this is the idea of a *process for solving* the equation $f(x) \doteq 0$. However, we will not adopt this idea here. For, in the first place—apart from the special case wherein $q(x)$ has the degree 1 and therefore $f(x)$ resolves into linear factors in K—either we are *no more able to solve* the equation $f(x) \doteq 0$ than the equation $q(x) \doteq 0$ (namely, there is *no rational process for solving* either equation), or we can *solve* one *just as well* as the other (namely, by the *constructions* in Sections 8, 10). In the second place, for reasons similar to those cited in the introduction regarding 1) there does not exist in principle a rational process for determining the coefficients of a Galois resolvent $q(x)$ from those of $f(x)$. Rather, for us the Galois resolvent has merely a *theoretical* significance in that its roots ϑ will permit the root field $K(\alpha_1, \ldots, \alpha_r)$ to be put in the "simple" form $K(\vartheta)$.

Theorem 99, (I) immediately yields in addition:

Theorem 102. *$f(x)$ is the Galois resolvent of itself if and only if it is a normal polynomial.*

For this reason the normal polynomials are also occasionally called, as mentioned in Def. 29, 30 [255, 258], Galois polynomials. Accordingly, since normal extensions, so long as they are simple, are stem fields of Galois polynomials, they are also called Galois extensions.

5) We now return to the question of the totality of conjugates to $\beta = h(\alpha)$, which was put aside on p. 258. Analogously to Theorems 96, 97 [257] we prove the following theorem, however, only for separable $f(x)$:

Theorem 103. *Let the data of Theorem* 95 [257] *be given and besides let $f(x)$ be separable. Then the elements $\beta_1, \ldots, \beta_r$ are the only conjugates to β within* W *or within any arbitrary extension of* W.

Proof: Let β^* be an element conjugate to β (in an extension of W). By Theorem 73 [230] β^* is then a root of the same irreducible polynomial in K as β. Hence by Theorems 74, 75

[231, 235] the stem field $K(\beta^*)$ belonging to it is isomorphic to the stem field $K(\beta)$ relative to K on the basis of the correspondence $\beta \longleftrightarrow \beta^*$.

Now, according to Theorem 101 let $W = K(\vartheta)$. Furthermore, let $q(x)$ and $\varphi(x)$ be the irreducible polynomials in K and $K(\beta)$ belonging to ϑ. Then $\varphi(x) \mid q(x)$ (Theorem 53 [210]); and $W = K(\vartheta) = K(\beta, \vartheta)$ is a stem field of $\varphi(x)$ over $K(\beta)$ (Theorem 75 [235]).

The above-mentioned isomorphism relative to K maps $q(x)$ into itself. At the same time $\varphi(x)$ generates a polynomial $\varphi^*(x)$ with the following properties: $\varphi^*(x)$ is irreducible in $K(\beta^*)$; $\varphi^*(x) \mid q(x)$ (therefore the roots of $\varphi^*(x)$ are contained among those of $q(x)$, that is, they are conjugates to ϑ); if ϑ^* is a root of $\varphi^*(x)$, then (cf. Theorems 101, 99) $W = K(\vartheta^*) = K(\beta^*, \vartheta^*)$ is a stem field of $\varphi^*(x)$ over $K(\beta^*)$.

Therefore, by the expositions to Vol. 1, Def. 7, Addendum [30] the correspondences $\beta \longleftrightarrow \beta^*$, $\vartheta \longleftrightarrow \vartheta^*$ generate (just as in the proof to Theorem 87 under b) [243]) an isomorphism of W to itself relative to K (a so-called *automorphism* of W relative to K — for further details, see the following Section 14). In other words, the isomorphism of $W = K(\vartheta) = K(\vartheta^*)$ to itself generated by $\vartheta \longleftrightarrow \vartheta^*$ yields $\beta \longleftrightarrow \beta^*$. By this isomorphism the element $\alpha = k(\vartheta)$ (represented according to Theorem 101) is now mapped on the element $\alpha^* = k(\vartheta^*)$ which by Theorem 96 [257] must be one of the α_i. Hence due to the representation $\beta = h(\alpha)$ the element β^* corresponding to the element β has the representation $\beta^* = h(\alpha^*)$ generated by that isomorphism; therefore, it is actually one of the $\beta_i = h(\alpha_i)$.

On taking Theorem 96 [257] and Theorem 58 [215] into consideration, Theorem 103 yields that those β_i which are *different* are the roots of the irreducible polynomial $g(x)$ belonging to β, that is, are the *conjugates* to β in the sense introduced there. Frequently, we find that *the* β_i *collectively* are also designated as *the conjugates to* β; in general, these are the roots of $g(x)$, each occurring a certain number of times. In Theorem 113 [284] we will study this more in detail.

14. The Automorphism Group of an Extension Domain

In this section we prepare the way for the application of group theory to the investigation of the structure of normal extensions of finite degree, which is to be made in the following, by introducing the groups in question. In order to obtain the elements of these groups we recall how we formed in Vol. 1, Section 2 the concept of *isomorphism* relative to domains from the concept of *one-to-one correspondence*, defined for sets, through the addition of the two postulates (3), (4) [29] relative to the rules of combination. In an entirely analogous manner we next create the corresponding concept of *automorphism*[5] relative to domains from the concept of permutation defined in Vol. 1, Section 16 for sets.

Definition 32. *A permutation of a domain* B, *that is, a one-to-one correspondence of* B *to itself with a definite mapping rule (designated by* $\rightarrow$*) is called an* ***automorphism*** *of* B *if in addition to the rules of combination defined in* B *it satisfies the relations:*

(1) $a \rightarrow a',\ b \rightarrow b'$ *imply* $a + b \rightarrow a' + b'$,

(2) $a \rightarrow a',\ b \rightarrow b'$ *imply* $ab \rightarrow a'b'$,

that is, if it satisfies the isomorphism conditions [*Vol.* 1, *Section* 2, (3), (4) [29]].

---

[5] The concept *automorphism* can also be introduced for groups just as *isomorphism* (Vol. 1, Def. 17 [65]); however, we have no need of this here.

This means that the remarks about permutations made in connection with Vol. 1, Def. 35 [117] can properly be applied to automorphisms.

Besides the comparison made above we can say that the two set concepts *one-to-one correspondence, permutation* and the two domain concepts *isomorphism, automorphism* bear the same relationship to one another, that is, *automorphism of* B means the same as *isomorphism of* B *to itself with a definite mapping rule*.

Therefore, the remarks about isomorphisms made in connection with Vol. 1, Def. 7 [30] can also properly be applied to automorphisms.

From Vol. 1, Theorems 56, 57 [118] we immediately obtain by means of Vol. 1, Theorem 19 [63] :

Theorem 104. *The automorphisms of a domain* B *form a group if by the product of two automorphisms of* B *we understand their product as permutations, that is, the automorphism of* B *generated by carrying them out one after the other. The type of this group is uniquely determined by the type of the domain* B.

We designate by a_A the element generated by applying the automorphism A to the element a. (1) and (2) can then also be put into the form

(1) $(a+b)_A = a_A + b_A$ (2) $(ab)_A = a_A b_A$.

The definition of the product of automorphisms further implies

(3) $(a_A)_B = a_{AB}$.

If a goes over into one and the same element by all automorphisms in a set of automorphisms $\mathfrak{M}$, then we designate this fact by $a_{\mathfrak{M}}$.

According to Theorem 104 every domain has at least the *identity* automorphism $a \to a$. That further automorphisms do not have to exist is shown by the example of the prime domains Γ, P, P_p. Thus, as in the case of isomorphisms, since for every automorphism of an integral domain we must also have $0 \to 0$, $e \to e$ (cf. the statement in Vol. 1 in connection with Def. 7 [30]), for the specified domains all remaining transitions according to (1), (2) must of necessity yield $a \to a$. In the following we will study in detail examples of domains (fields) with automorphism groups different from the unity group.

In the study of extension domains B of a domain B_0 we needed the sharper concept of isomorphism of B relative to B_0. Here, too, we have to have recourse to the sharper concept of automorphism of B relative to B_0.

Addendum to Definition 32. *If* B *is an extension domain of* B_0, *then those automorphisms of* B *whereby every element of* B_0 *goes over into itself are called* ***automorphisms*** *of* B *relative to* B_0.

Therefore, automorphism of B *relative to* B_0 *means the same as isomorphism of* B *to itself relative to* B_0 *with a definite mapping rule.*

Therefore, the remarks about relative isomorphisms made in connection with Vol. 1, Def. 7, Addendum [30] can properly be applied to relative automorphisms. Furthermore, corresponding to the expositions before Def. 20 [222] if $\mathsf{\Lambda} = \mathsf{K}(\mathsf{M})$ and an automorphism A of $\mathsf{\Lambda}$ relative to K carries the set M over into M', so that $\mathsf{\Lambda} = \mathsf{K}(\mathsf{M}')$ is also valid, then, as there, A will be completely described merely by specifying the substitutions taking M into M':

$$\alpha \to \alpha', \ \beta \to \beta', \ldots \quad \begin{pmatrix} \alpha, \beta, \ldots & \text{in} & \mathsf{M} \\ \alpha', \beta', \ldots & \text{in} & \mathsf{M}' \end{pmatrix}.$$

Analogously to Def. 20 [222] we further define in this regard:

Definition 33. *An automorphism of* $\mathsf{\Lambda} = \mathsf{K}(\mathsf{M})$ *relative to* K *is said to be* ***generated*** *by the substitutions of the elements of* M *performed under the automorphism.*

In particular, we can thereby have $\mathsf{M} = \mathsf{M}'$; in this case every substitution represents a permutation of M and A *is generated by these permutations of* M.

Finally, by means of Vol. 1, Theorem 19 [63] we immediately obtain from Theorem 104:

Corollary to Theorem 104. *The automorphisms of* B *relative to* B_0 *form a subgroup of the group of all automorphisms of* B. *The type of this subgroup is uniquely determined by the extension type of* B.

According to the above remarks this subgroup is the entire automorphism group of B if B is an integral domain (field) and B_0 is its prime integral domain (prime field); on the contrary, it is the unity group if B coincides with B_0.

15. The Galois Group of a Separable Normal Extension of Finite Degree

We next apply the concepts of Section 14, especially the Corollary to Theorem 104, to a normal extension N of finite degree over K, which (if separable) is by Theorem 100 [260] also simple algebraic over K. The following terminology is introduced in honor of *Galois* who first recognized[6] the far-reaching significance of the automorphism group for this case.

Definition 34.** *The group* $\mathfrak{G}$ *of the automorphisms relative to* K *of a* ***normal extension N ***of finite degree*** *over* K *is called the* ***Galois group*** *of* N *relative to* K.

In particular, if $\mathfrak{G}$ *is Abelian or cyclic,* N *is also called* ***Abelian*** *or* ***cyclic*** *over* K.

In the case of a *separable* N we obtain a general view of this Galois group through the following theorem:

Theorem 105. *Let* N *be a separable normal extension of degree n over* K, ϑ *a primitive element of* N *and* $\vartheta_1, \ldots, \vartheta_n$ *its*

[6] Although not in the abstract form given here, but in the concrete representation of Section 16. — *Evariste Galois* was killed in a duel on the 30th of May, 1832 at the age of 20. On the eve of his death he wrote a long letter to a friend in which he (among other things) added further important results to the first draft of his theory of algebraic equations, already presented to the Paris Academy. The letter is printed in his works.

conjugates. Then the Galois group $\mathfrak{G}$ *of* N *is finite of order* n, *and its* n *automorphisms are generated by the* n *substitutions* $\vartheta \rightarrow \vartheta_i$ $(i = 1, \ldots, n)$, *therefore every element* $\beta = h(\vartheta)$ *of* N *goes over into the* n *conjugates* $\beta_i = h(\vartheta_i)$.

Proof: a) By Def. 32, Addendum [266] an automorphism of N relative to K can also be regarded as an isomorphism of N to itself relative to K (with a definite mapping rule). Hence by Def. 26 [229] such an automorphism takes every element of N into a conjugate; in particular, ϑ into a ϑ_i (Theorem 96 [257]) and then the $\beta = h(\vartheta)$ into $\beta_i = h(\vartheta_i)$. Consequently, there are at most the n possibilities stated in the theorem for an automorphism of N relative to K.

b) Conversely, by Theorem 95 [257] each of these n possibilities gives rise to an isomorphism of $\mathsf{N} = \mathsf{K}(\vartheta)$ relative to K to one of its n conjugate stem fields $\mathsf{K}(\vartheta_i)$, therefore by Theorem 99, (II) [259] of N to itself. By Def. 32, Addendum this means that the isomorphism is an automorphism of N relative to K.

The statements of the theorem follow from a) and b) if we add that the separability of N implies that the n conjugates $\vartheta_1, \ldots, \vartheta_n$ to ϑ are different from one another, since they are the roots of the irreducible polynomial belonging to ϑ (Theorem 58 [215]). This means that the n automorphisms generated by the n substitutions $\vartheta \rightarrow \vartheta_i$ are also different.

In order to obtain a better idea of what it means to operate in the Galois group $\mathfrak{G}$, that is, to apply successively the automorphisms generated by the substitutions $\vartheta \rightarrow \vartheta_i$, we will set the elements of $\mathfrak{G}$ in a form which is more readily grasped. We will do so by passing over to an isomorphic group wherein these elements are no longer regarded as automorphisms or, as we say in group theory, by giving a suitable *representation of* $\mathfrak{G}$. This is brought about by

Theorem 106. *Let the assumptions and designations of Theorem 105 be valid; furthermore, let*

$$q(x) \equiv (x-\vartheta_1)\dots(x-\vartheta_n)$$

be the irreducible polynomial over K *belonging to* ϑ, *and according to Theorem* 99, (III) [259]

(1) $$\vartheta_i = g_i(\vartheta) \qquad (i = 1, \dots, n).$$

In the set $\mathfrak{F}$ *of the residue classes mod* $q(x)$ *represented by the* $g_i(x)$

(2) $$\{g_i\} \times \{g_k\} = \{g_l\}, \quad \textit{if} \quad \{g_i(g_k(x))\} = \{g_l(x)\}$$

then defines an operation which is unique, can be carried out without restriction and is isomorphic to $\mathfrak{G}$ *on the basis of the correspondences*

(3) $$(\vartheta \to \vartheta_i) \longleftrightarrow \{g_i(x)\} \qquad (i = 1, \dots, n).$$

Proof: First of all, let us recall the one-to-one correspondence (3) (p. 234) set up between the elements of N and the residue classes mod $q(x)$.

a) Since $g_i(g_k(\vartheta))$ is generated from $g_i(\vartheta)$ by $\vartheta \to g_k(\vartheta)$, therefore from ϑ_i by $\vartheta \to \vartheta_k$, then by Theorem 105 it is likewise a ϑ_l and therefore $g_i(g_k(\vartheta)) = g_l(\vartheta), \{g_i(g_k(x))\} = \{g_l(x)\}$. Consequently, (2) defines an operation in $\mathfrak{F}$ which is without restriction and single-valued.

b) Since the ϑ_i are different due to the separability of K, the $\{g_i\}$ are also different. Consequently (3) is a one-to-one correspondence between $\mathfrak{G}$ and $\mathfrak{F}$.

c) Now the successive application of the automorphisms generated by $\vartheta \to \vartheta_i$ and $\vartheta \to \vartheta_k$ takes ϑ first into $\vartheta_i = g_i(\vartheta)$ and then this into $g_i(\vartheta_k) = g_i(g_k(\vartheta)) = g_l(\vartheta) = \vartheta_l$. Hence on taking them together we obtain the automorphism generated by $\vartheta \to \vartheta_l$. This means that the operation in $\mathfrak{F}$ defined by (2) corresponds under the correspondence (3) to multiplication in $\mathfrak{G}$. Consequently, by (3) the isomorphism condition (Vol. 1, Theorem 23 [65]) is also satisfied.

The statements of the theorem follow from a), b), c).

Let a $q(x)$ be given (in the case of the application to the root field of a separable polynomial $f(x)$ let the Galois resolvent of this polynomial be given) as well as the representations (1). Then the *representation of the Galois group* $\mathfrak{G}$ *as the substitution group* $\mathfrak{F}$

of integral rational functions mod $q(x)$, given in Theorem 106, is immediately accessible for practical calculations. For this purpose it is appropriate to reduce each $g_i(x)$ to its uniquely determined residue mod $q(x)$ of degree lower than the n-*th* (Theorems 13, 27 [180, 192]; see in particular the remark after Theorem 13; a complete picture of the combinations within $\mathfrak{F}$ (therefore also those within $\mathfrak{G}$) is then obtained, if the same is done for all $g_i(g_k(x))$. In the prevailing literature this representation $\mathfrak{F}$ of $\mathfrak{G}$ is usually used to define the Galois group. However, this has the disadvantage that a definite *primitive element* ϑ is thereby singled out. It must then be proved that isomorphic groups $\mathfrak{F}, \mathfrak{F}', \ldots$ are obtained for all primitive elements $\vartheta, \vartheta', \ldots$. Our definition depending only on the *fields* N and K has the advantage of bringing this fact to the fore from the beginning. In so doing it penetrates one step deeper, namely, all groups $\mathfrak{F}, \mathfrak{F}', \ldots$ appear as representations of one and the same group $\mathfrak{G}$, the automorphism group of N relative to K.

16. The Galois Group of a Separable Polynomial

Let $\mathfrak{G}$ be the Galois group of the root field W of a separable polynomial $f(x)$ over K. If the methods of Section 15 are to be applied in order to obtain a concrete representation of this group, then we must know a Galois resolvent $q(x)$ of $f(x)$, to which Theorems 105, 106 can be applied. Now, by Theorem 102 [262] $f(x)$ is in general not a Galois resolvent of itself, and according to the remarks in connection with Def. 31 [261] a Galois resolvent cannot be derived from $f(x)$ by a rational process. Hence it is of interest to find a concrete representation of $\mathfrak{G}$ which does not depend on a Galois resolvent $q(x)$ of $f(x)$ but only on $f(x)$ and its roots.

We first define:

Definition 35.** *By the* ***Galois group of a polynomial $f(x)$ *over* K *we understand the Galois group* $\mathfrak{G}$ *of its root field* W *over* K.

In particular, if $\mathfrak{G}$ *is Abelian or cyclic, then* $f(x)$ *is also called* ***Abelian*** *or* ***cyclic*** *over* K *(as* W *was according to Def.* 34 [267] *).*

We now prove the following theorem which gives the desired representation of the Galois group of W or, as we can now say, the Galois group of a separable polynomial $f(x)$:

Theorem 107. *The Galois group* $\mathfrak{G}$ *of a separable polynomial* $f(x)$ *over* K *is isomorphic to the group* $\mathfrak{P}$ *of those permutations of the different roots among the roots* $\alpha_1, \ldots, \alpha_r$ *of* $f(x)$ *resulting from the automorphisms of* $\mathfrak{G}$. *These permutations can also be characterized by saying that their application preserves every integral rational relation*

$$f(\alpha_1, \ldots, \alpha_r) = 0$$

which may exist between the roots of $f(x)$.

Proof: 1) We first show that $\mathfrak{G}$ can generally be represented as a permutation group $\mathfrak{P}$ of the different $\alpha_1, \ldots, \alpha_{\bar{r}}$ among the roots $\alpha_1, \ldots, \alpha_r$.

a) By Theorem 105 [267] an automorphism A relative to K of the root field W of $f(x)$ takes each of the roots of $f(x)$ into a conjugate element, therefore by Theorem 73 [230] again into a root of $f(x)$. Since A is a one-to-one correspondence, it takes different elements into different elements. Consequently, through A the different $\alpha_1, \ldots, \alpha_{\bar{r}}$ are subjected to a uniquely determined permutation P.

b) Since $W = K(\alpha_1, \ldots, \alpha_r) = K(\alpha_1, \ldots, \alpha_{\bar{r}})$, A is generated by P (Def. 33 [266]), and therefore distinct A also correspond to distinct P. Consequently, the correspondence between the Galois group $\mathfrak{G}$ of W and the set $\mathfrak{P}$ of the permutations P of the $\alpha_1, \ldots, \alpha_{\bar{r}}$ produced by its automorphisms is one-to-one.

c) Since in the case of automorphisms as for permutations multiplication is defined as the successive application, the isomorphism condition (Vol. 1, Theorem 23 [65]) is also satisfied by this correspondence.

By a), b), c) $\mathfrak{P}$ is a permutation group isomorphic to $\mathfrak{G}$.

2) We next show that the permutations of $\mathfrak{P}$ are characterized by the property specified in the theorem.

a) That every existing relation $\bar{f}(\alpha_1, \ldots, \alpha_r) = 0$ is preserved by applying the permutations of $\mathfrak{P}$ is clear. For, according to 1) the application of such a permutation amounts to the application of the automorphism of $\mathfrak{G}$ generated by it, and this is actually the case here by Def. 32, Addendum [266] and the expositions to Vol. 1, Def. 7, Addendum [30].

b) According to Theorem 101 [261] let ϑ be a primitive element of W, $q(x) \equiv (x - \vartheta_1) \cdots (x - \vartheta_n)$ the Galois resolvent of $f(x)$ belonging to it and

$$\alpha_\nu = k_\nu(\vartheta) \qquad (\nu = 1, \ldots, r),$$
$$\vartheta = h(\alpha_1, \ldots, \alpha_r).$$

By Theorem 105 [267] the Galois group $\mathfrak{G}$ of W then consists of the automorphisms generated by the substitutions $\vartheta \to \vartheta_i$ ($i = 1, \ldots, n$). Now, if $\begin{pmatrix} \alpha_1, \ldots, \alpha_{\bar{r}} \\ \alpha_{i_1}, \ldots, \alpha_{i_{\bar{r}}} \end{pmatrix}$ is a permutation of the $\alpha_1, \ldots, \alpha_{\bar{r}}$ which preserves every existing relation $\bar{f}(\alpha_1, \ldots, \alpha_r) = 0$, and the transitions for the entire sequence $\alpha_1, \ldots, \alpha_r$ produced by it are designated by $\begin{pmatrix} \alpha_1, \ldots, \alpha_r \\ \alpha_{i_1}, \ldots, \alpha_{i_r} \end{pmatrix}$, then the application of these transitions will take the special relations

$$\alpha_\nu = k_\nu(h(\alpha_1, \ldots, \alpha_r)) \qquad (\nu = 1, \ldots, r),$$
$$q(h(\alpha_1, \ldots, \alpha_r)) = 0$$

into the relations

$$\alpha_{i_\nu} = k_\nu(h(\alpha_{i_1}, \ldots, \alpha_{i_r})) \qquad (\nu = 1, \ldots, r),$$
$$q(h(\alpha_{i_1}, \ldots, \alpha_{i_r})) = 0.$$

Therefore these, too, are valid. Now, the latter relation implies that $h(\alpha_{i_1}, \ldots, \alpha_{i_r}) = \vartheta_i$ is one of the conjugates of ϑ; consequently, by the former relations we have that $\alpha_{i_\nu} = k_\nu(\vartheta_i)$ is generated from $\alpha_\nu = k_\nu(\vartheta)$ by the automorphism $\vartheta \to \vartheta_i$. Hence according to 1) the permutation $\begin{pmatrix} \alpha_1, \ldots, \alpha_{\bar{r}} \\ \alpha_{i_1}, \ldots, \alpha_{i_{\bar{r}}} \end{pmatrix}$ actually arises from an automorphism of $\mathfrak{G}$ and consequently belongs to $\mathfrak{P}$.

This completes the proof of Theorem 107. Incidentally, from a practical standpoint it does not achieve as much as Theorem 106 [269], which is based on the knowledge of a Galois resolvent of $f(x)$. For, the decision as to which permutations have the property of Theorem 107 cannot be made in general in a finite number of steps without the knowledge of a Galois resolvent of $f(x)$. We note in addition that Theorem 107 yields

Theorem 108. *If $f(x)$ is a separable polynomial of degree r over K and $\bar{r}$ is the number of the distinct elements among its roots, then the degree n of its root field W over K is a divisor of $\bar{r}!$ (therefore, even more so, a divisor of $r!$).*

Proof: By Theorem 105 [267] n is at the same time the order of the Galois group $\mathfrak{G}$ of W. Now, since by Theorem 107 the permutation group $\mathfrak{P}$ isomorphic to $\mathfrak{G}$ is a subgroup of the symmetric group $\mathfrak{S}_{\bar{r}}$ of $\bar{r}$ elements, by Vol. 1, Theorems 25, 58 [68, 121] we have $n \mid \bar{r}!$.

17. The Fundamental Theorem of Galois Theory

The Galois group $\mathfrak{G}$ of a separable normal extension N of finite degree of K is studied because it is very useful for obtaining a more precise insight into the structure of the extension type of N. For, by means of the Galois group we are able to survey completely the building stones leading from K to N, that is, the fields lying between K and N together with their mutual relations, as soon as we know the structure of $\mathfrak{G}$, especially the totality of the subgroups of $\mathfrak{G}$ with their mutual relations. Since $\mathfrak{G}$ is a finite group, the latter, at least in any concrete case, is a problem which can be handled in finitely many steps.

1) We prove the following **Fundamental Theorem of the Galois Theory:**

Theorem 109. *Let N be a separable normal extension of degree n over K and $\mathfrak{G}$ its Galois group of order n. Then there exists a one-to-one correspondence between the totality of the extension fields Λ of K contained in N and the totality (containing $\mathfrak{E}$[7]) of the subgroups $\mathfrak{H}$ of $\mathfrak{G}$. This correspondence is*

[7] As in Vol. 1, $\mathfrak{E}$ designates the identity subgroup (unity group). The enclosed remarks refer to this superfluous addendum.

completely established by each of the following two facts (I a), (I b) *valid for a* $\mathsf{\Lambda}$ *and* $\mathfrak{H}$ *corresponding to one another:*

(I a) $\mathfrak{H}$ *consists of all and only the automorphisms of* $\mathfrak{G}$ *which leave every element of* $\mathsf{\Lambda}$ *invariant.*

(I aa) *Hence* $\mathfrak{H}$ *is the Galois group of* N *relative to* $\mathsf{\Lambda}$, *and therefore the order* m *of* $\mathfrak{H}$ *(the index of* $\mathfrak{E}$ *in* $\mathfrak{H}$) *is equal to the degree of* N *over* $\mathsf{\Lambda}$ *and the index* j *of* $\mathfrak{H}$ *in* $\mathfrak{G}$ *is equal to the degree of* $\mathsf{\Lambda}$ *over* K.

(I b) $\mathsf{\Lambda}$ *consists of all and only the elements of* N *which remain invariant under every automorphism of* $\mathfrak{H}$.

Moreover, if we say that the $\mathsf{\Lambda}$ *and* $\mathfrak{H}$ *with the same indices correspond to one another, then these correspondences also satisfy:*

(II) *If* $\mathsf{\Lambda}$ *is an extension field of* $\mathsf{\Lambda}'$ *of degree* k *over* $\mathsf{\Lambda}'$, *then* $\mathfrak{H}$ *is a subgroup of* $\mathfrak{H}'$ *of index* k *in* $\mathfrak{H}'$, *and conversely.*

(III) *If* $\mathsf{\Lambda}$, $\overline{\mathsf{\Lambda}}$ *are conjugate extension fields of* K, *then* $\mathfrak{H}$, $\overline{\mathfrak{H}}$ *are conjugate subgroups of* $\mathfrak{G}$, *and conversely. To be more exact: If* $\overline{\mathsf{\Lambda}}$ *is generated from* $\mathsf{\Lambda}$ *by the automorphism* S, *then* $\overline{\mathfrak{H}}$ *is generated from* $\mathfrak{H}$ *by transformation with the element* S, *and conversely.*

(IV) *If* $\mathsf{\Lambda}$ *is a normal field over* K, *then* $\mathfrak{H}$ *is a normal divisor of* $\mathfrak{G}$, *and conversely.*

(V) *In the case* (IV) *(besides the statement in* (I aa)) *the factor group* $\mathfrak{G}/\mathfrak{H}$ *is isomorphic to the Galois group of* $\mathsf{\Lambda}$ *relative to* K; *for, if every automorphism of a coset of* $\mathfrak{G}$ *relative to* $\mathfrak{H}$ *is applied to the elements of* $\mathsf{\Lambda}$ *one and the same automorphism of* $\mathsf{\Lambda}$ *relative to* K *is always obtained.*

The biuniqueness of the correspondence characterized by (I a) *or* (I b) *implies, in particular, that the number of fields* $\mathsf{\Lambda}$ *between* K *and* N *is finite.*

Remarks: For the better understanding of this theorem and its proof the one-to-one correspondence (I a), (I b) is illustrated by the following Fig. 1, in which fields and groups standing at the same height shall correspond to one another. In particular, by (I a) K and $\mathfrak{G}$ correspond to one another; by (I b) N and $\mathfrak{E}$.[8] Therefore "in $\mathfrak{G}$" always corresponds to "relative to K" and "relative to $\mathfrak{E}$," to "in N," as we tried to express as clearly as possible in the formulation of the theorem. Furthermore, by (II) to the "ascent" from K to N corresponds the "descent" from $\mathfrak{G}$ to $\mathfrak{E}$, and to the relative degrees n, m, j, k of the fields correspond the relative indices n, m, j, k of the corresponding groups, so that it is also appropriate to regard the orders of the groups as indices (of $\mathfrak{E}$ in them). As announced in the remark to Theorem 99, (II) [259] , (III) and (IV) justify the dual use of the words *normal* and *conjugate* in field theory and group theory (cf. also the remark in the case of Theorem 93 [256]). In (III) to (V) (analogous to (II)) the particular corresponding pair K, $\mathfrak{G}$ can be replaced[9] by any corresponding pair Λ', $\mathfrak{H}'$, as immediately follows by applying the entire theorem to Λ' as ground field and (according to (I aa)) $\mathfrak{H}'$ as the Galois group of N relative to Λ' (for this see also Theorems 66, 70 [224, 227]). Then (I aa) seems like a special case of (V), since in (V) $\mathfrak{G}$ and $\mathfrak{H}$ can be replaced by $\mathfrak{H}$ and $\mathfrak{E}$, and accordingly K and Λ by Λ and N. In fact we actually have $\mathfrak{H}/\mathfrak{E} \cong \mathfrak{H}$.

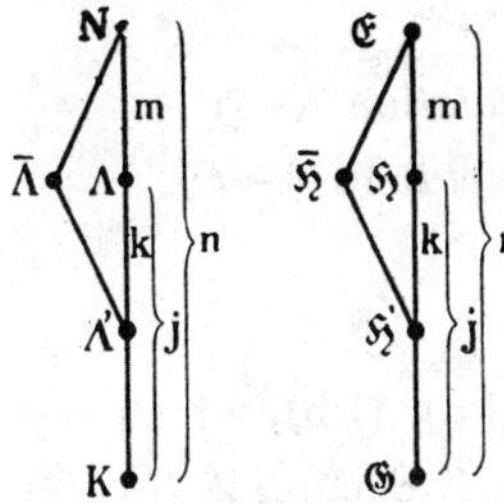

Fig. 1

[8] Therefore it is not N, as one might first think, which corresponds to its Galois group $\mathfrak{G}$. On the contrary, $\mathfrak{G}$ is the *Galois group of* N *relative to the* K *corresponding to* $\mathfrak{G}$, just as $\mathfrak{H}$ is the *Galois group of* N *relative to the* Λ *corresponding to* $\mathfrak{H}$.

[9] Fig. 1 corresponds to such a case, where this is also possible for (III), by taking Λ, $\bar{\Lambda}$ as conjugate even relative to Λ' and $\mathfrak{H}$, $\bar{\mathfrak{H}}$ as conjugate even relative to $\mathfrak{H}'$.

Proof of Part (I)

In order to show that (I a), (I b) yield one and the same biunique correspondence between all Λ and all $\mathfrak{H}$, it is sufficient to establish the following:

(1 a) (I a) *maps every* Λ *on a unique* $\mathfrak{H}$ (*notation* Λ→$\mathfrak{H}$).

(1 b) (I b) *maps* every $\mathfrak{H}$ *on a unique* Λ (*notation* $\mathfrak{H}$→Λ).

(2 a) Λ→$\mathfrak{H}$ *implies* $\mathfrak{H}$→Λ.

(2 b) $\mathfrak{H}$→Λ *implies* Λ→$\mathfrak{H}$.

For, that the unique correspondences (1 a), (1 b), which say the same thing by (2 a), (2 b), satisfy Vol. 1, Section 2, (δ), (ε) [23,24] is guaranteed by (1 a), and that they satisfy Vol. 1, Section 2, (δ′), (ε′) [24] is guaranteed by (1 b).

(1 a) This is clear, since by Vol. 1, Theorem 19 [63] and the definition of the product of automorphisms (Theorem 104 [265]) the set $\mathfrak{H}$ of those automorphisms of $\mathfrak{G}$ which leave every element of Λ invariant is a subgroup of $\mathfrak{G}$.

This means, as established in (I aa), that $\mathfrak{H}$ is the Galois group of N relative to Λ (Def. 34 [267]), and therefore the order of $\mathfrak{H}$ is equal to the degree of N over Λ (Theorem 105 [267]), and the index of $\mathfrak{H}$ in $\mathfrak{G}$ is equal to the degree of Λ over K (Theorem 71 [228] and Vol. 1, Theorem 25 [68]).

(1 b) This is clear, since by Vol. 1, Theorem 6 [25] and the conditions characterizing automorphisms relative to K [Def. 32, (1), (2) [264] and Addendum [266]] the set Λ of those elements of N which remain invariant under all automorphisms of $\mathfrak{H}$ is a subfield of N containing K.

(2 a) Let Λ→$\mathfrak{H}$ according to (1 a). Then we form $\mathfrak{H}\to\overline{\Lambda}$ according to (1 b) and $\overline{\Lambda}\to\overline{\mathfrak{H}}$ according to (1 a). In this case the

$$\left\{\begin{array}{l}\text{elements of } \Lambda\\ \text{automorphisms of } \mathfrak{H}\end{array}\right\},$$

since by $\left\{\begin{matrix}\text{(I a) they are invariant with respect to } \mathfrak{H} \\ \text{(I b) they leave the elements of } \bar{\mathsf{\Lambda}} \text{ invariant}\end{matrix}\right\}$

belong by $\left\{\begin{matrix}\text{(I b)} \\ \text{(I a)}\end{matrix}\right\}$, to the totality $\left\{\begin{matrix}\bar{\mathsf{\Lambda}} \\ \bar{\mathfrak{H}}\end{matrix}\right\}$ of all such $\left\{\begin{matrix}\text{elements of } \mathsf{N} \\ \text{automorphisms of } \mathfrak{G}\end{matrix}\right\}$, that is, we have $\left\{\begin{matrix}\mathsf{\Lambda} \leqq \bar{\mathsf{\Lambda}} \\ \mathfrak{H} \leqq \bar{\mathfrak{H}}\end{matrix}\right\}$. The first of these relations implies that $[\mathsf{N} : \mathsf{\Lambda}] \geqq [\mathsf{N} : \bar{\mathsf{\Lambda}}]$ (Theorem 70 [141]), whereas the last implies $[\mathsf{N} : \mathsf{\Lambda}] \leqq [\mathsf{N} : \bar{\mathsf{\Lambda}}]$, since by (I aa) $\mathfrak{H}$, $\bar{\mathfrak{H}}$ are the Galois groups of N relative to $\mathsf{\Lambda}$, $\bar{\mathsf{\Lambda}}$, whose orders by Theorem 105 [267] are equal to the degrees of N over $\mathsf{\Lambda}$, $\bar{\mathsf{\Lambda}}$. Consequently, $[\mathsf{N} : \mathsf{\Lambda}] = [\mathsf{N} : \bar{\mathsf{\Lambda}}]$, that is, $\mathsf{\Lambda} = \bar{\mathsf{\Lambda}}$ (Theorem 72 [143]); due to the choice of $\bar{\mathsf{\Lambda}}$ we therefore have $\mathfrak{H} \to \mathsf{\Lambda}$ according to (1 b), as stated in (2 a).

(2 b) Let $\mathfrak{H} \to \mathsf{\Lambda}$ according to (1 b). Then we form $\mathsf{\Lambda} \to \bar{\mathfrak{H}}$ according to (1 a).

On the one hand, it then follows as above that $\mathfrak{H} \leqq \bar{\mathfrak{H}}$. This means that the orders m, $\bar{m}$ of $\mathfrak{H}$, $\bar{\mathfrak{H}}$ satisfy the relation

$$m \leqq \bar{m}.$$

On the other hand, by means of a primitive element ϑ of N we form the polynomial

$$\psi(x) \equiv (x - \vartheta_{A_1}) \cdots (x - \vartheta_{A_m}),$$

where $A_1, \ldots, A_m$ are the automorphisms of $\mathfrak{H}$. Its coefficients are symmetric integral rational functions of the roots ϑ_{A_μ} ($\mu = 1, \ldots, m$). Now, an automorphism A of $\mathfrak{H}$ maps ϑ_{A_μ} into $(\vartheta_{A_\mu})_A = \vartheta_{A_\mu A}$, namely, merely permutes them with one another (Vol. 1, Theorem 16 [60]). Hence the coefficients of $\psi(x)$ are invariant with respect to all automorphisms A of $\mathfrak{H}$ and consequently according to (I b) belong to $\mathsf{\Lambda}$. $\psi(x)$ is therefore a polynomial in $\mathsf{\Lambda}$; it has $\vartheta = \vartheta_E$ as a root, and its degree is equal to the order m of $\mathfrak{H}$. This means that

$$[\mathsf{N} : \Lambda] = [\mathsf{K}(\vartheta) : \Lambda] = [\Lambda(\vartheta) : \Lambda] = [\vartheta : \Lambda] \leqq m$$

(Theorems 61, 77 [220, 236] Def. 22 [223] , Theorem 53 [210]). But by (I aa) and Theorem 105 [267] it follows from $\Lambda \to \bar{\mathfrak{H}}$ that $[\mathsf{N} : \Lambda] = \bar{m}$. Consequently we have

$$\bar{m} \leqq m.$$

These two inequalities yield $m = \bar{m}$, that is, $\mathfrak{H} = \bar{\mathfrak{H}}$; due to the choice of $\bar{\mathfrak{H}}$ we therefore have $\Lambda \to \mathfrak{H}$ according to (1 a), as stated in (2 b).

Incidentally, from $\bar{m} = [\mathsf{N} : \Lambda] = [\mathsf{K}(\vartheta) : \Lambda] = m$ together with Theorem 77 [236] and Def. 22 [223] it follows that $\psi(x)$ is the irreducible polynomial in Λ belonging to ϑ.

The unique correspondences (1 a), (1 b), which by (2 a), (2 b) form together one and the same biunique correspondence between all Λ and all $\mathfrak{H}$, are now designated by $\Lambda \longleftrightarrow \mathfrak{H}$.

Proof of Part (II)

a) If $\Lambda \longleftrightarrow \mathfrak{H}$, $\Lambda' \longleftrightarrow \mathfrak{H}'$ and $\Lambda \geqq \Lambda'$, then by (I a) the automorphisms of $\mathfrak{H}$ leave, in particular, the elements of the subfield Λ' of Λ invariant, therefore by (I a) belong to the totality $\mathfrak{H}'$ of all such automorphisms of $\mathfrak{G}$. Consequently we have $\mathfrak{H} \leqq \mathfrak{H}'$.

b) If $\Lambda \longleftrightarrow \mathfrak{H}$, $\Lambda' \longleftrightarrow \mathfrak{H}'$ and $\mathfrak{H} \leqq \mathfrak{H}'$, then by (I b) the elements of Λ' are left invariant, in particular, with respect to the automorphisms of the subgroup $\mathfrak{H}$ of $\mathfrak{H}'$, therefore by (I b) belong to the totality Λ of all such elements of N. Consequently we have $\Lambda \geqq \Lambda'$.

It immediately follows from (I aa) that in both cases the degree of Λ over Λ' is equal to the index of $\mathfrak{H}$ in $\mathfrak{H}'$ if we set there Λ', $\mathfrak{H}'$ instead of K, $\mathfrak{G}$.

Proof of Part (III)

For this purpose we first note that an automorphism S of N relative to K takes a field Λ between K and N into a field Λ_S between K and N isomorphic to it relative to K, namely, into a conjugate field. This immediately follows from Def. 32, Addendum [266] and Def. 26 [229]

Now, if $\Lambda \longleftrightarrow \mathfrak{H}$, $\Lambda_S \longleftrightarrow \mathfrak{H}_S$ and β is an element of Λ, β_S the element of Λ_S corresponding to it, then $\beta_{\mathfrak{H}} = \beta$ implies

$$(\beta_S)_{S^{-1}\mathfrak{H}S} = \beta_{SS^{-1}\mathfrak{H}S} = \beta_{\mathfrak{H}S} = \beta_S;$$

therefore β_S is invariant with respect to the subgroup $S^{-1}\mathfrak{H}S$ of $\mathfrak{G}$ conjugate to $\mathfrak{H}$. Consequently $S^{-1}\mathfrak{H}S \leqq \mathfrak{H}_S$. But S^{-1} takes Λ_S again into Λ since $SS^{-1} = E$. Hence it likewise follows that $S\mathfrak{H}_S S^{-1} \leqq \mathfrak{H}$, or also $\mathfrak{H}_S \leqq S^{-1}\mathfrak{H}S$. Consequently $\mathfrak{H}_S = S^{-1}\mathfrak{H}S$, that is, $\Lambda_S \longleftrightarrow S^{-1}\mathfrak{H}S$. In order to complete the proof of (III) we only have to establish in addition due to the biuniqueness of our correspondence that *all* conjugates to $\mathfrak{H}$ in $\mathfrak{G}$ or Λ in N are represented by $S^{-1}\mathfrak{H}S$ or Λ_S, respectively, if S runs through the group $\mathfrak{G}$.

a) For $\mathfrak{H}$ this is immediately clear by Vol. 1, Def. 21 [71]

b) For Λ it follows thus: If we set $\Lambda = \mathsf{K}(\beta)$, then $\Lambda_S = \mathsf{K}(\beta_S)$. Now, if S runs through the group $\mathfrak{G}$, then β_S runs through all conjugates to β (Theorem 105 [267]), therefore Λ_S runs through all conjugates to Λ (Theorem 97 [258]).

Proof of Part (IV)

By (III) and the biuniqueness of our correspondence we have that if the conjugates of Λ coincide so also do the conjugates of $\mathfrak{H}$ for a corresponding pair $\Lambda \longleftrightarrow \mathfrak{H}$, and conversely. (IV) immediately follows, on the one hand, from Theorem 99, (II) [259] and, on the other hand, from Vol. 1, Theorem 31 [73].

Proof of Part (V)

Let $\Lambda \longleftrightarrow \mathfrak{H}$ and according to (IV) let Λ be a normal field over K, $\mathfrak{H}$ a normal divisor of $\mathfrak{G}$. Then, due to $\Lambda_S = \Lambda$ (cf. proof to part (III)) every automorphism S of $\mathfrak{G}$ produces an automorphism P of Λ relative to K; and since every element of Λ is invariant with respect to $\mathfrak{H}$, all automorphisms of a residue class $\mathfrak{H}S$ produce one and the same automorphism P of Λ. Conversely, every automorphism P of Λ relative to K is generated in this way from an automorphism S of $\mathfrak{G}$. For, if β is a primitive element of Λ, then by Theorem 105 [267] β_P is one of the conjugates to β, and therefore there exists, again by Theorem 105, an automorphism S of $\mathfrak{G}$ which takes β into β_P and consequently produces the automorphism P for the elements of $\Lambda = K(\beta)$. Accordingly, to the totality of cosets of $\mathfrak{G}$ relative to $\mathfrak{H}$, that is, to the totality of elements of the factor group $\mathfrak{G}/\mathfrak{H}$, there uniquely corresponds the totality of elements of the Galois group of Λ relative to K. This correspondence is also one-to-one in this case, since by (I aa) the order of $\mathfrak{G}/\mathfrak{H}$, that is, the index of $\mathfrak{H}$, is equal to the degree of Λ, therefore by Theorem 105 is equal to the order of the Galois group of Λ. Finally, the definition of coset multiplication (Vol. 1, Theorem 22, [65]) implies that the correspondence under consideration also satisfies the isomorphism condition (Vol. 1, Theorem 23 [65]). Consequently, the Galois group of Λ relative to K is isomorphic to the factor group $\mathfrak{G}/\mathfrak{H}$ and is generated by it in the manner specified in (V).

This completes the proof of the Fundamental Theorem. Now, under the one-to-one correspondence specified in the theorem by (II) all containing relations and therefore also maximal and minimal properties relative to such relations likewise correspond to each other in inverted order. On taking this fact into consideration we obtain the following additional properties of that correspondence:

Theorem 110. *If in the sense of Theorem* 109

$$\mathsf{\Lambda}_1 \longleftrightarrow \mathfrak{H}_1, \ldots, \mathsf{\Lambda}_r \longleftrightarrow \mathfrak{H}_r$$

and $[\cdots]$ *designates the intersection,* $\{\cdots\}$ *the composite of the fields and groups,*[10] *then*

$$[\mathsf{\Lambda}_1, \ldots, \mathsf{\Lambda}_r] \longleftrightarrow \{\mathfrak{H}_1, \ldots, \mathfrak{H}_r\},$$
$$\{\mathsf{\Lambda}_1, \ldots, \mathsf{\Lambda}_r\} \longleftrightarrow [\mathfrak{H}_1, \ldots, \mathfrak{H}_r]$$

is valid.

In particular, by the remark made with respect to Theorem 62 [220] we have

Corollary. *If* $\alpha_1, \ldots, \alpha_r$ *are elements of* N *and in the sense of Theorem* 109

$$\mathsf{K}(\alpha_1) \longleftrightarrow \mathfrak{H}_1, \ldots, \mathsf{K}(\alpha_r) \longleftrightarrow \mathfrak{H}_r,$$

then

$$\mathsf{K}(\alpha_1, \ldots, \alpha_r) \longleftrightarrow [\mathfrak{H}_1, \ldots, \mathfrak{H}_r].$$

2) The Fundamental Theorem enables us to draw conclusions about the structure of N over K from the structure of the Galois group $\mathfrak{G}$ of N relative to K. According to the introductory remarks we think of the latter as known[11] in applying the Fundamental Theorem to the investigation of the structure of the extension N of K. In order to break up the *step* from K to N *to be investigated* into a sequence of *simpler steps* by inserting a chain of intermediate fields

$$\mathsf{K} = \mathsf{\Lambda}_0 < \mathsf{\Lambda}_1 < \cdots < \mathsf{\Lambda}_s = \mathsf{N},$$

---

[10] In regard to this, cf. Vol. 1, Theorem 7 [26], Def. 5 [27], Theorem 21 [64], Def. 15 [64], especially the characterization of intersection and composite given in connection with Def. 5.

[11] Cf. Theorem 106 [269] as well as the remark before Def. 35 [270] and after Theorem 107 [271].

we have to determine, starting from a chain of subgroups

$$\mathfrak{G} = \mathfrak{H}_0 > \mathfrak{H}_1 > \cdots > \mathfrak{H}_s = \mathfrak{E},$$

the Λ_i as the intermediate fields corresponding to the subgroups $\mathfrak{H}_i$. If we regard the intermediate links Λ_i themselves as new ground fields, the successive *expansion* from K to N is then tied to a successive *reduction* of the Galois group $\mathfrak{G}$ of N relative to K to the subgroups $\mathfrak{H}_i$, which according to (I aa) are actually the Galois groups of N relative to the Λ_i. The entire step from K to N is covered when $\mathfrak{G}$ is reduced completely, that is, to $\mathfrak{E}$. In particular, if $\mathfrak{H}_i$ is chosen so that $\mathfrak{H}_{i+1}$ is a normal divisor of $\mathfrak{H}_i$, then by (IV) Λ_{i+1} is a normal field over Λ_i, and the Galois group corresponding to this step is $\mathfrak{H}_i/\mathfrak{H}_{i+1}$.

In order to reduce the Galois group $\mathfrak{G}$ of N to a subgroup $\mathfrak{H}$ in the stated sense we have to determine the subfield Λ of N corresponding to $\mathfrak{H}$. This can certainly be done by the correspondence rule (I b); however, this does not enable us to control the field Λ as completely as if we were to give a primitive element β of Λ. For such a primitive element we introduce the following definition:

Definition 36. *If* $\Lambda \longleftrightarrow \mathfrak{H}$ *in the sense of Theorem* 109 *and* $\Lambda = K(\beta)$, *that is, if* β *is a primitive element of the* Λ *corresponding to* $\mathfrak{H}$, *then* β *is called an* ***element*** *of* N ***belonging to*** $\mathfrak{H}$.

Here we will not go into the question of how such a β is determined from a primitive element ϑ of N (cf. Vol. 3, Section 17, Exer. 4). In the following we will only derive a series of facts, which are of theoretical significance in this regard.

Conversely, it is naturally valid that *every* element β of N also belongs to a certain subgroup $\mathfrak{H}$ of $\mathfrak{G}$, namely, the subgroup (uniquely) determined according to $K(\beta) = \Lambda \longleftrightarrow \mathfrak{H}$. Hence these facts, in addition, extend, and yield a deeper group-theoretic basis for the statements made earlier about the conjugates of an algebraic element (Theorems 95, 96, 103 [257, 257, 262]).

Theorem 111. *Under the assumptions of Theorem* 109 *let* β *be an element of* N *belonging to the subgroup* $\mathfrak{H}$ *of* $\mathfrak{G}$, *and* j *the index of* $\mathfrak{H}$; *furthermore let*

$$\mathfrak{G} = \mathfrak{H}S_1 + \cdots + \mathfrak{H}S_j$$

be the right decomposition of $\mathfrak{G}$ *relative to* $\mathfrak{H}$. *Then, on applying the automorphisms* S *of* $\mathfrak{G}$ *one and the same conjugate* $\beta_{\mathfrak{H}S}$ *of* β *is always generated by all automorphisms of a coset* $\mathfrak{H}S$. *Furthermore, the conjugates* $\beta_{\mathfrak{H}S_1}, \ldots, \beta_{\mathfrak{H}S_j}$ *corresponding to the* j *cosets* $\mathfrak{H}S_1, \ldots, \mathfrak{H}S_j$ *are different from one another. Or, in short, the element* β *is invariant with respect to* $\mathfrak{H}$ *and* j*-valued with respect to* $\mathfrak{G}$.

In particular, therefore

(1) $$g(x) \equiv (x - \beta_{\mathfrak{H}S_1}) \cdots (x - \beta_{\mathfrak{H}S_j})$$

is the irreducible polynomial in K *belonging to* β.

Proof: According to Def. 36 the elements of $\Lambda = \mathsf{K}(\beta)$ remain invariant with respect to the automorphisms of $\mathfrak{H}$. This means, in particular, that $\beta_{\mathfrak{H}} = \beta$ and therefore $\beta_{\mathfrak{H}S} = \beta_S$ for any S of $\mathfrak{G}$. Now the β_S represent all the conjugates to β (Theorems 103, 105 [262, 267]). Furthermore, by Theorem 109 $\Lambda = \mathsf{K}(\beta)$, so that β has the degree j. Hence there are generally *exactly* j different conjugates to β (Theorems 96, 58 [257, 215]). But, in view of what has already been shown, there are among the β_S *at most* the j elements $\beta_{\mathfrak{H}S_\nu}$ $(\nu = 1, \ldots, j)$ different from one another. Therefore none of these can be equal. The statement of the theorem follows from this.

Theorem 111 can also be reversed:

Theorem 112. *Under the assumptions of Theorem* 109 *let* β *be an element of* N *invariant with respect to the subgroup* $\mathfrak{H}$ *of* $\mathfrak{G}$ *of index* j *and* j*-valued with respect to* $\mathfrak{G}$. *Then* β *is an element belonging to* $\mathfrak{H}$.

Proof: *If* $\mathsf{K}(\beta) = \Lambda \longleftrightarrow \mathfrak{H}'$, that is, β is an element belonging to $\mathfrak{H}'$, then by (I a) we first have $\mathfrak{H} \leqq \mathfrak{H}'$, since by the assumption the elements of $\Lambda = \mathsf{K}(\beta)$ are surely invariant with respect to $\mathfrak{H}$. Furthermore, by Theorem 111 β is j'-valued with respect to $\mathfrak{G}$, where j' designates the index of $\mathfrak{H}'$. Therefore, according to the assumption $j' = j$, that is, $\mathfrak{H}' = \mathfrak{H}$, and consequently β is an element belonging to $\mathfrak{H}$, as stated.

The two extreme cases of Theorems 111, 112 are worthy of note:

Corollary. *Under the assumptions of Theorem* 109 *an element* β *of* N *is a primitive element of* N *if and only if it is n-valued with respect to* $\mathfrak{G}$, *and an element of* K *if and only if it is one-valued (invariant) with respect to* $\mathfrak{G}$.[12]

The results expressed in Theorem 111 can be applied (by Theorem 94 [256]) to the data taken as a basis in Theorem 95 [257] , if the irreducible polynomial $f(x)$, whose stem field $\Lambda = \mathsf{K}(\alpha)$ and root field $\mathsf{W} = \mathsf{K}(\alpha_1, \ldots, \alpha_r)$ are to be studied, is again (as was already done in Theorem 103 [262]) assumed to be separable. As a supplement to Theorem 95 and Theorem 103 we prove in this regard:

Theorem 113. *Let the data of Theorem* 95 [257] *be given, and in addition let* $f(x)$ *be separable. If we set*

$$[\mathsf{K}(\alpha) : \mathsf{K}(\beta)] = k, \quad [\mathsf{K}(\beta) : \mathsf{K}] = j,$$

therefore

$$kj = [\mathsf{K}(\alpha) : \mathsf{K}] = r,$$

---

[12] These facts follow most simply directly from the fact that the correspondences (I a) and (I b) coincide, as established in the Fundamental Theorem. For this purpose we only have to state that K and $\mathfrak{G}$ correspond, not only (as already stressed in the remarks included there, trivially) according to (I a), but also according to (I b); and similarly that N and $\mathfrak{E}$ not only correspond according to (I b) but also according to (I a).

then the elements $\beta_1, \ldots, \beta_r$ *conjugate to* β *fall into* j *different sets each consisting of* k *elements equal to one another.*

In particular, therefore,

$$\bar{g}(x) \equiv (x-\beta_1)\cdots(x-\beta_r)$$

is a polynomial in K *which is related to the irreducible polynomial* $g(x)$ *in* K *belonging to* β *as follows:*

$$\bar{g}(x) \equiv g(x)^k.$$

Proof: We apply to α, and with this to $\beta = h(\alpha)$, all automorphisms of the Galois group $\mathfrak{G}$ of W. (Besides the degree relations already introduced in the theorem for the fields $\mathsf{W} \geqq \mathsf{K}(\alpha) \geqq \mathsf{K}(\beta) \geqq \mathsf{K}$) let

$$l = [\mathsf{W} : \mathsf{K}(\alpha)], \quad m = [\mathsf{W} : \mathsf{K}(\beta)], \quad n = [\mathsf{W} : \mathsf{K}],$$

therefore

$$lk = m, \quad mj = n.$$

On the one hand, by Theorem 111 the set of the r different $\alpha_1, \ldots, \alpha_r$ conjugate to α is now generated l times from α by applying $\mathfrak{G}$ (Theorem 58 [215]), and therefore the set of conjugates $\beta_1, \ldots, \beta_r$ is generated, likewise l times, from β by applying $\mathfrak{G}$. On the other hand, however, the set of the j different conjugates to β is generated m times from β by applying $\mathfrak{G}$ according to Theorem 111. Therefore, the set $\beta_1, \ldots, \beta_r$ (written only once) must represent these different conjugates exactly $k = \frac{m}{l}$ times, as stated.

In analogy to the Corollary to Theorems 111, 112, it further follows from Theorem 113 that:

Corollary. *Let the data of Theorem* 95 [257] *be given and in addition let* $f(x)$ *be separable. Then an element* β *of* Λ *is a primitive element of* Λ *if and only if the conjugates* $\beta_1, \ldots, \beta_r$ *are all different from one another, and it is an element of* K *if and only if these conjugates are all equal to one another.*

In connection with Theorem 111 we further establish:

Theorem 114. *Let* $\mathsf{\Lambda} \longleftrightarrow \mathfrak{H}$ *in the sense of Theorem* 109 [273]. *Furthermore, let* ϑ *be an element belonging to* $\mathfrak{E}$ *and* β *an element of* N *belonging to* $\mathfrak{H}$, *therefore* $\mathsf{N} = \mathsf{K}(\vartheta)$ *and* $\mathsf{\Lambda} = \mathsf{K}(\beta)$. *Finally, let* $A_1, \ldots, A_m$ *be elements of* $\mathfrak{H}$ *and* $\mathfrak{H}S_1, \ldots, \mathfrak{H}S_j$ *right cosets of* $\mathfrak{G}$ *relative to* $\mathfrak{H}$. *Then the* j *conjugate elements* $\beta_{\mathfrak{H}S_\nu}$ *each belong to the* j *conjugate subgroups* $S_\nu^{-1}\mathfrak{H}S_\nu$.

Furthermore,

(2) $$\psi(x) \equiv (x - \vartheta_{A_1}) \cdots (x - \vartheta_{A_m})$$

is the irreducible polynomial over $\mathsf{\Lambda}$ *belonging to* ϑ. *The irreducible polynomial* $q(x)$ *over* K *belonging to* ϑ *has the decomposition*

(3) $$q(x) \equiv \psi_{\mathfrak{H}S_1}(x) \cdots \psi_{\mathfrak{H}S_j}(x),$$

where

(4) $$\psi_{\mathfrak{H}S_\nu}(x) \equiv (x - \vartheta_{A_1 S_\nu}) \cdots (x - \vartheta_{A_m S_\nu}) \quad (\nu = 1, \ldots, j).$$

Here the factors $\psi_{\mathfrak{H}S_\nu}(x)$ *are the conjugates to* $\psi(x)$; *therefore they too are irreducible polynomials in the conjugate fields*

$$\mathsf{\Lambda}_{\mathfrak{H}S_\nu} = \mathsf{K}(\beta_{\mathfrak{H}S_\nu}) \text{ to } \mathsf{\Lambda}.$$

In particular, if $\mathfrak{H}$ *is a normal divisor of* $\mathfrak{G}$, *so that* $\mathsf{\Lambda}$ *is a normal field over* K, *then* (3) *accordingly represents the decomposition of* $q(x)$ *into its irreducible factors* (4) *in the field* $\mathsf{\Lambda}$. *Therefore, these are all of the same degree and consist of the linear factors of* $q(x)$ *corresponding to the decomposition of* $\mathfrak{G}$ *relative to* $\mathfrak{H}$.

Proof: The statement regarding the $\beta_{\mathfrak{H}S_\nu}$ follows from (III). The statement about $\psi(x)$ was already shown in the proof of part (I) to Theorem 109 under (2b). On applying the automorphisms S_ν to $\mathsf{\Lambda}_{\mathfrak{H}} = \mathsf{\Lambda}$, $\psi_{\mathfrak{H}}(x) \equiv \psi(x)$ it finally follows that the $\psi_{\mathfrak{H}S_\nu}(x)$ are polynomials over the $\mathsf{\Lambda}_{\mathfrak{H}S_\nu}$.

If N is the root field of a separable polynomial $f(x)$ over K, hence $q(x)$ a Galois resolvent of $f(x)$, then in the older literature the relations described in Theorems 111, 114 were expressed as follows (here too remarks similar to those made in connection with Def. 31 [261] are appropriate):

The Galois group $\mathfrak{G}$ of the polynomial $f(x)$ over K will reduce to $\mathfrak{H}$ by the adjunction of an irrationality β of N belonging to the subgroup $\mathfrak{H}$ (index j, order m), that is, with respect to $\Lambda = \mathsf{K}(\beta)$ as ground field. This adjunction is made possible by solving the resolvent of j-th degree (1) and produces a decomposition (3) of the Galois resolvent $q(x)$ into irreducible factors of m-th degree (4) which belong to the j conjugate fields to $\Lambda = \mathsf{K}(\beta)$. After the adjunction of β, in order to determine a root ϑ of the Galois resolvent $q(x)$ we must still solve the resolvent of m-th degree (2), the Galois resolvent of $f(x)$ relative to Λ, which is obtained from those of the factors (4) of $q(x)$ corresponding to the field Λ. In particular, if $\mathfrak{H}$ is a normal divisor of $\mathfrak{G}$, then $\Lambda = \mathsf{K}(\beta)$ is a normal field over K and the resolvent (1) is the Galois resolvent of itself with the Galois group $\mathfrak{G}/\mathfrak{H}$.

The conjugates $\beta_{\mathfrak{H}S_\nu}$ of β are irrationalities over N belonging to the conjugate subgroups $S_\nu^{-1}\mathfrak{H}S_\nu$ of $\mathfrak{H}$. Consequently, by Theorem 110, Corollary [281] the simultaneous adjunction of *all* conjugates $\beta_{\mathfrak{H}S_\nu}$, that is, of *all* roots of the auxiliary equation (1), reduces the Galois group $\mathfrak{G}$ to the intersection $[S_1^{-1}\mathfrak{H}S_1, \ldots, S_j^{-1}\mathfrak{H}S_j]$ of all subgroups conjugate to $\mathfrak{H}$. By Vol. 1, Theorem 33 [74] as well as by Theorem 94 [256] and Theorem 109, (IV) [274] this means that this intersection is a normal divisor of $\mathfrak{G}$.

3) Finally, it should be noted that the Fundamental Theorem also can be used to investigate the structure of *an arbitrary* (not necessarily normal) separable extension Λ of finite degree over K. For, if $\Lambda = \mathsf{K}(\alpha)$ and $\alpha_1, \ldots, \alpha_r$ are the conjugates to α, then Λ is a subfield of the normal field $\mathsf{N} = \mathsf{K}(\alpha_1, \ldots, \alpha_r)$ over K. In this case, if $\mathfrak{G}$ is its Galois group, $\mathfrak{H}$ the subgroup corresponding to Λ, then a one-to-one correspondence with the properties of Theorem 109 can be set up mapping the groups

between $\mathfrak{G}$ and $\mathfrak{H}$ on the fields between K and $\mathsf{\Lambda}$. The proof of Theorem 113 [284] is an example of this kind of approach.

A. Loewy[13] has actually shown much more by carrying out the entire train of ideas of the Galois theory *from the beginning* for an *arbitrary* finite separable algebraic extension $\mathsf{\Lambda} = \mathsf{K}(\alpha_1, \ldots, \alpha_r)$ (where $\alpha_1, \ldots, \alpha_r$ are, therefore, not necessarily *the* roots *of a single* polynomial) rather than restricting himself to a normal extension. Instead of the *automorphisms* and *permutations* he used *isomorphisms* and so-called *transmutations* (one-to-one correspondences with a definite mapping rule of the $\alpha_1, \ldots, \alpha_r$ to a system of conjugates $\alpha_{1\nu_1}, \ldots, \alpha_{r\nu_r}$, cf. the proof of Theorem 90 [251]) which no longer form a *group* but a so-called *groupoid.* Incidentally in this way Loewy was likewise able to establish the Galois theory independently of the symmetric functions (cf. footnote 1 to Theorem 90).

18. Dependence on the Ground Field

The Fundamental Theorem of the Galois theory and the expositions related to it enabled us to determine how the structure of a separable normal extension N of finite degree over a ground field K is affected if an extension $\mathsf{\Lambda}$ of K *contained* in N is used as ground field instead of K. In addition we now wish to see what happens to the relations if the ground field K is replaced by an *arbitrary* extension $\overline{\mathsf{K}}$ of K. This question arises, as the considerations at the end of Section 17, from the effort to attain a given extension N of K of the stated kind by steps as simple as possible or — and this is the point which represents

[13] *Neue elementare Begründung und Erweiterung der Galoisschen Theorie* (New Elementary Foundation and Extension of the Galois Theory), Sitzungsberichte der Heidelberger Akademie der Wissenschaften, Mathematisch-naturwissenschaftlicher Klub, 1925 (Records of the Heidelberg Academy of Sciences, Department of Mathematics and Natural Science, 1925).

a generalization of Section 17 — merely to include it. Above all we intend to impose on these steps some general simplicity condition, which has nothing to do with the given N; for instance, as will be done in Chapter V, the condition that the extension take place through the adjunction of *roots* $\sqrt[n]{a}$ in the special sense of the word.

1) If N is the root field W of a polynomial $f(x) \equiv (x-\alpha_1) \cdots (x-\alpha_r)$ over K, then on passing over to an extension $\bar{K}$ of K as ground field the root field $W = K(\alpha_1, \ldots, \alpha_r)$ of $f(x)$ over K is also replaced by the extended root field $\bar{W} = \bar{K}(\alpha_1, \ldots, \alpha_r)$ of $f(x)$ over $\bar{K}$, and by Theorem 60 [220] $\bar{W} = W$ if and only if $\bar{K} \leqq W$, namely, if we have the same situation as in the previous section. Since by Theorem 100 [260] any extension N of K of the stated kind can be represented as a root field W of a polynomial $f(x)$ over K, we can also explain in this way what is to be understood by N *with respect to an extension* $\bar{K}$ *of* K *as ground field,* namely, the passage to the extension $\bar{N} = \bar{W}$ of $\bar{K}$. This explanation seems at first dependent on the choice of the polynomial $f(x)$. However, we prove:

Theorem 115. *If* N *is a separable normal extension of finite degree of* K *and* $\bar{K}$ *an arbitrary extension of* K, *then the root fields over* $\bar{K}$ *of all polynomials over* K, *for which* N *is the root field over* K, *establish altogether one and the same separable normal extension* $\bar{N}$ *of finite degree over* $\bar{K}$.

Proof: Let

$$f(x) \equiv (x-\alpha_1) \cdots (x-\alpha_r),$$
$$f^*(x) \equiv (x-\alpha_1^*) \cdots (x-\alpha_{r^*}^*)$$

be two polynomials over K for which N is the root field over K, and let $\overline{N}, \overline{N}^*$ be the root fields of $f(x), f^*(x)$ over $\overline{K}$. In this case since

$$\overline{N}^* = \overline{K}(\alpha_1^*, \ldots, \alpha_{r^*}^*) \geqq K(\alpha_1^*, \ldots, \alpha_{r^*}^*) = N = K(\alpha_1, \ldots, \alpha_r),$$

$\overline{N}^*$ contains $\overline{K}$, on the one hand, and $\alpha_1, \ldots, \alpha_r$, on the other hand. Therefore, we also have $\overline{K}(\alpha_1, \ldots, \alpha_r) = \overline{N}$, that is, $\overline{N}^* \geqq \overline{N}$. Likewise, $\overline{N} \geqq \overline{N}^*$. Consequently $\overline{N} = \overline{N}^*$.

The extension $\overline{N}$ of $\overline{K}$, independent, according to this, of the choice of the polynomial $f(x)$, is naturally separable and normal of finite degree over $\overline{K}$ (Theorem 100 [260]).

The extension $\overline{N}$ of $\overline{K}$ in Theorem 115 is determined uniquely[14] by the property of being a root field over $\overline{K}$ for all polynomials over K for which N is a root field over K, in the same sense as the root field of a polynomial is determined according to Theorems 87, 89 [242, 246]. This means that any two such extensions of $\overline{K}$ are isomorphic relative to $\overline{K}$, and no extension of $\overline{K}$ contains two different such extensions. We can therefore define:

Definition 37. *The extension $\overline{N}$ of $\overline{K}$ in Theorem 115 determined uniquely by $K, N, \overline{K}$ is called **the extension N of K with respect to $\overline{K}$ as ground field.***

It is important for us to characterize this extension $\overline{N}$ still in another way:

---

[14] This uniqueness depends essentially on the normality of N. For arbitrary extensions of finite degree $\Lambda = K(\alpha_1, \ldots, \alpha_r)$, where $\alpha_1, \ldots, \alpha_r$ are not necessarily *the* roots of *a single* polynomial over K, the conjugates of $\overline{\Lambda} = \overline{K}(\alpha_1, \ldots, \alpha_r)$ would necessarily have to be characterized with respect to $\overline{K}$.

Theorem 116. *If, under the assumption of Theorem* 115, $\overline{\mathsf{N}}$ *is the extension* N *of* K with respect to $\overline{\mathsf{K}}$ *as ground field, then*

1) $\overline{\mathsf{N}}$ *contains* N,

2) *no field between* $\overline{\mathsf{K}}$ *and* $\overline{\mathsf{N}}$ *contains* N *except* $\overline{\mathsf{N}}$ *itself.*

$\overline{\mathsf{N}}$ *is determined uniquely by* 1), 2).

Proof: That 1), 2) are valid for $\overline{\mathsf{N}}$ follows immediately from the property used to define $\overline{\mathsf{N}}$ as well as the minimal property of root fields (Theorem 88 [245]).

b) The extension $\overline{\mathsf{N}}^*$ of $\overline{\mathsf{K}}$ has the properties 1), 2). In this case by 1) $\overline{\mathsf{N}}^*$ contains the roots $\alpha_1, \ldots, \alpha_r$ of every polynomial $f(x)$ over K for which N is the root field over K, therefore it also contains the field $\overline{\mathsf{N}}$ of Theorem 115. Hence $\overline{\mathsf{N}}$ is a field between $\overline{\mathsf{K}}$ and $\overline{\mathsf{N}}^*$ which contains N, and therefore $\overline{\mathsf{N}} = \overline{\mathsf{N}}^*$, since we have assumed that $\overline{\mathsf{N}}^*$ satisfies 2).

The properties 1), 2) say that $\overline{\mathsf{N}}$ is the smallest subfield of $\overline{\mathsf{N}}$ containing N and $\overline{\mathsf{K}}$; therefore, it is *the composite* $\{\mathsf{N}, \overline{\mathsf{K}}\}$.

Here $\overline{\mathsf{N}}$ itself is to be regarded as the auxiliary field (field K of Vol. 1, Def. 5 [27]) containing both N and $\overline{\mathsf{K}}$, whose existence is required in order to be able to form the composite $\{\mathsf{N}, \overline{\mathsf{K}}\} = \overline{\mathsf{N}}$. Hence $\overline{\mathsf{N}}$ cannot be *defined* from the beginning as the composite $\{\mathsf{N}, \overline{\mathsf{K}}\}$. On the contrary, the representation of $\overline{\mathsf{N}}$ as the composite $\{\mathsf{N}, \overline{\mathsf{K}}\}$ is only made possible by the *construction* of $\overline{\mathsf{N}}$ carried out according to Theorem 115, and the use of the definite expression "the composite $\{\mathsf{N}, \overline{\mathsf{K}}\}$" is based on the fact that $\overline{\mathsf{N}}$ is determined uniquely by N and $\overline{\mathsf{K}}$ alone as proved in Theorem 115. Before the composite is formed according to Theorem 115 the fields N and $\overline{\mathsf{K}}$ are "free" from one another, that is, are not contained in a common extension. We express this logical relation as follows, in connection with Def. 37:

Addendum to Definition 37. *The extension* N *of* K *with respect to* $\overline{K}$ *as ground field, which exists in the sense of Theorem* 115 *and Def.* 37, *is also called the* ***free composite*** *of* N *and* $\overline{K}$ (*notation* $\{N, \overline{K}\}$).

It may help to clarify the point under consideration if we make the following additional statement: Steinitz proved that the free composite can be defined from the beginning as the ordinary composite of N and $\overline{K}$ if we make use of the existence and uniqueness of the field $\overline{A}$ of all algebraic elements over $\overline{K}$ (see Section 11). Then this field $\overline{A}$, which also contains the field A of all algebraic elements over K and therefore, in particular, the field N, can be used as an auxiliary field for forming the composite of N and $\overline{K}$.[15]

In Theorem 116 we characterized the extension N of K with respect to $\overline{K}$ as the *free composite* $\{N, \overline{K}\}$. This characterization is important because it shows that the ground field K entering in Theorem 115 and Def. 37 essentially plays only the role of an auxiliary field. Namely, since in Theorem 116, 1), 2) no mention of K is made, we have

Theorem 117. *If* N *is a separable normal extension of finite degree over* K, $\overline{K}$ *an extension of* K *and* $\overline{N}$ *the extension* N *of* K *with respect to* $\overline{K}$, *then* $\overline{N}$ *is also the extension* N *of* K^* *with respect to* $\overline{K}$ *if* K^* *designates any common subfield of* N *and* $\overline{K}$ *over which* N *is separable and normal of finite degree.*

[15] This is also valid for an arbitrary algebraic extension Λ of K, and even uniquely. This follows from the fact that the conjugates of $\overline{\Lambda} = \{\Lambda, \overline{K}\}$ which are not distinguishable "from below," that is, with respect to free composition by a process generalizing Theorem 115, are, from the beginning, distinct "from above," that is, inside $\overline{A}$.

Therefore, in particular, the largest common subfield of N and $\bar{K}$, that is, the intersection [N, $\bar{K}$], can also be regarded as ground field, since it satisfies the required conditions (Theorems 70, 92, 93 [227, 255, 256]). In order to be in harmony in the future with the designations of Section 17 we now write $\bar{\Lambda}$ instead of $\bar{K}$, so that $\bar{N} = \{N, \bar{\Lambda}\}$; furthermore, we set $\Lambda = [N, \bar{\Lambda}]$ and illustrate the fields under consideration and their relations to one another by the adjoining Fig. 2, which is an extension of the graphic illustration used in Fig. 1 for Theorem 109 [275]. By Theorem 117 $\bar{N}$ also has in this case the property of Theorem 115 for Λ as ground field. Furthermore, due to the symmetry of the composite $\{N, \bar{\Lambda}\}$ in N and $\bar{\Lambda}$ we have:

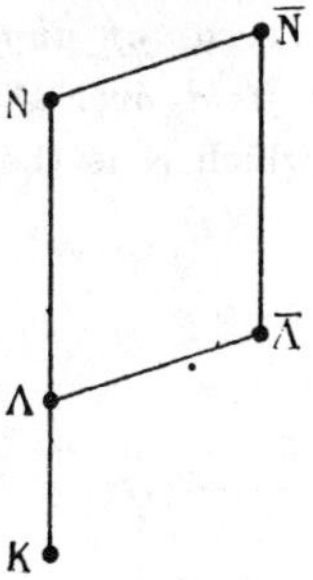

Fig. 2.

Theorem 118. *If* N *and* $\bar{\Lambda}$ *are separable normal extensions of finite degree over* K, *then the free composite* $\bar{N} = \{N, \bar{\Lambda}\}$ *is the extension* N *of* K *with respect to* $\bar{\Lambda}$ *as well as the extension* $\bar{\Lambda}$ *of* K *with respect to* N. *Consequently,* $\bar{N}$ *is separable and normal of finite degree over* $\bar{\Lambda}$ *as well as over* N.

2) We now prove the following basic theorem, which completely answers the question asked at the beginning:

Theorem 119. *Let* N *be a separable normal extension of finite degree over* K *and* $\mathfrak{G}$ *the Galois group of* N *relative to* K. *Furthermore, let* $\bar{\Lambda}$ *be any extension of* K *and*

$$\bar{N} = \{N, \bar{\Lambda}\}, \quad \Lambda = [N, \bar{\Lambda}].$$

Finally, let $\mathfrak{H}$ *be the subgroup of* $\mathfrak{G}$ *corresponding to the field* Λ *between* K *and* N. *Then*

(I) *The Galois group* $\bar{\mathfrak{H}}$ *of* $\bar{\mathsf{N}}$ *relative to* $\bar{\Lambda}$ *is isomorphic to the Galois group* $\mathfrak{H}$ *of* N *relative to* Λ. *Namely, the automorphisms of* $\mathfrak{H}$ *and* $\bar{\mathfrak{H}}$ *can be generated:*

a) *By the same substitutions of any primitive element* ϑ *of* N *relative to* Λ (therefore, in particular, by such a one from N relative to K).

b) *By the same permutations of the roots* $\alpha_1, \ldots, \alpha_r$ *of any polynomial* $\varphi(x)$ *over* Λ *for which* N *is the root field over* Λ (therefore, in particular, by such a one over K for which N is the root field over K).

In particular, according to this (Fig. 3)

$$[\bar{\mathsf{N}} : \bar{\Lambda}] = [\mathsf{N} : \Lambda],$$

and, if $\bar{\Lambda}$ *has finite degree over* Λ, *also*

$$[\bar{\mathsf{N}} : \mathsf{N}] = [\bar{\Lambda} : \Lambda].$$

(II) *If the fields* Λ^* *between* Λ *and* N, *and the fields* $\bar{\Lambda}^*$ *between* $\bar{\Lambda}$ *and* $\bar{\mathsf{N}}$ *correspond to one another on the basis of the isomorphism between* $\mathfrak{H}$ *and* $\bar{\mathfrak{H}}$ *described under* (I) *and according to Theorem* 109 [273] , *then this is a one-to-one correspondence between the* Λ^* *and* $\bar{\Lambda}^*$, *in which the relations "contained, conjugate, normal" correspond to one another as*

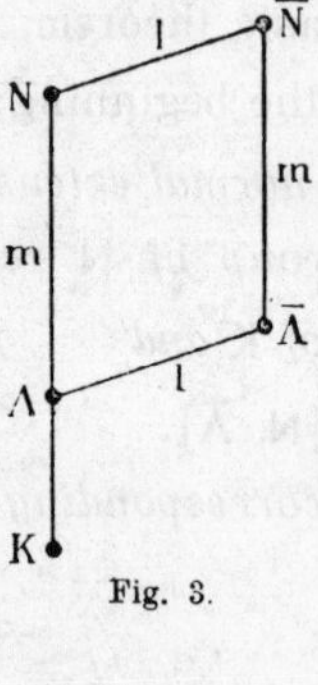

Fig. 3.

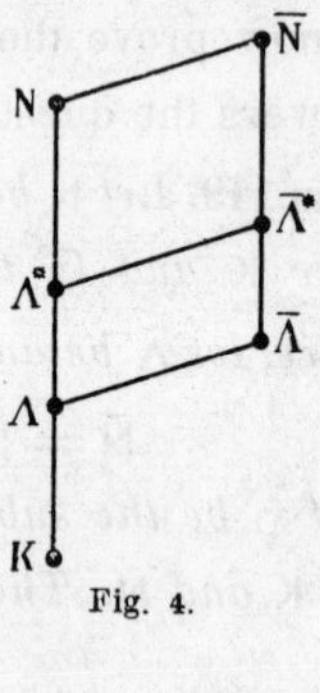

Fig. 4.

long as they refer to fields corresponding to one another and ground fields of the stated kind. With respect to this correspondence we have further (Fig. 4):

$$\mathsf{\Lambda}^* = [\mathsf{N}, \overline{\mathsf{\Lambda}}^*], \quad \overline{\mathsf{N}} = \{\mathsf{N}, \overline{\mathsf{\Lambda}}^*\},$$

$$\mathsf{\Lambda} = [\mathsf{\Lambda}^*, \overline{\mathsf{\Lambda}}], \quad \overline{\mathsf{\Lambda}}^* = \{\mathsf{\Lambda}^*, \overline{\mathsf{\Lambda}}\}.$$

(III) *If, in particular,* $\overline{\mathsf{\Lambda}}$ *is normal over* K, *then* $\mathsf{\Lambda}$ *is also normal over* K *(the converse, however, need not be valid).*

Proof of Part (I)

a)[16] Let ϑ be a primitive element of N relative to $\mathsf{\Lambda}$, and $\psi(x)$ and $\overline{\psi}(x)$ the irreducible polynomials over $\mathsf{\Lambda}$ and $\overline{\mathsf{\Lambda}}$, respectively, belonging to this element. Then $\overline{\psi}(x)$ is first of all a divisor of $\psi(x)$ (Theorem 53 [109]). Furthermore, since $\psi(x)$ resolves into linear factors in N (Theorems 93 [256] , 98 [258], 99, (III) [259]), $\overline{\psi}(x)$ is a product of certain of these linear factors; therefore it, too, is a polynomial in N. Consequently, $\overline{\psi}(x)$ actually belongs to the intersection $\mathsf{\Lambda} = [\mathsf{N}, \overline{\mathsf{\Lambda}}]$. Due to the irreducibility of $\psi(x)$ we therefore have $\overline{\psi}(x) \equiv \psi(x)$.

From $\overline{\mathsf{N}} = \{\mathsf{N}, \overline{\mathsf{\Lambda}}\} = \{\mathsf{\Lambda}(\vartheta), \overline{\mathsf{\Lambda}}\} = \overline{\mathsf{\Lambda}}(\vartheta)$ it further follows that ϑ is also a primitive element of $\overline{\mathsf{N}}$ relative to $\overline{\mathsf{\Lambda}}$.

This result and the fact $\overline{\psi}(x) \equiv \psi(x)$ previously proved yield the statement (I) a) by Theorem 105 [267] .

b) Let N be the root field of $\varphi(x) \equiv (x - \alpha_1) \cdots (x - \alpha_r)$ over $\mathsf{\Lambda}$, therefore $\overline{\mathsf{N}}$ the root field of $\varphi(x)$ over $\overline{\mathsf{\Lambda}}$ (Theorems 115, 117). Then by Theorem 107 [271] the automorphisms of the Galois

---

[16] For this proof we must realize that the elements of N belong to $\overline{\mathsf{N}}$ (Theorem 116, 1 [[291]), therefore can be replaced by those of $\overline{\mathsf{\Lambda}}$ in calculating relations. Without the existence of a common extension of N and $\overline{\mathsf{\Lambda}}$ this would not be permissible. In such a case, for instance, the polynomial $\overline{\psi}(x)$ could not be defined as in the text.

groups $\mathfrak{H}$ and $\overline{\mathfrak{H}}$ are generated by those permutations of the different elements among the $\alpha_1, \ldots, \alpha_r$, whose application takes any existing integral rational relation $\chi(\alpha_1, \ldots, \alpha_r) = 0$ and $\overline{\chi}(\alpha_1, \ldots, \alpha_r) = 0$ with coefficients in $\mathsf{\Lambda}$ and $\overline{\mathsf{\Lambda}}$, respectively, over into a relation which is also correct. The groups $\mathfrak{P}$ and $\overline{\mathfrak{P}}$ of these permutations, which are isomorphic to $\mathfrak{H}$ and $\overline{\mathfrak{H}}$, respectively, are also isomorphic to one another due to the isomorphism of $\mathfrak{H}$ and $\overline{\mathfrak{H}}$ proved by a); therefore, in particular, they have the same finite order. Now, the permutations in $\mathfrak{P}$ have the specified property relative to the field $\overline{\mathsf{\Lambda}}$ a fortiori for the subfield $\mathsf{\Lambda}$, because the relations $\chi(\alpha_1, \ldots, \alpha_r) = 0$ occur among the relations $\overline{\chi}(\alpha_1, \ldots, \alpha_r) = 0$. Hence $\overline{\mathfrak{P}} \leqq \mathfrak{P}$ and consequently by the above $\overline{\mathfrak{P}} = \mathfrak{P}$, as stated under (I) b).

The degree relations specified under (I) immediately follow from Theorem 109, (I aa), [274] and the double application of Theorem 71 [142] according to Fig. 3.

Proof of Part (II)

The first part of statement (II) is clear by (I) and Theorem 109 [273]. Furthermore, let $\mathsf{\Lambda}^*, \overline{\mathsf{\Lambda}}^*$ be a corresponding pair of fields. To complete the proof use the elementary properties of intersections and composites:

First, $\mathsf{\Lambda}^* = [\mathsf{N}, \overline{\mathsf{\Lambda}}^*]$. To prove this we let $\mathfrak{H}^*$, $\overline{\mathfrak{H}}^*$ be the subgroups of $\mathfrak{H}, \overline{\mathfrak{H}}$ corresponding to $\mathsf{\Lambda}^*, \overline{\mathsf{\Lambda}}^*$, and ϑ be a primitive element of N relative to $\mathsf{\Lambda}$, therefore by the proof for (I) a) also of $\overline{\mathsf{N}}$ relative to $\overline{\mathsf{\Lambda}}$. Then by our correspondence rule in (II) and by Theorem 109, (I b) [274] $\mathsf{\Lambda}^*$ and $\overline{\mathsf{\Lambda}}^*$ consist of all rational functions over $\mathsf{\Lambda}$ and $\overline{\mathsf{\Lambda}}$, respectively; of ϑ which are invariant with respect to $\mathfrak{H}^*$ and $\overline{\mathfrak{H}}^*$, respectively. Therefore, by (I) a) $\mathsf{\Lambda}^* \leqq \overline{\mathsf{\Lambda}}^*$, and consequently also $\mathsf{\Lambda}^* \leqq [\mathsf{N}, \overline{\mathsf{\Lambda}}^*]$. Conversely, the elements of the intersection $[\mathsf{N}, \overline{\mathsf{\Lambda}}^*]$ are, as elements of N, rational functions of ϑ over $\mathsf{\Lambda}$; and as elements of $\overline{\mathsf{\Lambda}}^*$ they are invariant with respect to $\bar{\mathfrak{H}}^*$. Hence by (I) a) they are invariant with respect to $\mathfrak{H}^*$, that is, we also have $[\mathsf{N}, \bar{\Lambda}^*] \leqq \Lambda^*$. Taken together this means that $\Lambda^* = [\mathsf{N}, \bar{\Lambda}^*]$, as stated.

Secondly, $\bar{\mathsf{N}} = \{\mathsf{N}, \bar{\Lambda}^*\}$ follows trivially from
$\bar{\mathsf{N}} \geqq \{\mathsf{N}, \bar{\Lambda}^*\} \geqq \{\mathsf{N}, \bar{\Lambda}\} = \bar{\mathsf{N}}$.

Thirdly, $\Lambda = [\Lambda^*, \bar{\Lambda}]$ follows trivially from
$\Lambda \leqq [\Lambda^*, \bar{\Lambda}] \leqq [\mathsf{N}, \bar{\Lambda}] = \Lambda$.

Fourthly, $\bar{\Lambda}^* = \{\Lambda^*, \bar{\Lambda}\}$. Namely, from the relation $\Lambda^* \leqq \bar{\Lambda}^*$ previously proved it follows, at any rate, that $\bar{\Lambda}^* \geqq \{\Lambda^*, \bar{\Lambda}\}$. Now, suppose that $\bar{\Lambda}^* > \{\Lambda^*, \bar{\Lambda}\}$ were valid. Then if the one-to-one correspondence established in the first part of (II) were carried out using the intersection mechanism already proved as valid under "first," it would also follow that

$$\Lambda^* = [\mathsf{N}, \bar{\Lambda}^*] > [\mathsf{N}, \{\Lambda^*, \bar{\Lambda}\}],$$

while $\Lambda^* \leqq [\mathsf{N}, \{\Lambda^*, \bar{\Lambda}\}]$ is trivially true.

The latter proof justifies the technique of drawing the cross connection between Λ^* and $\bar{\Lambda}^*$ in Fig. 4.

Proof of Part (III)

If, besides $\mathsf{N}, \bar{\Lambda}$ also is normal over K, then by Theorems 98 [258] ; 99, (III) [259] ; 103 [262] the conjugates relative to K of a primitive element of the intersection $\Lambda = [\mathsf{N}, \bar{\Lambda}]$ are contained in N as well as in $\bar{\Lambda}$, therefore also in the intersection Λ. By these theorems, therefore, Λ is then normal over K. This completes the proof of Theorem 119.

3) The result expressed in Theorem 119 under (I) will now be interpreted in terms of the expositions in Section 17, 2) [281] . From this point of view it says that in the transition

to an *arbitrary* extension $\bar{\mathsf{\Lambda}}$ of K as ground field the Galois group $\mathfrak{G}$ of N relative to K is reduced just as in the transition to the intersection $\mathsf{\Lambda} = [\mathsf{N}, \bar{\mathsf{\Lambda}}]$, that is, to the part $\mathsf{\Lambda}$ of $\bar{\mathsf{\Lambda}}$ *contained in* N.

Accordingly, the adjunction of elements to K not contained in N furthers the construction of N no more than the adjunction of suitable elements to K contained in N. Hence, following *Kronecker*, we call the former (so far as they are algebraic over K) *accessory irrationals*, the latter *natural irrationals* for the extension N of K. That the accessory irrationals must be taken into account with respect to certain investigations in spite of the results contained in Theorem 119, (I) goes back to the fact that the adjunction of an accessory irrational may very well satisfy a prescribed simplicity condition, whereas this is not the case for the adjunction of an equivalent natural irrational according to Theorem 119, (I).

The result expressed in Theorem 119, (II) says that the step from $\bar{\mathsf{\Lambda}}$ to $\bar{\mathsf{N}}$ still to be made for the inclusion of N after passing over to $\bar{\mathsf{\Lambda}}$ as ground field [cf. Theorem 116, 2)] is equivalent to the step from $\mathsf{\Lambda}$ to N in any consideration that may concern us. Moreover, it says that any pair of fields $\mathsf{\Lambda}^*$ and $\bar{\mathsf{\Lambda}}^*$ corresponding to one another in the sense of Theorem 119, (II) can take on the roles of $\mathsf{\Lambda}$ and $\bar{\mathsf{\Lambda}}$.

Now, to generalize the expositions in Section 17, 2) [281] take an arbitrary chain of extensions

(1) $$\mathsf{K} = \bar{\mathsf{\Lambda}}_0 < \bar{\mathsf{\Lambda}}_1 < \bar{\mathsf{\Lambda}}_2 < \cdots < \bar{\mathsf{\Lambda}}_r$$

as a basis. Then there corresponds to this a chain

(2) $$\mathsf{K} = \mathsf{\Lambda}_0 \leqq \mathsf{\Lambda}_1 \leqq \mathsf{\Lambda}_2 \leqq \cdots \leqq \mathsf{\Lambda}_r \leqq \mathsf{N}$$

of fields between K and N, the development of which can be illustrated by the following Fig. 5.

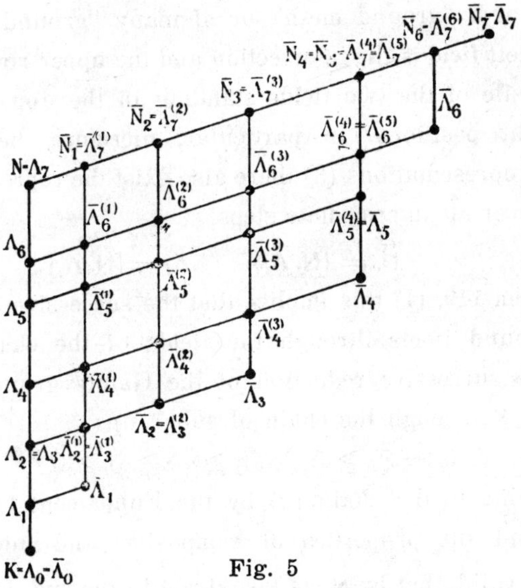

Fig. 5

By the successive construction we thereby have

(3) $\overline{\mathsf{N}}_i = \{\overline{\mathsf{N}}_{i-1}, \overline{\Lambda}_i\}, \quad \overline{\Lambda}_i^{(i-1)} = [\overline{\mathsf{N}}_{i-1}, \overline{\Lambda}_i],$

and the fields $\overline{\Lambda}_i^{(i-1)}, \overline{\Lambda}_i^{(i-2)}, \ldots, \overline{\Lambda}_i^{(1)}, \Lambda_i$ are the subfields of $\overline{\mathsf{N}}_{i-1}, \overline{\mathsf{N}}_{i-2}, \ldots, \overline{\mathsf{N}}_1, \mathsf{N}$ corresponding to $\overline{\Lambda}_i^{(i-1)}$ in the sense of Theorem 119, (II).

Theorem 119, (III) yields that of these $\overline{\Lambda}_i^{(i-1)}$ is normal over $\overline{\Lambda}_{i-1}$, therefore by Theorem 119, (II), Λ_i is also normal over Λ_{i-1} if $\overline{\Lambda}_i$ is normal over $\overline{\Lambda}_{i-1}$ (but the converse need not be true).

By the successive application of Theorem 119, (II) it easily follows in view of the minimal property of composites (Vol. 1, after Def. 5 [27] or Vol. 2, Theorem 116, 2)) and the maximal property of intersections (Vol. 1, after Def. 5) that in any parallelogram of our schematic figure (it may be composed of a "ground mesh" or of many "ground meshes") the lower left field is the intersection and the upper right field is the composite of the two fields standing in the upper left and lower right positions. In particular, therefore, besides the recursive representations (3) there also exist the representations skipping over all intermediate steps

$$(4) \qquad \overline{\mathsf{N}}_i = \{\mathsf{N}, \overline{\Lambda}_i\}, \qquad \Lambda_i = [\mathsf{N}, \overline{\Lambda}_i].$$

By Theorem 119, (I) this implies that the successive expansion of the ground fields through the fields of the chain (1) is tied to the successive reduction of the Galois group $\mathfrak{G}$ of N relative to K through the chain of subgroups

$$(5) \qquad \mathfrak{G} = \mathfrak{H}_0 \geqq \mathfrak{H}_1 \geqq \mathfrak{H}_2 \geqq \cdots \geqq \mathfrak{H}_r \geqq \mathfrak{E}$$

corresponding to the chain (2) by the Fundamental Theorem. By (4) and the properties of composites and intersections $\overline{\Lambda}_r \geqq \mathsf{N}$ is valid, that is, N, as visualized in the end, is included in chain (1) if and only if $\Lambda_r = \mathsf{N}$ and therefore $\overline{\Lambda}_r = \overline{\mathsf{N}}_r$, that is, if, according to (5), the Galois group $\mathfrak{G}$ is reduced to $\mathfrak{H}_r = \mathfrak{E}$.

V. Solvability of Algebraic Equations by Radicals

The theory developed in Chapter IV owes its origin to the celebrated question already mentioned at the beginning of Section 18, namely, *under what conditions is an algebraic equation solvable by radicals.* Accordingly, this theory forms the foundation for the handling of this question. The last chapter to be given is devoted to answering this question for ground fields of characteristic 0. For this purpose we will first state the question in a more precise form by *defining* what we mean by *solvable by radicals* (Section 19). Then we will develop as a necessary tool the theory of *cyclotomic fields* (Section 20) as well as the theory of *pure* and *cyclic extensions of prime degree* (Section 21). From this by applying the Galois theory considered in Chapter IV we will deduce a group-theoretic *criterion for the solvability by radicals* (Section 22). Finally, we will sketch in addition the proof based on the Galois theory for the *non-solvability by radicals of the generic algebraic equation of degree higher than the fourth,* which was first established by *Abel* in another way, (Section 23).

In Section 20 we add a short sketch of the theory of finite fields and thereby, in particular, fill up the gap still remaining in the proof of Theorem 90 [251] regarding such fields.

19. Definition of Solvability by Radicals

In this section we give an exact formulation for what is to be understood by the expression *solvable by radicals.* The concept $\sqrt[n]{a}$ familiar from the elements of arithmetic, where a is an element of a field K and n is a natural number, is explained there, as is well known, as the solution of the equation $x^n - a \doteq 0$. Since $\sqrt[n]{a}$ is in general a many-valued function we will not use this notation. Instead we will use the equation belonging to the radical rather than the radical itself.

Definition 38. *A **polynomial** of the form $x^n - a$ is called **pure.***

In order that the question posed at the beginning of this chapter be not trivial, we naturally have to admit into the circle of the allowable operations not only the specified operation of root extraction but also the four elementary operations, subordinate to the former from this standpoint.[1] Along with a root α of a pure polynomial we then consider all its rational functions over the ground field K as known, that is, all elements of K(α). However, the significance of our question goes still further: It would be unsystematic if we were to hold the operation of root extraction in check by *one* such step. On the contrary, it is reasonable to regard not only the roots of pure polynomials as known but also those of polynomials belonging to the extended field K(α), etc. Our question amounts then to this: What are the conditions under which we can reach or introduce the roots, that is, the root field of a polynomial $f(x)$ over K or in general any extension Λ of K, by the *successive*[2] adjunction of roots of pure polynomials starting from K. This immediately enables us to curtail the type of radicals to be drawn into consideration: Namely, if $x^n - a$ is a pure polynomial over K of compound degree $n = n_1 n_2$ and α one of its roots, then $\alpha^{n_2} = \alpha_1$ is a root of the pure polynomial $x^{n_1} - a$ over K and further α is a root of the pure polynomial $x^{n_2} - \alpha_1$ over K(α_1). Consequently, we

---

1 Otherwise, only pure equations could be solved by radicals.

2 Not only by *simultaneous* adjunction. This actually says (in contrast to the case of Theorem 62 [220]) more than this, for α can very well be a root of a pure polynomial over an extension $\overline{K}$ of K without still being a root of a pure polynomial over K.

can restrict ourselves to the successive adjunction of roots of pure polynomials of prime degree. According to one's wish the restriction can also be imposed here that these polynomials shall or shall not be irreducible in the field reached at any given time. Since the irreducible polynomials are the simplest building stones for the construction of algebraic extensions, it seems theoretically more proper to adopt this restriction.[3] Accordingly, we define:

* **Definition 39.** *An **extension** Λ of K is called **pure** over K if it can be derived by the adjunction of a root of an irreducible pure polynomial over K.*

* **Definition 40.** *An **extension** of finite degree Λ of K is called **solvable by radicals** over K if a chain of extensions*

$$\mathsf{K} = \overline{\Lambda}_0 < \overline{\Lambda}_1 < \cdots < \overline{\Lambda}_r \text{ with } \overline{\Lambda}_r \geqq \Lambda$$

exists in which $\overline{\Lambda}_i$ is pure and of prime degree over $\overline{\Lambda}_{i-1}$.

*A **polynomial** $f(x)$ over K is said to be **solvable by radicals** over K if its root field over K is also.*

20. Cyclotomic Fields. Finite Fields

In order to be able to handle the question of the solvability by radicals we have to make some preliminary statements about the theory of the special pure polynomial $x^n - e$. We remark that if the roots of this equation in the case of the rational ground field P are represented as complex numbers in accordance with the so-called Fundamental Theorem of Algebra, they will effect the division of the circumference of the unit circle into n equal parts. In view of our applications we will

---

[3] Actually the answer to our question (for ground fields of characteristic 0) given in Theorem 127 [319] is independent of this restriction, as easily follows from Theorems 123, 126 [312, 316] given later. Out of regard to Theorem 126 it appears to me, however, more proper to demand the irreducibility, since the "cruder" statement of the question entirely overlooks the algebraically interesting "finer" structure of cyclotomic fields.

not restrict ourselves here to the special case P. Instead, we will allow more general ground fields K, though in general we will still call the equation $x^n - e \doteq 0$, due to its association with this special case, the ***cyclotomic equation*** and its root field T_n the ***cyclotomic field*** for n over K. Regarding the roots of the cyclotomic equation for n over K, the so-called ***n-th roots of unity*** over K, we first of all prove the following theorem:

Theorem 120. *Let K be a field whose characteristic is 0 or a prime number which is not an exact divisor of n. Then the n-th roots of unity over K form a cyclic group $\mathfrak{Z}$ of order n with respect to multiplication. Therefore, there exist n different n-th roots of unity over K which can be represented as the powers*

$$\zeta^0 = e, \quad \zeta^1, \ldots, \zeta^{n-1}$$

*of one among them, a so-called **primitive n-th root of unity** ζ.*

Proof: Let $\zeta_1, \ldots, \zeta_n$ be the roots of $f_n(x) \equiv x^n - e$. Then the derivative is

$$f'_n(\zeta_i) = n\zeta_i^{n-1} \neq 0 \quad (i = 1, \ldots, n),$$

since naturally $\zeta_i \neq 0$, which by the assumption regarding the characteristic of K in this case also implies $n\zeta_i^{n-1} \neq 0$ (Theorem 43 [203]). Therefore, by Theorem 56 [213] the n roots ζ_i are different from one another. Furthermore, since $\zeta_i^n = e$, $\zeta_k^n = e$ implies $(\zeta_i\zeta_k)^n = e$, the n different n-th roots of unity form an Abelian group $\mathfrak{Z}$ of order n (Vol. 1, Theorem 20 [64] applied to the multiplicative group of the elements $\neq 0$ of the cyclotomic field T_n).

By Theorem 34 [198] the order of each element ζ_i of $\mathfrak{Z}$ is then a particular divisor m_i of n. Now, let ζ be an element of $\mathfrak{Z}$ of highest possible order m. We wish to show that $m = n$, for this result will imply that the n powers $\zeta^0, \zeta^1, \ldots, \zeta^{n-1}$ are different and consequently exhaust the group $\mathfrak{Z}$. To prove this equality let p be an arbitrary prime number and set (according to Theorems 12, 22 [178, 187].

$$m = p^{\mu}\overline{m}, \quad m_i = p^{\mu_i}\overline{m}_i \quad \text{with} \quad (\overline{m}, p) = 1, \quad (\overline{m}_i, p) = 1.$$

Then, the orders of $\zeta_i^{\overline{m}_i}, \zeta^{p^{\mu}}$ are obviously p^{μ_i}, m, therefore by Theorem 35 [198] the order of $\zeta_i^{\overline{m}_i}\zeta^{p^{\mu}}$ *is* $p^{\mu_i}\overline{m}$. The maximal choice of m implies $p^{\mu_i}\overline{m} \leqq p^{\mu}\overline{m}$, that is, $\mu_i \leqq \mu$. Therefore, m_i contains any prime number p at most to the power to which p occurs in m, that is, $m_i \mid m$ (Theorem 20 [187]) and consequently $\zeta_i^m = e$. The n different n-th roots of unity ζ_i are therefore, all of them, roots of the polynomial of m-th degree $x^m - e$. This implies that $m \geqq n$ (Theorem 48 [208]), which together with $m \mid n$ gives $m = n$. This completes the proof of the theorem.

By Theorem 37 [200] (cf. also the statement to Theorem 31 [195]) we immediately have in addition:

Corollary. *If ζ is a primitive n-th root of unity over K, then all and only the powers ζ^m, which correspond to the $\varphi(n)$ prime residue classes of m mod n, are likewise primitive.*

This is the basis for the determination of the Galois group of the cyclotomic field T_n given in the following theorem:

Theorem 121. *If K is a field as in Theorem* 120 *and ζ a primitive n-th root of unity over K, then the polynomial*

$$g_n(x) \equiv \prod_{\substack{m=0 \\ (m,n)=1}}^{n-1} (x - \zeta^m)$$

whose roots are the $\varphi(n)$ different primitive roots of unity, is a polynomial in K. If

$$\overline{g}_n(x) \equiv \prod_{\overline{m}} (x - \zeta^{\overline{m}})$$

is the irreducible (separable by Theorem 59 [215], *normal by Theorem* 99, (III) [259]) *factor of* $g_n(x)$ *belonging to* ζ, *then the* $\overline{m}$ *represent a subgroup* $\overline{\mathfrak{P}}_n$ *of the prime residue class group* $\mathfrak{P}_n$ *mod* n. *The Galois group* $\mathfrak{G}_n$ *of the (separable, normal) cyclotomic field* T_n *is then isomorphic to this group* $\overline{\mathfrak{P}}_n$ *on the basis of the correspondence of the automorphism of* T_n *generated by* $\zeta \to \zeta^{\overline{m}}$ *to the residue class* $\overline{m}$ *mod* n.

In particular, T_n *is Abelian (Def.* 34 [267]), *and furthermore the degree of* T_n *over* K *is a divisor of* $\varphi(n)$ *(Theorem* 105 [267]).

Proof: a) By Theorem 107 [271] an automorphism of T_n relative to K, on the one hand, permutes the n different roots ζ_i of $x^n - e$ only among themselves and, on the other hand, leaves their power representations $\zeta_i = \zeta^{i-1}$ invariant. Hence such an automorphism takes ζ again into a primitive n-th root of unity, so that the $\varphi(n)$ different primitive n-th roots of unity are again permuted only among themselves by such automorphisms. Accordingly, the coefficients of $g_n(x)$ are invariant under all automorphisms of T_n relative to K and consequently belong to K (Theorem 112, Corollary [284]).

b) $\mathsf{T}_n = \mathsf{K}(\zeta^0, \ldots, \zeta^{n-1}) = \mathsf{K}(\zeta)$, therefore a primitive n-th root of unity over K is at the same time also a primitive element of T_n relative to K. This implies that the automorphisms of T_n relative to K can (Theorem 105 [267]) be written in terms of the substitutions of ζ corresponding to them. Therefore, if $\bar{g}_n(x)$ has the significance specified in the theorem, then the Galois group $\mathfrak{G}_n$ of T_n relative to K is represented by the substitutions $\zeta \to \zeta^{\overline{m}}$, and their elements correspond biuniquely through this to the set $\overline{\mathfrak{P}}_n$ of the prime residue classes mod n represented by the $\overline{m}$. Now, since $\zeta \to \zeta^{\overline{m}_1}$ and $\zeta \to \zeta^{\overline{m}_2}$ carried out one after the other yield $\zeta \to (\zeta^{\overline{m}_2})^{\overline{m}_1} = \zeta^{\overline{m}_1 \overline{m}_2}$ under this correspondence, the multiplication in $\mathfrak{G}_n$ amounts to the multiplication of the residue classes in $\overline{\mathfrak{P}}_n$. Hence this correspondence is an isomorphism and $\overline{\mathfrak{P}}_n$ is a subgroup of $\mathfrak{P}_n$ isomorphic to $\mathfrak{G}_n$.

In investigating the solvability by radicals the roots of unity of prime order $n = p$ play, according to Def. 40 [303], a special role. For this case we prove an extension of Theorem 121:

Theorem 122. *Let p be a prime number and* K *a field with characteristic different from p. Then the cyclotomic field* T_p *is cyclic over* K *and its degree is an exact divisor of* $p-1$.

Proof: By Theorem 121 the degree of T_p over K is a divisor of $\varphi(p)$ and the Galois group $\mathfrak{G}_p$ of T_p relative to K is isomorphic to a subgroup $\overline{\mathfrak{P}}_p$ of the prime residue class group $\mathfrak{P}_p$. Now, by Theorem 28 [193] the residue classes mod p actually form a field, the prime field P_p (Def. 13 [201], Theorem 41 [202]). The $\varphi(p)$ elements of $\mathfrak{P}_p$ are then the $p-1$ elements of P_p different from zero (Theorem 17 [185]) and as such are roots of the cyclotomic equation $x^{p-1} - e = 0$ (Theorem 29 [194]), therefore are the totality of $(p-1)$-th roots of unity over P_p. Consequently, by Theorem 120 [304] they form a cyclic group with respect to multiplication. Hence $\mathfrak{P}_p$ is cyclic, so that by Theorem 36 [199] the subgroup $\overline{\mathfrak{P}}_p$, that is, $\mathfrak{G}_p$, is also. Therefore, T_p is cyclic over K (Def. 34 [267]) and its degree is an exact divisor of $p-1$.

Moreover, Theorem 44 [204] trivially implies:

Corollary. *If* K *has characteristic p, then* $x^p - e \equiv (x-e)^p$, *therefore e is the single p-th root of unity over* K, *and* $T_p = K$.

It is worth noting how the abstract theory of fields yields in a very simple way the conclusion that the prime residue class group $\mathfrak{P}_p$ is cyclic. For this purpose we extend, without further difficulty, Theorem 120 to P_p; in number theory this theorem is usually proved only for the ground field P. In number theory we describe this conclusion by saying that there exists a **primitive root mod** p, namely, there is an integer r such that for every integer m prime to p there exists the power representation

$$m \equiv r^{\mu} \bmod p \; (\mu = 0, \ldots, p-2).$$

We add a further remark about the special case of the cyclotomic field T_p over the rational ground field P. By number-theoretic methods (*Theorem of Eisenstein-Schönemann*, see Vol. 3, Section 20, Exer. 6) we can show that the polynomial

$$g_p(x) \equiv \frac{x^p - 1}{x - 1} \equiv x^{p-1} + x^{p-2} + \cdots + x + 1$$

of Theorem 121 is irreducible in P, therefore that T_p has the degree $\varphi(p) = p - 1$ over P. Now, if $p - 1 = 2^{\nu}$ $(\nu \geqq 0)$ is a power of 2, then by Theorem 109 [273] T_p can be reached from P by the successive adjunction of quadratic irrationals. This follows from the fact that the Galois group $\mathfrak{G}_p$ of T_p relative to P, which is cyclic by Theorem 122, has the order 2^{ν}, and consequently by Theorem 36 [199] there is a chain of subgroups

$$\mathfrak{G}_p = \mathfrak{H}_0 > \mathfrak{H}_1 > \cdots > \mathfrak{H}_{\nu} = \mathfrak{E}$$

such that $\mathfrak{H}_i$ is a subgroup of $\mathfrak{H}_{i-1}$ of index 2. Conversely, if T_p can be reached from P by successive adjunction of quadratic irrationals (or even only included), then by the expositions in Section 17, 2) [281] and Section 18, 3) [297] the group $\mathfrak{G}$ contains a chain of subgroups of the kind[4] just described, and consequently its order $p - 1$ is then a power of 2. This implies the famous

Result of Gauss. *The regular p-gon for a prime number p can be constructed by ruler and compass if and only if p is a prime number of the form* $2^{\nu} + 1$.

[4] For the general case of inclusion, cf. the detailed proof to Theorem 127, part a), footnote 6 [320] given later.

We do not know, even today, whether or not the sequence beginning with $p = 2, 3, 5, 17, 257, 65537$ of prime numbers of this form breaks off (see, for this, also Vol. 3, Section 20, Exer. 14, 15).

In the next section we will analogously deduce the solvability of T_p by radicals over definite ground fields K. This is the main reason for the digression of this section.

On the basis of Theorem 120 [304] we can now easily give:

Brief Sketch of the Theory of Finite Fields

A. We have already met finite fields, that is, fields which contain only a finite number of elements. For instance, for any prime number p the prime field P_p (residue class field mod p) is a finite field having exactly p elements (Section 4).

Next, let E be an arbitrary finite field. Then the prime field contained in E is also finite, therefore not isomorphic to the rational number field. Hence we have (Theorem 41 [202]):

(I) *The characteristic of* E *is a prime number* p.

By the statements in connection with Theorem 41, E can then be regarded as an extension of the prime field P_p. It is trivial by this that E has finite degree over P_p (Def. 25 [225]). From the unique representation $\alpha = a_1\alpha_1 + \cdots + a_m\alpha_m$ of the elements α of E in terms of a basis $\alpha_1, \ldots, \alpha_m$ of E relative to P_p with coefficients $a_1, \ldots, a_m$ in P_p it then follows:

(II) *If* $[\mathsf{E} : \mathsf{P}_p] = m$, *then* E *has exactly* p^m *elements.*

Next, we generalize to E the inferences applied to the prime field P_p itself in the proof to Theorem 122. The multiplicative group of the elements of E different from zero (Vol. 1, Section 6, Example 1 [61]) has by (II) the order $p^m - 1$. Hence these $p^m - 1$ elements different from zero satisfy the equation $x^{p^m-1} - e \doteq 0$ (Theorem 34 [198]), therefore are the totality of $(p^m - 1)$-th roots of unity over P_p. Consequently, the group formed from these elements is cyclic (Theorem 120):

(III) *If* $[\mathsf{E} : \mathsf{P}_p] = m$, *then* E *is the cyclotomic field* T_{p^m-1} *over* P_p.

The elements of E *different from zero are the roots of the equation* $x^{p^m-1} - e \doteq 0$; *therefore the totality of elements of* E *are the roots of the equation* $x^{p^m} - x \doteq 0$.

There exists in E *a primitive element* ϱ *such that the* p^m-1 *elements of* E *different from zero can be represented as the powers*

$$\varrho^0 = e, \varrho^1, \ldots, \varrho^{p^m-2}.$$

Conversely we have:

(IV) *For arbitrary* m *the cyclotomic field* T_{p^m-1} *over* P_p *is a finite field with* $[\mathsf{T}_{p^m-1} : \mathsf{P}_p] = m$.

For, T_{p^m-1} is itself a finite field (Def. 25, Addendum [226]) as it is an extension of finite degree of the finite field P_p (Theorem 83 [240]). This has exactly p^m elements. Its elements are already exhausted by zero and the p^m-1 roots of $x^{p^m-1}-e$, that is, by the p^m roots of $x^{p^m}-x$. For these p^m roots already form a field, since $\alpha^{p^m}=\alpha$, $\beta^{p^m}=\beta$ not only (as in the proof to Theorem 120) implies that $(\alpha\beta)^{p^m}=\alpha\beta$ and (in case $\beta \neq 0$) $\left(\frac{\alpha}{\beta}\right)^{p^m} = \frac{\alpha}{\beta}$, but also by Theorem 44 [204] that $(\alpha \pm \beta)^{p^m} = \alpha \pm \beta$. Hence by (II) we have $p^{[\mathsf{T}_{p^m-1}:\mathsf{P}_p]} = p^m$, that is, $[\mathsf{T}_{p^m-1}:\mathsf{P}_p] = m$.

Since the characteristic p and the degree m are determined uniquely by the number of elements p^m, by (III) and (IV) we have:

(V) *For any number of elements of the form* p^m *there is exactly one finite field type, namely, the cyclotomic field* T_{p^m-1} *over* P_p.

Furthermore we have;

(VI) T_{p^m-1} *has only the totality of fields* $\mathsf{T}_{p^\mu-1}$ *with* $\mu \mid m$ as *subfields and thereby*

$$[\mathsf{T}_{p^m-1} : \mathsf{T}_{p^\mu-1}] = \frac{m}{\mu}.$$

For, on the one hand, if $\mathsf{T}_{p^\mu-1} \leqq \mathsf{T}_{p^m-1}$, by Theorem 71 [228] we have that $\mu = [\mathsf{T}_{p^\mu-1} : \mathsf{P}_p] \mid [\mathsf{T}_{p^m-1} : \mathsf{P}_p] = m$ and $[\mathsf{T}_{p^m-1} : \mathsf{T}_{p^\mu-1}] = \frac{m}{\mu}$. On the other hand, if $\mu \mid m$ and we accordingly set $m = \mu\mu'$, then

$$p^m-1 = p^{\mu\mu'}-1 = (p^\mu-1)(p^{\mu(\mu'-1)}+\cdots+p^\mu+1),$$

therefore $p^\mu-1 \mid p^m-1$. Consequently $\mathsf{T}_{p^\mu-1} \leqq \mathsf{T}_{p^m-1}$, since the $(p^\mu-1)$-th roots of unity occur in this case among the (p^m-1)-th roots of unity.

(V) and (VI) yield a complete survey of all finite field types and there mutual relations.

B. Next, let $\mathsf{E} = \mathsf{T}_{p^m-1}$ be a finite ground field and H a finite extension of E. First of all it is trivial that H has in this case finite degree n over E (Def. 25 [225]) and therefore is again a finite field (Def. 25, Addendum [226]), which by (VI) has the form $\mathsf{H} = \mathsf{T}_{p^{mn}-1}$. Then, if ϱ is a primitive element of H in the sense of (III), ϱ is all the more a primitive element of H relative to that subfield in the sense of Def. 19 [221]. Therefore:

(VII) H *is simple over* E.

This fills the gap still remaining in the proof of Theorem 90 [251].

Since the characteristic p of H is not an exact divisor of the order $p^{mn}-1$ of the roots of unity, which form H, it is further valid by the remarks to Theorem 121 [305]:

(VIII) H *is separable over* E.

Finally, by Theorem 94 [256] we have:

(IX) H *is normal over* E.

Hence the theorems of the Galois theory can be applied to the extension H of E. Although we have already obtained a general view of the fields between H and E by (VI) without using the Galois theory — they are the totality of $\mathsf{T}_{p^{m\nu}-1}$ with $\nu \mid n$ —, it is still of interest from a theoretical point of view to establish:

(X) H *is cyclic over* E.

Namely, the Galois group of H *relative to* E *consists of the powers of the automorphism*

$$A : \alpha \to \alpha^{p^m} \text{ for every } \alpha \text{ in } \mathsf{H}$$

with $A^n = E$, *that is, of the* n *automorphisms*

$$A : \alpha \to \alpha^{p^{m\nu}} \text{ for every } \alpha \text{ in } \mathsf{H}\ (\nu = 0, 1, \ldots, n-1).$$

Namely, by Theorem 44 [204] [see as well the deductions in the proof to (IV)] these are actually automorphisms of H which leave every element of E invariant, since each element is a root of $x^{p^m} - x$. Hence these automorphisms are automorphisms of H relative to E. Furthermore, these n automorphisms of H relative to E are different from one another, since for a primitive element ϱ of H (in the sense of (III)) the totality of powers ϱ^i $(i = 1, \ldots, p^{mn}-1)$ are different from one another, therefore, in particular, so also are the n powers $\varrho^{p^{m\nu}}$ $(\nu = 0, 1, \ldots, n-1)$. Hence they are all $n = [\mathsf{H} : \mathsf{E}]$ automorphisms of the Galois group of H relative to E (Theorem 105 [267]).

21. Pure and Cyclic Extensions of Prime Degree

In order to be able to handle the question of the solvability by radicals we still have to supplement the special developments of the previous sections by the theory of irreducible pure polynomials of prime degree on which the Def. 40 [303] of the solvability by radicals rests. We first prove the following theorem regarding the irreducibility of a pure polynomial of prime degree:

Theorem 123. *Let p be a prime number and $x^p - a$ a pure polynomial with $a \neq 0$ in K. Then the root field W of this polynomial contains the cyclotomic field T_p over K, and only the following two cases are possible:*

a) *$x^p - a$ has a root in K, that is, a is a p-th power in K. Then $x^p - a$ is reducible in K and $W = T_p$.*

b) *$x^p - a$ has no root in K, that is, a is not a p-th power in K. Then $x^p - a$ is irreducible in K and even in T_p. Moreover, it is normal over T_p, and therefore W is pure of degree p over T_p.*

Proof: Let $\alpha_1, \ldots, \alpha_p$ be the roots of $x^p - a$ and α one of these. Since $a \neq 0$, it then follows from $\alpha^p = a$ that $\alpha \neq 0$, and

$$\left(\frac{x}{\alpha}\right)^p - e \equiv \frac{x^p - \alpha^p}{\alpha^p} \equiv \frac{x - \alpha_1}{\alpha} \cdots \frac{x - \alpha_p}{\alpha} \equiv \left(\frac{x}{\alpha} - \frac{\alpha_1}{\alpha}\right) \cdots \left(\frac{x}{\alpha} - \frac{\alpha_p}{\alpha}\right).$$

By the principle of substitution (Vol. 1, Theorem 12 [47], applied to $I[x']$ with $I = W[x]$ and the substitution $x' = \alpha x$) αx can be substituted for x in this, so that

$$x^p - e \equiv \left(x - \frac{\alpha_1}{\alpha}\right) \cdots \left(x - \frac{\alpha_p}{\alpha}\right)$$

follows. The quotients $\frac{\alpha_i}{\alpha}$ are therefore the p-th roots of unity over K, that is, $W \geqq T_p$. Furthermore, if ζ is a primitive p-th root of unity (Theorem 120 [304]; — in case K has characteristic p, $\zeta = e$ [Theorem 122, Corollary]), then by a suitable ordering we have

$$\alpha_i = \zeta^i \alpha \ (i = 1, \ldots, p).$$

a) Now, if α lies in K, then according to this the α_i lie in T_p that is, $W \leqq T_p$ and consequently by the above $W = T_p$.

b) If, however, none of the α_i lie in K and if, in this case,

$$h(x) \equiv x^\nu + \cdots + a_0 \ (1 \leqq \nu \leqq p-1)$$

is an irreducible factor of $x^p - a$ in K, then $\pm a_0$ would have a representation as a product of certain ν factors α_i, namely,

$$\pm a_0 = \zeta^\mu \alpha^\nu.$$

If by Theorems 14, 17 [182, 185] we were to set $\nu\nu' = 1 + kp$, then since $\alpha^p = a$ it would follow that

$$(\pm a_0)^{\nu'} = \zeta^{\mu\nu'} \alpha\, a^k,$$

so that, since $a \neq 0$, the root $\alpha_{\mu\nu'} = \zeta^{\mu\nu'}\alpha = \frac{(\pm a_0)^{\nu'}}{a^k}$ would still lie in K. Hence $x^p - a$ is in this case irreducible in K and consequently $K(\alpha)$ has degree p over K. Now, if in the above line of reasoning we had made the assumption that $h(x)$ was to be an irreducible factor of $x^p - a$ in T_p, then it would follow that α, and consequently $K(\alpha)$, would be contained in T_p. Hence the degree of T_p over K would be a multiple of p, whereas by Theorem 121 [305] this degree is at the same time an exact divisor of $p - 1$. Consequently $x^p - a$ is in this case also irreducible in T_p and by Theorem 99, (III) [259] normal over T_p as well; therefore by Theorem 99, (I) $W = T_p(\alpha)$ and consequently pure of degree p over T_p (Def. 39 [303]).

For the question of the solvability by radicals we are naturally especially interested in the case b) of Theorem 123. If K has characteristic p, then $x^p - a$ is an *inseparable* irreducible polynomial (Def. 17 [214]). Its single root α is a p-fold root. In the sense of our prevailing restriction to separable extensions we exclude this possibility in the following by assuming in the case of the consideration of pure extensions of prime degree p that the characteristic of K is different from p. Then $x^p - a$ (and generally any irreducible polynomial over K of degree p) is a fortiori separable (Def. 17).

Furthermore, in the case b) $x^p - a$ is in general not *normal* over K though it is over T_p, so that it seems appropriate for the application that we have in mind to adjoin at any given time first a primitive p-th root of unity ζ to K before the adjunction of a root of a pure polynomial $x^p - a$ of prime degree p. This means that we should first go over to the extended ground field $\overline{\mathsf{K}} = \mathsf{K}(\zeta) = \mathsf{T}_p$ which coincides with the field $\overline{\mathsf{T}}_p = \{\mathsf{T}_p, \overline{\mathsf{K}}\}$ (Def. 37, Addendum [292]) of the p-th roots of unity over $\overline{\mathsf{K}}$.

In this regard the following theorem, which is an immediate consequence of Theorem 123, is of interest to us (in which K, so to speak, is to be identified with the $\overline{\mathsf{K}}$ just specified):

Theorem 124. *If p is a prime number and K a field with characteristic different from p which contains the p-th roots of unity over K, then every pure extension of p-th degree Λ of K is normal (separable and cyclic)* over K.

That Λ is *cyclic* over K is trivial, since it is a separable normal extension of prime degree p. For, by Theorem 105 [267] its Galois group relative to K has the prime order p and by Theorem 34 [198] must therefore coincide with the period of any of its elements different from E.

As a converse to Theorem 124 we now prove the theorem upon which our application is based:

Theorem 125. *If p is a prime number and* K *a field with characteristic different from p which contains the p-th roots of unity over* K, *then any normal extension of p-th degree* Λ *of* K *is (a fortiori separable, cyclic and) pure over* K.

Proof: Let A be a primitive element of the cyclic Galois group of Λ relative to K, ϑ a primitive element of Λ relative to K and ζ a primitive *p-th* root of unity over K. Then we form the so-called **Lagrange resolvent** of ϑ:

$$\alpha = \vartheta_E + \zeta^{-1}\vartheta_A + \cdots + \zeta^{-(p-1)}\vartheta_{A^{p-1}}.$$

If this element α of Λ is different from zero, we proceed as follows:

Let A be applied to α. Due to $A^p = E$, $\zeta^p = e$ and the invariance of the element ζ of K with respect to A we generate

$$\begin{aligned}\alpha_A &= \vartheta_A + \zeta^{-1}\vartheta_{A^2} + \cdots + \zeta^{-(p-1)}\vartheta_{A^p}\\ &= (\vartheta_E + \zeta^{-1}\vartheta_A + \cdots + \zeta^{-(p-1)}\vartheta_{A^{p-1}})\zeta = \alpha\zeta;\end{aligned}$$

therefore by the repeated application of A

$$\alpha_A^{\nu} = \alpha\zeta^{\nu}.$$

This means that the elements $\alpha, \alpha\zeta, \ldots, \alpha\zeta^{p-1}$ different from one another due to the assumption $\alpha \neq 0$ are the conjugates to α relative to K, that is,

$$g(x) \equiv (x-\alpha)\,(x-\alpha\zeta)\cdots(x-\alpha\zeta^{p-1})$$

is the irreducible polynomial over K belonging to α, and α is a primitive element of Λ (Theorems 111, 112 [283, 283] together with Corollary). Hence

$$x^p - e \equiv (x-e)\,(x-\zeta)\cdots(x-\zeta^{p-1}),$$

implies, as in the proof to Theorem 123, that

$$g(x) \equiv x^p - \alpha^p$$

and consequently

$$g(x) \equiv x^p - a$$

with $a = \alpha^p$ in K, therefore α is a root of the irreducible pure polynomial $x^p - a$ over K. Hence $\Lambda = K(\alpha)$ is in this case actually pure over K (Def. 39 [303]·).

We now show that by a suitable choice of the primitive p-th root of unity ζ we can obtain an $\alpha \neq 0$. Namely, if for each of the $p-1$ primitive p-th roots of unity ζ^ν $(\nu = 1, \ldots, p-1)$ the Lagrange resolvent belonging to it were $\alpha_\nu = 0$, then the system of equations

$$\alpha_\nu = \sum_{\mu=0}^{p-1} (\zeta^\nu)^{-\mu} \vartheta_{A^\mu} = 0 \qquad (\nu = 1, \ldots, p-1)$$

would exist. If we were to multiply the ν-th equation by $\zeta^{\nu\mu'}$ and sum over ν, then by interchanging the order of summation it would follow that

$$\sum_{\mu=0}^{p-1} \left(\sum_{\nu=1}^{p-1} \zeta^{\nu(\mu'-\mu)} \right) \vartheta_{A^\mu} = 0.$$

Now,

$$\sum_{\nu=1}^{p-1} (\zeta^{\mu'-\mu})^\nu = \begin{cases} -e & \text{for } \mu' \not\equiv \mu \bmod p \\ pe - e & \text{for } \mu' \equiv \mu \bmod p, \end{cases}$$

because in the former case $\zeta^{\mu-\mu'}$ is a primitive p-th root of unity, therefore a root of $\dfrac{x^p - e}{x - e} \equiv x^{p-1} + x^{p-2} + \cdots + x + e$, whereas in the latter case e stands $(p-1)$ times as the summand. From this we obtain the relations

$$\sum_{\mu=0}^{p-1} \vartheta_{A^\mu} = p \vartheta_{A^{\mu'}} \qquad (\mu' = 0, 1, \ldots, p-1).$$

Since K does not have the characteristic p, this would mean that all $\vartheta_{A^{\mu'}}$ would be equal to one another, which by Theorem 112, Corollary [284] is not the case for a primitive element ϑ of Λ.

In conclusion we will make further use of the preceding results in order to prove the solvability of T_p by radicals over fixed ground fields K:

Theorem 126. *Let p be a prime number and K a field whose characteristic is 0 or a prime number $> p$. Then the cyclotomic field T_p is solvable by radicals over K, and besides there actually exists a chain of fields*

$$K=\overline{\Lambda}_0<\overline{\Lambda}_1<\cdots<\overline{\Lambda}_r \text{ with } \overline{\Lambda}_r \geqq T_p,$$

in which $\overline{\Lambda}_i$ *is not only (according to Def.* 40 [303] *) pure of prime degree but also normal over* $\overline{\Lambda}_{i-1}$.

Proof: Use mathematical induction, assuming for this purpose the statements as already proved for all prime numbers $<p$ (and all ground fields allowable according to the formulation of the theorem). Now, let d be the degree of T_p over K which by Theorem 122 [307] is an exact divisor of $p-1$, and let $d=p_1\cdots p_\nu$ be the factorization of d into (not necessarily different) prime numbers p_k. Now, by assumption the characteristic of K, if $\neq 0$, is also greater than each of these prime numbers. Hence by the induction assumption there first of all exists in this case a chain of fields

$$K=\overline{\Lambda}_0<\overline{\Lambda}_1<\cdots<\overline{\Lambda}_{r_1} \text{ with } \overline{\Lambda}_{r_1} \geqq T_{p_1},$$

in which $\overline{\Lambda}_i$ is pure and normal of prime degree over $\overline{\Lambda}_{i-1}$. Secondly, (starting next from $\overline{\Lambda}_{r_1}$ instead of K as ground field) there is a chain of fields

$$\overline{\Lambda}_{r_1}<\overline{\Lambda}_{r_1+1}<\cdots<\overline{\Lambda}_{r_2} \text{ with } \overline{\Lambda}_{r_2} \geqq T_{p_1}, T_{p_2},$$ [5]

in which $\overline{\Lambda}_{r_1+i}$ is pure and normal of prime degree over $\overline{\Lambda}_{r_1+i-1}$, etc. Therefore taken together there is a chain of fields

$$K=\overline{\Lambda}_0<\overline{\Lambda}_1<\cdots<\overline{\Lambda}_{r_\nu} \text{ with } \overline{\Lambda}_{r_\nu} \geqq T_{p_1},\dots,T_{p_\nu},$$

in which every $\overline{\Lambda}_i$ is pure and normal of prime degree over $\overline{\Lambda}_{i-1}$. Now, let $\overline{T}_p$ be the cyclotomic field for p over $\overline{\Lambda}_{r_\nu}$ and $\overline{d}$ its degree over $\overline{\Lambda}_{r_\nu}$, which by Theorem 119 [293] is an exact divisor of d. Then by inferences entirely similar to those in the case of the Result of Gauss [308] (Theorems 36, 109,

[5] The cyclotomic field $\overline{T}_{p_2}$ for p_2 over $\overline{\Lambda}_{r_1}$ naturally contains the cyclotomic field T_{p_2} for p_2 over K.

122 [199, 273, 307]) there exists a chain of fields

$$\bar{\mathsf{\Lambda}}_{r_\nu} < \bar{\mathsf{\Lambda}}_{r_\nu+1} < \cdots < \bar{\mathsf{\Lambda}}_r = \bar{\mathsf{T}}_p,$$

in which $\bar{\mathsf{\Lambda}}_{r_\nu+i}$ is normal of prime degree over $\bar{\mathsf{\Lambda}}_{r_\nu+i-1}$. The successive degrees in the last chain are, as divisors of $\bar{d}$, certain of the prime numbers p_k. Now, since by construction the p_k-th roots of unity are contained in $\bar{\mathsf{\Lambda}}_{r_\nu+i}$, $\bar{\mathsf{\Lambda}}_{r_\nu+i}$ is pure over $\bar{\mathsf{\Lambda}}_{r_\nu+i-1}$ by Theorem 125 which can be applied in this case (cf. also Theorem 42 [203]), due to the assumption regarding the characteristic of K. Consequently the complete chain

$$\mathsf{K} = \bar{\mathsf{\Lambda}}_0 < \cdots < \bar{\mathsf{\Lambda}}_r = \bar{\mathsf{T}}_p,$$

if we further bear in mind that $\mathsf{T}_p \leqq \bar{\mathsf{T}}_p$, has all properties required for the statements of the theorem.

Since the theorem is trivially valid for the smallest prime number $p = 2$ because $\mathsf{T}_2 = \mathsf{K}$, this completes the proof of the theorem by mathematical induction.

22. Criterion for the Solvability by Radicals

In this section we will derive the criterion for the solvability by radicals. In order to be able to express this criterion we make the following definition:

* **Definition 41.** *A separable normal extension N of finite degree of a field K is called* ***metacyclic*** *over K if a chain of intermediate fields*

$$\mathsf{K} = \mathsf{\Lambda}_0 < \mathsf{\Lambda}_1 < \cdots < \mathsf{\Lambda}_r = \mathsf{N}$$

exists such that $\mathsf{\Lambda}_i$ is normal of prime degree over $\mathsf{\Lambda}_{i-1}$, or — which by the Fundamental Theorem of the Galois theory amounts to the same — if the Galois group $\mathfrak{G}$ of N relative to K contains a chain of subgroups

$$\mathfrak{G} = \mathfrak{H}_0 > \mathfrak{H}_1 > \cdots > \mathfrak{H}_r = \mathfrak{E}$$

such that $\mathfrak{H}_i$ is a normal divisor of prime index of $\mathfrak{H}_{i-1}$.

A separable ***polynomial*** *$f(x)$ over K is called metacyclic over K if its root field is* ***metacyclic*** *over K.*

Therefore, the expression *metacyclic* says that the individual steps Λ_i over Λ_{i-1} and $\mathfrak{H}_{i-1}/\mathfrak{H}_i$ are cyclic. Incidentally, a ***group*** $\mathfrak{G}$ of the kind specified in Def. 41 is likewise called ***metacyclic.***

We will now state and prove a criterion for the solvability by radicals of normal extensions of finite degree. Here we restrict ourselves to ground fields of characteristic 0 due to the complications arising in the previous sections in the case of prime characteristics. This means, in particular, that the assumption of separability is always trivially satisfied.

Theorem 127. *A normal extension N of finite degree over a field K of characteristic 0 is solvable by radicals if and only if it is metacyclic.*

A polynomial $f(x)$ over K is solvable by radicals if and only if it is metacyclic.

Proof: a) Let N be solvable by radicals over K. According to Def. 40 [303] there exists in this case a chain of fields

$$\mathsf{K} = \overline{\Lambda}'_0 < \overline{\Lambda}'_1 < \cdots < \overline{\Lambda}'_r \text{ with } \overline{\Lambda}'_r \geqq \mathsf{N},$$

in which $\overline{\Lambda}'_i$ is pure of prime degree p_i over $\overline{\Lambda}'_{i-1}$. By Theorem 126 there exists (just as in the proof of that theorem) a chain of fields

$$\mathsf{K} = \overline{\Lambda}_0 < \overline{\Lambda}_1 < \cdots < \overline{\Lambda}_s \text{ with } \overline{\Lambda}_s \geqq \mathsf{T}_{p_1}, \ldots, \mathsf{T}_{p_r},$$

in which $\overline{\Lambda}_i$ is (pure and) normal of prime degree over $\overline{\Lambda}_{i-1}$. Now, let α_i be a sequence of elements of $\overline{\Lambda}'_i$ such that α_i is a root of a pure irreducible polynomial $x^{p_i} - a_i$ over $\overline{\Lambda}'_{i-1}$, therefore $\overline{\Lambda}'_i = \overline{\Lambda}'_{i-1}(\alpha_i)$ and $\overline{\Lambda}'_r = \mathsf{K}(\alpha_1, \ldots, \alpha_r)$. Either $x^{p_1} - a_1$ is also irreducible in $\overline{\Lambda}_s$; then by Theorem 123 [312] and due to $\mathsf{T}_{p_1} \leqq \overline{\Lambda}_s$ its root field $\overline{\Lambda}_{s+1}$ over $\overline{\Lambda}_s$ is (pure and) normal of prime degree p_1 over $\overline{\Lambda}_s$ and in addition $\overline{\Lambda}_{s+1} = \overline{\Lambda}_s(\alpha_1)$. Or $x^{p_1} - a_1$ is reducible in $\overline{\Lambda}_s$; then by the same theorem $\overline{\Lambda}_{s+1} = \overline{\Lambda}_s$ and in addition $\overline{\Lambda}_{s+1} = \overline{\Lambda}_s(\alpha_1)$. Similarly, we conclude that the root field $\overline{\Lambda}_{s+2}$ of $x^{p_2} - a_2$ over $\overline{\Lambda}_{s+1}$ is either (pure and) normal of prime degree p_2 over $\overline{\Lambda}_{s+1}$ or $= \overline{\Lambda}_{s+1}$ and in both cases in addition to this we have $\overline{\Lambda}_{s+2} = \overline{\Lambda}_{s+1}(\alpha_2)$, etc. By continuing on to $\overline{\Lambda}_{s+r}$ and counting only once fields successively appearing many times we obtain the chain of fields

$$\mathsf{K} = \overline{\Lambda}_0 < \overline{\Lambda}_1 < \cdots < \overline{\Lambda}_{\bar{r}} \text{ with } \overline{\Lambda}_{\bar{r}} \geqq \mathsf{N}$$

(the latter on account of $\overline{\Lambda}_{\bar{r}} = \overline{\Lambda}_s(\alpha_1, \ldots, \alpha_r) \geqq \mathsf{K}(\alpha_1, \ldots, \alpha_r) = \overline{\Lambda}'_r \geqq \mathsf{N}$), in which every $\overline{\Lambda}_i$ is (pure and) normal of prime degree over $\overline{\Lambda}_{i-1}$. By the expositions in Section 18, 3) (cf. Fig. 5 [299]) to this corresponds a chain of intermediate fields

$$\mathsf{K} = \Lambda_0 \leqq \Lambda_1 \leqq \cdots \leqq \Lambda_{\bar{r}} = \mathsf{N},$$

in which Λ_i is normal over Λ_{i-1} and, more specifically, of prime degree unless $\Lambda_i = \Lambda_{i-1}$ (which means that Λ_i could be omitted). For, the degree $[\Lambda_i : \Lambda_{i-1}]$, as a divisor of the prime degree $[\overline{\Lambda}_i : \overline{\Lambda}_{i-1}]$, is either 1 or this very prime number itself.[6] According to Def. 41 N is then metacyclic over K.

b) Let N be metacyclic over K. According to Def. 41 there exists in this case a chain of intermediate fields

$$\mathsf{K} = \Lambda_0 < \Lambda_1 < \cdots < \Lambda_r = \mathsf{N},$$

in which Λ_i is normal of prime degree p_i over Λ_{i-1}. As under a) there exists a chain of fields

---

[6] Incidentally, the same conclusion — without calling express attention to it — was already made in the proof of the Result of Gauss in Section 20 [308] for the prime degree 2 appearing there.

$$\mathsf{K}=\overline{\Lambda}_0<\overline{\Lambda}_1<\cdots<\overline{\Lambda}_s \text{ with } \overline{\Lambda}_s \geqq \mathsf{T}_{p_1},\ldots,\mathsf{T}_{p_r},$$

in which $\overline{\Lambda}_i$ is pure (and normal) of prime degree over $\overline{\Lambda}_{i-1}$. Now, let ϑ_i be a sequence of elements of Λ_i such that ϑ_i is a root of a normal polynomial $g_i(x)$ of prime degree p_i over Λ_{i-1}, therefore $\Lambda_i=\Lambda_{i-1}(\vartheta_i)$ and $\mathsf{N}=\Lambda_r=\mathsf{K}(\vartheta_1,\ldots,\vartheta_r)$. Either $g_1(x)$ is irreducible and consequently also normal in $\overline{\Lambda}_s$; then due to $\mathsf{T}_{p_1}\leqq\overline{\Lambda}_s$ by Theorem 125 [315] its root field $\overline{\Lambda}_{s+1}=\overline{\Lambda}_s(\vartheta_1)$ over $\overline{\Lambda}_s$ is pure (and normal) of prime degree p_1 over $\overline{\Lambda}_s$. Or $g_1(x)$ is reducible in $\overline{\Lambda}_s$; then $\overline{\Lambda}_{s+1}=\overline{\Lambda}_s(\vartheta_1)=\overline{\Lambda}_s$, since $[\overline{\Lambda}_{s+1}:\overline{\Lambda}_s]$ is in this case, on the one hand, $<p_1$ ($\leqq$ on account of the normality of $g_1(x)$ in Λ_0 and actually $<$ on account of the reducibility in $\overline{\Lambda}_s$); on the other hand, a divisor of p_1 (by Theorem 119 [293], applied to $\mathsf{K}=\Lambda_0$, $\mathsf{N}=\Lambda_1$, $\overline{\Lambda}=\overline{\Lambda}_s$, $\overline{\mathsf{N}}=\overline{\Lambda}_{s+1}$), therefore $[\overline{\Lambda}_{s+1}:\overline{\Lambda}_s]=1$. Similarly, we conclude that the root field $\overline{\Lambda}_{s+2}=\overline{\Lambda}_{s+1}(\vartheta_2)$ of $g_2(x)$ over $\overline{\Lambda}_{s+1}$ is either pure (and normal) of prime degree p_2 over $\overline{\Lambda}_{s+1}$ or $=\overline{\Lambda}_{s+1}$, etc. By continuing on to $\overline{\Lambda}_{s+r}$ and counting only once fields appearing successively many times, we obtain a chain of fields

$$\mathsf{K}=\overline{\Lambda}_0<\overline{\Lambda}_1<\cdots<\overline{\Lambda}_{\bar r} \text{ with } \overline{\Lambda}_{\bar r}\geqq\mathsf{N}$$

(the latter due to $\overline{\Lambda}_{\bar r}=\overline{\Lambda}_s(\vartheta_1,\ldots,\vartheta_r)\geqq\mathsf{K}(\vartheta_1,\ldots,\vartheta_r)=\mathsf{N}$), in which every $\overline{\Lambda}_i$ is pure (and normal) of prime degree over $\overline{\Lambda}_{i-1}$. According to Def. 40 [303] N is then solvable by radicals over K.

As is evident from each of the two parts of the proof, a refinement similar to that already obtained in the special Theorem 126 [316] is also generally valid:

Corollary. *If* N *is solvable by radicals over* K *under the assumptions of Theorem* 127, *then there actually exists a chain of fields*

$$K = \overline{\Lambda}_0 < \overline{\Lambda}_1 < \cdots < \overline{\Lambda}_r \quad \textit{with} \quad \overline{\Lambda}_r \geqq N,$$

in which $\overline{\Lambda}_i$ *is not only* (*according to Def.* 40) *pure of prime degree but also normal over* $\overline{\Lambda}_{i-1}$.

Theorem 127, together with the statements already made in Def. 41, answers the question asked at the beginning of this section, namely: Under what conditions is an algebraic equation $f(x) = 0$ in a ground field K of characteristic 0 solvable by radicals,[7] that is, when can its roots be represented in terms of calculating expressions which are formed by means of the four elementary operations and the operation of root extraction? There is another question, somewhat different from the above, which could be asked: When can one root of an *irreducible* polynomial $f(x)$ over K be represented in this manner? It amounts to the question of the solvability by radicals of an *arbitrary* extension Λ of finite degree of K, which conversely is not more general either since any such extension Λ can be regarded as the stem field of an irreducible polynomial $f(x)$. In this regard we cite that the conditions for the latter question are exactly the same as those for the question considered above. *Namely, an arbitrary extension of finite degree* Λ *of* K *is solvable by radicals if and only if this is the case for the normal extension* N *belonging to it* (the root field of any irreducible polynomial $f(x)$ for which Λ is a stem field). It is clear that if N is solvable by radicals so also is Λ. Conversely, by passing over according to Def. 41 from a chain of fields for Λ to their conjugates we can show that if Λ is solvable by radicals so also are all conjugate extensions. This easily yields that N is solvable by radicals.

Examples of Algebraic Equations over Ground Fields of Characteristic 0 Which Are Solvable by Radicals

1) *All equations of second, third and fourth degree.*

Namely, their Galois groups are isomorphic to subgroups of the symmetric groups $\mathfrak{S}_2$, $\mathfrak{S}_3$, $\mathfrak{S}_4$ (Theorem 107 [271]), and it is easy

[7] Strictly speaking, however, this does not *answer* the question, for it merely *reduces* it to the statement and investigation of the Galois group.

to prove that the latter (together with their subgroups) are metacyclic.

2) *All cyclic and,* more generally, *Abelian equations*; in particular, by Theorem 121 [305] *the generic cyclotomic equation* $x^n - 1 \doteq 0$.

Namely, by Theorem 36 [199] any finite cyclic group is metacyclic. It is especially easy to show from the general theory of finite Abelian groups that these groups are all metacyclic. Here, however, we cannot give more details.[8]

23. Existence of Algebraic Equations not Solvable by Radicals

The existence of equations not solvable by radicals was discovered by *Abel*, who first proved the *impossibility of solving by radicals the generic equation of degree higher than the fourth.* In this last section we will sketch a modern proof of this Abelian Theorem.

First we define:

Definition 42. *If* $\mathsf{K}_n = \mathsf{K}(x_1, \ldots, x_n)$ *is the field of rational functions of* n *indeterminates* $x_1, \ldots, x_n$ *over* K, *then the polynomial*

$$(1) \qquad f_n(x) \equiv x^n + x_1 x^{n-1} + \cdots + x_n$$

over K_n *is called the **generic polynomial of n-th degree** over* K.

This *generic* polynomial of n-th degree over K can be regarded as an "indeterminate" condensation of all *special* polynomials of n-th degree over K, which, conversely, can be obtained from it by *substituting* in the generic polynomial any *system of elements* $a_1, \ldots, a_n$ *of* K *for the indeterminates* $x_1, \ldots, x_n$ *over* K.

[8] For this we refer to Vol. 3, Section 3, Exer. 9 to 20. In regard to further theorems about metacyclic groups cf. the text of *A. Speiser* Theorie der Gruppen von endlicher Ordnung (Theory of Groups of Finite Order) 3rd ed., Berlin 1937.

We now consider the decomposition into linear factors

(2) $f_n(x) \equiv x^n + x_1 x^{n-1} + \cdots + x_n \equiv (x - \xi_1) \cdots (x - \xi_n)$

of the generic polynomial of n-th degree over K in its root field $\mathsf{W}_n = \mathsf{K}_n(\xi_1, \ldots, \xi_n)$. If we think of the n linear factors on the right as multiplied out, then by Vol. 1, Theorem 11 [39] the coefficients of the same powers of x on the left and the right must be equal. Thus, we obtain the system of formulae[9]

$$(3)\quad \begin{cases} x_1 = -(\xi_1 + \cdots + \xi_n) \\ x_2 = \xi_1 \xi_2 + \cdots + \xi_{n-1} \xi_n \\ \cdots\cdots\cdots\cdots\cdots\cdots \\ x_n = (-1)^n \xi_1 \cdots \xi_n \end{cases}$$

or on collecting them together

$$x_\nu = (-1)^\nu \sum_{\{i_1, \ldots, i_\nu\}} \xi_{i_1} \cdots \xi_{i_\nu} \qquad (\nu = 1, \ldots, n),$$

where the sum on the right extends over all $\binom{n}{\nu}$ combinations taken ν at a time (Vol. 1, Section 16 [121]) of the numerals $1, \ldots, n$. According to these formulae we have, in particular,

$$(4)\qquad \mathsf{W}_n = \mathsf{K}_n(\xi_1, \ldots, \xi_n) = \mathsf{K}(x_1, \ldots, x_n;\ \xi_1, \ldots, \xi_n) = \mathsf{K}(\xi_1, \ldots, \xi_n).$$

Besides the foregoing interpretation leading from (1) over (2) to (3) and (4), we can conversely also give another. For this purpose we start from (4), that is, the field $\mathsf{W}_n = \mathsf{K}(\xi_1, \ldots, \xi_n)$ of rational functions of $\xi_1, \ldots \xi_n$ over K now taken to be n indeterminates; then we define $x_1, \ldots, x_n$ by the formulae (3) as elements of this field W_n and define $f_n(x)$ by the formula (2) as a polynomial in the subfield $\mathsf{K}_n = \mathsf{K}(x_1, \ldots, x_n)$ of $\mathsf{W}_n = \mathsf{K}(\xi_1, \ldots, \xi_n)$, whereby W_n is again the root field to

[9] Here, deviating from the convention in Vol. 1, p. 50, we designate equality in $\mathsf{K}_n = \mathsf{K}(x_1, \ldots, x_n)$ and in the algebraic extension $\mathsf{W}_n = \mathsf{K}_n(\xi_1, \ldots, \xi_n)$ only by $=$, in order to reserve $\equiv$ for equality in the case of the addition of further indeterminates (say x in (1) and (2) as well as $\overline{x}_1, \ldots, \overline{x}_n$ in the proof of the following Theorem 128).

$f_n(x)$ over K_n and has the representations (4). Of course, in the case of this latter interpretation the question remains unanswered whether the polynomial $f_n(x)$ so formed is the generic polynomial of n-th degree over K. Since the specified second interpretation is handier for the application which we have in mind, it is important to answer this question affirmatively:

Theorem 128. *If* $W_n = K(\xi_1, \ldots, \xi_n)$ *is the field of the rational functions of* n *indeterminates* $\xi_1, \ldots, \xi_n$ *over* K, *then the elements* $x_1, \ldots, x_n$ *of* W_n *defined by formulae* (3) *likewise have the character of* n *indeterminates over* K,[10] *that is, the subfield* $K_n = K(x_1, \ldots, x_n)$ *of* $W_n = K(\xi_1, \ldots, \xi_n)$ *is likewise of the extension type of the field of the rational functions of* n *indeterminates over* K. *In particular, the polynomial* $f_n(x)$ *over* K_n *defined by* (2) *is in this case the generic polynomial of* n-*th degree over* K.

Proof: We have to show that the normal representations (Vol. 1, Def. 9 [45]) of the elements of the integral domain $K[x_1, \ldots, x_n]$ in terms of $x_1, \ldots, x_n$ are unique. For this purpose it is sufficient to prove that a relation

(5) $$g(x_1, \ldots, x_n) = 0,$$

where $g(\bar{x}_1, \ldots, \bar{x}_n)$ is an integral rational function of n indeterminates $\bar{x}_1, \ldots, \bar{x}_n$ over K, implies the relation

(6) $$g(\bar{x}_1, \ldots, \bar{x}_n) \equiv 0.$$

We will prove this by double mathematical induction,[11] first on the number n of indeterminates, secondly on the degree ν_n of g in $\bar{x}_n$.

---

[10] Cf. Vol. 1, Def. 9 [45] together with the accompanying explanation.

[11] For the idea of applying *double* mathematical induction in this proof, I am indebted to a communication by letter from *Ph. Furtwängler.*

For $n=1$, $x_1 = -\xi_1$, therefore the theorem is obviously valid on the basis of the assumed indeterminate character of ξ_1. Let us assume that the theorem has been proved up to $n-1$. Then, let

(7) $$g(\bar{x}_1, \ldots, \bar{x}_n) \equiv \sum_{k=0}^{\nu_n} \bar{x}_n^k \, g_k(\bar{x}_1, \ldots, \bar{x}_{n-1})$$

be the representation of g (following from the normal representation by combining as an integral rational function of $\bar{x}_n$ over $\mathsf{K}[\bar{x}_1, \ldots, \bar{x}_{n-1}]$, therefore, in particular,

(8) $$g(\bar{x}_1, \ldots, \bar{x}_{n-1}, 0) \equiv g_0(\bar{x}_1, \ldots, \bar{x}_{n-1}).$$

Now, if we set $\xi_n = 0$ in (5), then by the principle of substitution (Vol. 1, Theorem 12 [47]), which can be used due to the indeterminate character of ξ_n, the relation

(9) $$g(x_1', \ldots, x_{n-1}', 0) = 0$$

is generated, where $x_1', \ldots, x_{n-1}'$ arise from $x_1, \ldots, x_{n-1}$ by the substitution $\xi_n = 0$ in (3); if we then set $(\bar{x}_1, \ldots, \bar{x}_{n-1}) = (x_1', \cdots, x_{n-1}')$ in (8), by the principle of substitution we further obtain from (9) the relation

(10) $$g_0(x_1', \ldots, x_{n-1}') = 0.$$

Now, since the significance of $x_1', \ldots, x_{n-1}'$ according to their definition in terms of $\xi_1, \ldots, \xi_{n-1}$ corresponds to that of $x_1, \ldots, x_n$ in terms of $\xi_1, \ldots, \xi_n$, it follows from (10) according to the induction assumption first made that the relation

$$g_0(\bar{x}_1, \ldots, \bar{x}_{n-1}) \equiv 0$$

is valid: therefore by (7) the relation

(11) $$g(\bar{x}_1, \ldots, \bar{x}_n) \equiv \bar{x}_n \sum_{k=0}^{\nu_n - 1} \bar{x}_n^k \, g_{k+1}(\bar{x}_1, \ldots, \bar{x}_{n-1}) \equiv \bar{x}_n g^{(1)}(\bar{x}_1, \ldots, \bar{x}_n),$$

is further valid, where $g^{(1)}(\bar{x}_1, \ldots, \bar{x}_n)$ is again an integral rational function of $\bar{x}_1, \ldots, \bar{x}_n$ over K, which (in case $\nu_n > 0$) has the degree $\nu_n - 1$ in $\bar{x}_n$.

Now, if the degree is $\nu_n = 0$, then $g^{(1)}(\bar{x}_1, \ldots, \bar{x}_n) \equiv 0$ and therefore the statement (6) is true by (11). Let us assume that it has been proved up to the degree $\nu_n - 1$ (for fixed n). Then by the substitution $(\bar{x}_1, \ldots, \bar{x}_n) = (x_1, \ldots, x_n)$ we obtain from (11) the relation

$$g(x_1, \ldots, x_n) = x_n g^{(1)}(x_1, \ldots, x_n)$$

and by (5) and the fact that $x_n \neq 0$ we further obtain from this the relation

$$g^{(1)}(x_1, \ldots, x_n) = 0.$$

Hence by this second induction assumption we have

$$g^{(1)}(\bar{x}_1, \ldots, \bar{x}_n) \equiv 0,$$

which by (11) implies statement (6). This completes the proof of the statement of the theorem by double mathematical induction.

Incidentally, Theorem 128 easily yields the converse, namely, the fact that the elements $\xi_1, \ldots, \xi_n$ defined by (2), starting from the indeterminates $x_1, \ldots, x_n$, have the character of indeterminates over K. However, here we have no need of this result.

We now prove:

Theorem 129. *The generic polynomial of n-th degree over* K *is separable and its Galois group relative to* K_n *is isomorphic to the symmetric group* $\mathfrak{S}_n$.

Proof: According to Theorem 128 we think of the generic polynomial of n-th degree $f_n(x)$ over K in terms of the second interpretation discussed before Theorem 128, that is, as formed through the formulae (3), (2) starting from the root field $\mathsf{W}_n = \mathsf{K}(\xi_1, \ldots, \xi_n)$. First, that $f_n(x)$ is separable immediately follows in this case from the distinctness of its roots $\xi_1, \ldots, \xi_n$ chosen as n indeterminates over K (Theorem 59, Corollary [216]). Furthermore, let $\begin{pmatrix} 1 \ldots n \\ i_1 \ldots i_n \end{pmatrix}$ be an arbitrary permutation in $\mathfrak{S}_n$. By Vol. 1, Theorems 10, 11 [33, 39], $\mathsf{K}(\xi_{i_1}, \ldots, \xi_{i_n})$ is then isomorphic to $\mathsf{K}(\xi_1, \ldots, \xi_n)$ relative to K on the basis of the correspondences

$$\xi_1 \longleftrightarrow \xi_{i_1}, \ldots, \xi_n \longleftrightarrow \xi_{i_n}.$$

However, since the formulae (3) are symmetric in $\xi_1, \ldots, \xi_n$, the elements $x_1, \ldots, x_n$, and consequently all elements of $\mathsf{K}_n = \mathsf{K}(x_1, \ldots, x_n)$, are mapped onto themselves under this correspondence, so that the specified isomorphism is valid even relative to K_n. Since

$$\mathsf{W}_n = \mathsf{K}(\xi_1, \ldots, \xi_n) = \mathsf{K}(\xi_{i_1}, \ldots, \xi_{i_n}),$$

any permutation in $\mathfrak{S}_n$ generates an automorphism of W_n relative to K_n, and conversely is therefore obtained by such an automorphism in the sense of Theorem 107 [271]. On taking into consideration the distinctness of the roots $\xi_1, \ldots, \xi_n$, pointed out before, it follows from this theorem that the Galois group of W_n, that is, the Galois group of $f_n(x)$ relative to K_n, is isomorphic to the symmetric group $\mathfrak{S}_n$.

Moreover, Theorem 129 yields in particular:

Theorem 130. *The generic polynomial of n-th degree over* K *is irreducible in* K_n.

Proof: If $\overline{f}_n(x)$ is the irreducible polynomial in K_n belonging to a root ξ of $f_n(x)$, then, on the one hand, $\overline{f}_n(x) | f_n(x)$ (Theorem 53 [210]), on the other hand, $\overline{f}_n(\xi_i) = 0$ for every root ξ_i of $f_n(x)$ (Theorems 73 [230], 129). Therefore, since the roots ξ_i are distinct, it also follows that $f_n(x) | \overline{f}_n(x)$ (Theorem 47 [207]). These two facts taken together yield $\overline{f}_n(x) \equiv f_n(x)$, as stated.

We will dwell a moment on formulae (3), again from the second point of view discussed before Theorem 128 [325]. In this case we call the elements $x_1, \ldots, x_n$ of $\mathsf{K}(\xi_1, \ldots, \xi_n)$ the ***elementary symmetric functions*** of the indeterminates $\xi_1, \ldots, \xi_n$. Furthermore, we generally call a rational function over K of the indeterminates $\xi_1, \ldots, \xi_n$ *symmetric* in $\xi_1, \ldots, \xi_n$, if it goes into itself by all permutations of the n elements $\xi_1, \ldots, \xi_n$. By applying Theorems 107, 112 [271, 283] along with Corollary, Theorem 129 immediately yields:

Theorem 131. *A rational function over* K *of the indeterminates* $\xi_1, \ldots, \xi_n$ *[that is, an element of* $\mathsf{K}(\xi_1, \ldots, \xi_n)$*], is symmetric if and only if it is a rational function over* K *of the elementary symmetric functions* $x_1, \ldots, x_n$ *of* $\xi_1, \ldots, \xi_n$*, that is, an element of the subfield* $\mathsf{K}(x_1, \ldots, x_n)$ *of* $\mathsf{K}(\xi_1, \ldots, \xi_n)$.

The deeper-lying statement of this theorem, namely, the statement "only if," which says that every symmetric rational function over K of $\xi_1, \ldots, \xi_n$ is a rational function over K of $x_1, \ldots, x_n$, is a substatement of the theorem known under the name of the ***Theorem on Symmetric Functions,*** which in the past was nearly always taken as a basis for the Galois theory (cf. footnote 1 to the proof of Theorem 90 [251]). This theorem goes beyond the statement of Theorem 131, in as much as it states that:

1) Any *integral* rational symmetric function over K of $\xi_1, \ldots, \xi_n$ is an *integral* rational function of $x_1, \ldots, x_n$.

2) The latter is also valid even if an *integral domain* I is used instead of the *field* K.

However, in contrast to Theorem 131, these further statements cannot be inferred from the Galois theory.[12]

We now return to the proper problem of this section, which we can next attack on the basis of Theorem 129. Since the symmetric group $\mathfrak{S}_n$ for $n > 1$ always has the normal divisor $\mathfrak{A}_n$ of index 2 (Vol. 1, Theorem 63 [126]), we can reduce the root field $\mathsf{W}_n = \mathsf{K}_n(\xi_1, \ldots, \xi_n)$ of degree $n!$ over K_n to a field of degree $\frac{n!}{2}$ over a field V_n generated from K_n by the adjunction of a square root:

[12] Here we cannot give a proof — communicated to me by Ph. Furtwängler — of the statements 1), 2) by means of double mathematical induction, which is entirely analogous to the proof of Theorem 128. See, Vol. 3, Section 23, Exer. 3.

Theorem 132. *The root field* $W_n = K_n(\xi_1, \ldots, \xi_n)$ *of the generic polynomial of n-th degree* $(n > 1)$ *over* K *has a subfield* V_n *of degree* 2 *over* K_n. *This is obtained, in case* K *does not have the characteristic* 2, *by the adjunction of the element*

$$\delta = \begin{vmatrix} 1 & \xi_1 & \xi_1^2 & \cdots & \xi_1^{n-1} \\ \cdot & \cdot & \cdot & \cdot & \cdot \\ 1 & \xi_n & \xi_n^2 & \cdots & \xi_n^{n-1} \end{vmatrix}$$

to K_n, *which is the root of a pure polynomial* $x^2 - d$ *of second degree over* K_n.[13]

Proof: That $V_n = K_n(\delta)$ is the field between K_n and W_n corresponding to $\mathfrak{A}_n$ follows according to Theorems 112, 129 [283, 327] from two facts: first, δ is unchanged by the even permutations of $\xi_1, \ldots, \xi_n$, but changes its sign under the odd permutations (Vol. 1, Theorem 65 [130]); secondly, $\delta \neq 0$ (see Vol. 3, part 1, Section 19, Exer. 4), so that the assumption about the characteristic implies $\delta \neq -\delta$. Furthermore, this means that $\delta^2 = d$ is unchanged by all permutations of $\xi_1, \ldots, \xi_n$; therefore it must be an element of K_n (Theorem 112, Corollary [284]).

The element $d = \delta^2$ is called the ***discriminant of*** $f_n(x)$. Naturally, it even belongs to $K[\xi_1, \ldots, \xi_n]$ and therefore is an *integral* rational function over K of the roots $\xi_1, \ldots, \xi_n$.

Now, in the theory of groups it is proved that the *alternating group* $\mathfrak{A}_n$ *for* $n \neq 4$ *has no proper normal divisor,*[14] *and that* $\mathfrak{A}_n$ *is the only normal divisor of* $\mathfrak{S}_n$.[15] *Since* $\frac{n!}{2}$ is not a prime

[13] Regarding the case where K has the characteristic 2, see Vol. 3, Section 23, Exer. 20.

[14] *Speiser*, l. c. (cf. footnote 8 of this Chapter), Theorem 94. See also Vol. 3, Section 23, Exer. 13, 14.

[15] This is a consequence of the so-called *Jordan Theorem* (*Speiser*, same place, Theorem 27) together with the obvious nonexistence of normal divisors of $\mathfrak{S}_n$ of order 2. See also Vol. 3, Section 23, Exer. 16.

number *for* $n \geqq 4$, there can therefore exist for $n > 4$ no chain of subgroups of $\mathfrak{S}_n$ of the kind specified in Def. 41 [318], so that $\mathfrak{S}_n$ is not metacyclic in this case. Theorem 127 [319] therefore implies:

Result of Abel. *The generic polynomial of n-th degree over a field* K *of characteristic* 0 *is not solvable by radicals for* $n > 4$.

This theorem insures the existence of equations not solvable by radicals, first of all, only for the particular ground field K_n of Def. 42 [323]. Another question which arises is then the following: *In a given ground field* K *are there special* (that is, situated in K itself) *equations of any degree* $n > 4$ *not solvable by radicals*? This question is answered affirmatively for the special case of the rational ground field P by the

Irreducibility Theorem of Hilbert.[16] *If* $g(x; x_1, \ldots, x_n)$ *is an integral rational function of the indeterminates* $x; x_1, \ldots, x_n$ *over* P, *which is a polynomial in* x *irreducible over* $\mathsf{P}_n = \mathsf{P}(x_1, \ldots, x_n)$, *then there are infinitely many systems of elements* $a_1, \ldots, a_n$ *of* P *such that* $g(x; a_1, \ldots, a_n)$ *is irreducible in* P.

This theorem gives the following answer to the question asked above regarding the ground field P: If $\xi_1, \ldots, \xi_n$ are the roots of the generic polynomial of n-th degree $f_n(x) = x^n + x_1 x^{n-1} + \cdots + x_n$ over P, then by Theorem 112, Corollary [284] and Theorem 129 [327]

$$\vartheta = c_1\xi_1 + \cdots + c_n\xi_n$$

is a primitive element of the root field $\mathsf{W}_n = \mathsf{P}_n(\xi_1, \ldots, \xi_n)$ relative to $\mathsf{P}_n = \mathsf{P}(x_1, \ldots, x_n)$ provided that the coefficients c_ν are

---

[16] *D. Hilbert, Über die Irreduzibilität ganzer rationaler Funktionen mit ganzzahligen Koeffizienten* (On the Irreducibility of Integral Rational Functions with Integral Coefficients), Crelle 110, 1892.

chosen from P_n so that all permutations $\begin{pmatrix} \nu \\ i_\nu \end{pmatrix}$ of the ξ_ν yield different conjugates

$$\vartheta_i = c_1 \xi_{i_1} + \cdots + c_n \xi_{i_n}.$$

We think of the c_ν as chosen in this way; in doing so we can even take them, as seen in Theorem 49 [208], as elements of the integral domain $\Gamma_n = \mathsf{P}[x_1, \ldots, x_n]$. Then

$$g(x; x_1, \ldots, x_n) \equiv \prod_{i=1}^{n!} (x - \vartheta_i)$$

is a Galois resolvent of W_n relative to P_n and satisfies the assumptions of Hilbert's Irreducibility Theorem. Therefore, there are infinitely many systems of elements $a_1, \ldots, a_n$ in P such that $g(x; a_1, \ldots, a_n)$ is irreducible in P. The root fields W over P of the special $f(x)$ corresponding to these systems $a_1, \ldots, a_n$ then have the highest possible degree $n!$ over P (Theorem 108 [273]), since they each contain an element ϑ of degree $n!$ and, consequently, have a Galois group isomorphic to $\mathfrak{S}_n$ itself (Theorem 107 [271]). Hence by the expositions of these sections these $f(x)$ are not solvable by radicals for $n > 4$. We therefore have:

Corollary. *For every degree n there are in* P *infinitely many algebraic equations whose Galois group is isomorphic to* $\mathfrak{S}_n$ *(so-called equations without affect; in particular, therefore, for every degree* $n > 4$ *there are infinitely many algebraic equations not solvable by radicals.*

Whether this result is also valid for general ground fields K, as well as for any subgroups of $\mathfrak{S}_n$ as prescribed Galois groups, is undecided even today except for simple cases.

AUTHOR AND SUBJECT INDEX

(The numbers refer mainly to the pages on which the terms appear for the first time.)

INDEX

INDEX

INDEX